DEIRDRE MADDEN'S

# DESIGN FOR LIVING

## COMPLETE JUNIOR CERTIFICATE HOME ECONOMICS

3RD EDITION
*Revised by Lorna Freeborn*

Gill & Macmillan

Gill & Macmillan

Hume Avenue

Park West

Dublin 12

with associated companies throughout the world

www.gillmacmillan.ie

© Deirdre Madden 1998 and Lorna Freeborn 2010

978 0 7171 4673 4

Index compiled by Cover to Cover

Design and print origination by Design Image

Illustrations by Peter Bull Art Studio

The paper used in this book is made from the wood pulp of managed forests.
For every tree felled, at least one tree is planted, thereby renewing natural resources.

Original front cover photographic images supplied by:
Grain: George Bosela; First-aid Box: Adam Elliston; Energy-saving Globe: Jenny Rollo; Stairs 2: Ilja Wanka; The Hands: Christian Wilke-Zhang; Still Life: Peter Mrhar; Gas Burner: Hagit; Fork Series: Ramasamy Chidambaram; Grater: Joh Tal; Sewing Machine Detail 2: Iwan Beijes; Yellow Pepper Macro: Nicolas Raymond.

# Contents

Introduction

## Part 1 Food

1. Healthy eating — 2
2. Nutrition — 7
3. Digestion of food — 24
4. Balancing the diet — 31
5. Special diets — 39
6. Meal planning — 53
7. Practical cookery exam — 60
8. Food hygiene and storage — 68
9. Food preparation — 75
10. Cooking food — 83
11. Breakfasts and packed meals — 90
12. Soups and sauces — 95
13. The cereal group — 101
14. Fruit and vegetables — 111
15. The milk, cheese and yoghurt group — 122
16. The protein group – meat, fish and eggs — 130
17. Food preservation and processing — 149
18. Recipes — 162

## Part 2 Consumer Studies

19. What is a consumer? — 206
20. Consumer rights and responsibilities — 211
21. Consumer protection — 216
22. Quality — 223
23. Money management — 229
24. Shopping — 234
25. Advertising and marketing — 240

## Part 3 Social and Health Studies

26. Good health — 246
27. Personal hygiene — 252
28. The teeth — 257
29. The circulatory system — 260
30. The respiratory system — 263
31. The family — 265
32. Adolescence — 272
33. Becoming an adult — 278
34. Health hazards — 283

## Part 4 Resource Management and Home Studies

35. Management — 292
36. Home and community — 297
37. Design in the home — 300
38. Room planning — 304
39. Technology in the home — 311
40. Services to the home — 321
41. The environment and you — 329
42. Hygiene in the home — 333
43. Safety and first aid — 336

## Part 5 Textile Studies

44. Textiles in clothing — 344
45. Textiles in the home — 350
46. Fibres and fabrics — 354
47. Textile care — 364
48. Textile skills — 372

## Part 6 Options

Option 1    Childcare — 384
Option 2    Design and craftwork — 402
Option 3    Textile skills — 408

Index — 419

## eTest.ie – what is it?

A revolutionary new website-based testing platform that facilitates a social learning environment for Irish schools. Both students and teachers can use it, either independently or together, to make the whole area of testing easier, more engaging and more productive for all.

## Students – do you want to know how well you are doing? Then take an eTest!

At eTest.ie, you can access tests put together by the author of this textbook. You get instant results, so they're a brilliant way to quickly check just how your study or revision is going.

Since each eTest is based on your textbook, if you don't know an answer, you'll find it in your book.

Register now and you can save all of your eTest results to use as a handy revision aid or to simply compare with your friends' results!

## Teachers – eTest.ie will engage your students and help them with their revision, while making the jobs of reviewing their progress and homework easier and more convenient for all of you.

Register now to avail of these exciting features:

- Create tests easily using our pre-set questions OR you can create your own questions

- Develop your own online learning centre for each class that you teach

- Keep track of your students' performances

eTest.ie has a wide choice of question types for you to choose from, most of which can be graded automatically, like multiple-choice, jumbled-sentence, matching, ordering and gap-fill exercises. This free resource allows you to create class groups, delivering all the functionality of a VLE (Virtual Learning Environment) with the ease of communication that is brought by social networking.

# Introduction

Now that the Junior Certificate Home Economics syllabus and practical examination have been in operation for many years, the important elements required in a textbook have become clear —

- A text which is concise and to the point, omitting unnecessary detail.
- Simple, clear language.
- Difficult concepts such as design and management explained in a simple way.
- Important facts listed or numbered for easy learning.
- Definitions highlighted for easy revision.
- Cross-referencing to facilitate integration of different sections.
- Clear but unobtrusive illustrations.
- Advice and assistance for conducting practical work, such as step-by-step instructions for cookery assignments.
- Higher level material highlighted.
- Activities included.
- Clear explanations of how to construct design briefs, together with examples.
- Revision questions included.
- Options included.
- Advice on production and presentation of project and practical work on options.

*Design for Living* incorporates all these factors to produce a textbook which meets the needs of both students and teachers. It emphasises the importance of practical work, investigative techniques and ongoing evaluation, and encourages the student to develop skills such as creativity, decision-making and good management.

# Part 1

# Food

# Chapter
# 1 Healthy Eating

## Why do we eat?

Most people eat because they feel hungry or because they like the taste of food. However, the most important reason we eat is to stay alive.

## Functions of food

Food is necessary

- for the growth and repair of body cells
- to provide heat and energy for the body
- to regulate and protect the body.

## Food choices

Most foods will keep us alive, but in order to keep the body healthy we must choose nourishing foods, i.e. those that will help maintain good health.

❖ *Poor food choice*

❖ *Good food choices*

Bad food choices lead to bad health – many diseases such as cancer, heart disease, diabetes and dental decay are associated with an unhealthy diet.

# Factors that affect our choice of food

**1 Senses:** Our senses help us to decide whether we like or dislike a food.

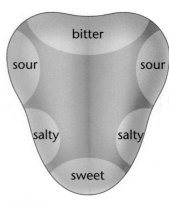

❧ **Smell** – Cells in the nose pick up the odour of food. This makes the mouth water and starts the digestive juices working.

❧ **Sight** – Food that is well presented and looks attractive makes us want to eat it.

❧ **Taste** – Cells on the tongue, called taste buds, pick out flavours (sweet, sour, salty, bitter).

❧ **Touch** – The tongue also senses the temperature and texture of food. Is it hot, cold, smooth, lumpy, soft or crunchy?

❖ *Taste areas on the tongue*

**2 Food value:** Is the food nourishing – has it a good balance of nutrients, with the right amount of kilocalories for the energy needs of the body?

**3 Lifestyle (family and friends):** Eating habits are formed at home, where children tend to eat the same diet as their family, whether this is a nourishing one or not. As children grow older, outside influences such as friends and advertising may encourage them to try other foods.

❖ *A family eating dinner at home*

**4 Culture:** The country we live in and the group or race we belong to influence what we eat. In Ireland, bread and potatoes are **staple foods** (see page 4); in Italy people eat lots of pasta. Some **religions** have rules about what foods may be eaten (e.g. Hindus do not eat beef). Eating traditions play a part in celebrations such as weddings, Christmas, Passover and Shrove Tuesday.

**5 Cost:** What foods can I afford to buy? Wealthy people may eat more expensive foods and eat out more often. Those on a limited budget, e.g. pensioners, have to settle for cheaper foods, though these are not necessarily less nourishing.

**6 Availability:** What types of food are available in the shops? Today we have a

❖ *Some exotic fruit from abroad*

greater choice of food than ever before. Improved transport and technology mean that foods from all over the world are available all the year round. In rural areas there is often less choice, although some families may produce some of their own food.

## Summary

Food choice is influenced by:

- senses
- food value
- lifestyle
- culture
- cost
- availability.

## Malnutrition

**Malnutrition means bad nutrition. It is an incorrect balance of nutrients in the body.**

It can be caused by:

- too little food (starvation)
- too much food (obesity)
- a lack of certain nutrients (deficiency diseases).

## Staple foods

A staple food is a food that is plentiful and is a main part of the diet in a country. Rice is a staple food in many countries in the East. In many Western countries, bread is a staple food. In the past the potato was the staple food in Ireland and much of Europe. Today, bread, rice and pasta are also staple foods.

**ACTIVITY**

1. Find out four ways in which the body is affected by starvation.
2. Food plays a central part in many of our customs and festivals. We celebrate special occasions, such as weddings, with a special meal. List some foods associated with the following festivals:
   - Hallowe'en
   - Easter
   - Shrove Tuesday
   - Christmas.

   Cook one dish associated with an occasion of your choice.
3. Find out what are typically Irish dishes.
4. List all the potato dishes you can find out about.

# Eating patterns today

Food not only satisfies our hunger, it is also a source of pleasure and a social activity. At mealtime the family has a chance to sit down to talk and eat together. Regular meals are important, and three meals a day is the usual pattern – breakfast, lunch and dinner/supper.

In recent years there have been many changes in eating habits.

**1** Many people lead busier lives; they have less time for cooking and sit-down meals, so they may not cook or eat together regularly.

**2** More fast foods (i.e. processed/convenience foods, such as McDonald's) are eaten.

**3** Young people often eat 'on the move', eating snacks such as sandwiches or takeaways.

**4** More people eat out in restaurants, both traditional and ethnic.

**5** There is greater interest in healthy eating. **Organic food** (food produced without the use of artificial chemicals) and vegetarianism (see page 39) have become popular.

**6** People tend to 'graze' more, i.e. they eat throughout the whole day, rather than just three times a day, even though they might not be hungry.

Vegetarian diets, page 39

# Unhealthy eating

Medical experts have found that we consume too much:

✦ fat (particularly animal fat)

✦ sugar

✦ salt

✦ alcohol

and that we do not consume enough:

✦ fibre

✦ fruit and vegetables.

To maintain good health we need to reverse this unhealthy eating pattern.

| Healthy eating guidelines | |
| --- | --- |
| ✦ Eat a wide variety of food. | ✦ Eat more fruit and vegetables – have four or more helpings a day. |
| ✦ Eat less fat (no more than 50% should be animal fats). | ✦ Increase iron and calcium intake (especially important for females). |
| ✦ Eat less sugar. | |
| ✦ Eat less salt. | ✦ Drink more water. |
| ✦ Eat more fibre – wholegrain cereals, pulses and pasta. | ✦ Drink alcohol only in moderation. |

The IUNA (Irish Universities Nutrition Alliance) Food Consumption Survey carried out in 2001 found the following:

- 75% of the population did not eat enough fibre
- people were eating too much fat
- 39% of the population were overweight
- 25% of all energy is consumed outside the home.

The IUNA National Teen Food Survey of 2008 states that:

- 42% of girls and 23% of boys don't eat enough calcium
- 11% of teenage boys are obese and 8% of teenage girls are obese.

**ACTIVITY**

1. Name four ways in which we could improve our lifestyle.
2. Name five ways in which we could reduce fat in our diet.

**REVISION QUESTIONS**

1. Name four factors which influence our choice of food.
2. What are the basic functions of food in the body?
3. What is malnutrition?
4. Explain the term 'staple food'.
5. Name three diseases associated with a poor diet.
6. Describe three changes in modern eating patterns.
7. List five healthy eating guidelines.
8. What is meant by the term 'organic' food?

Test Yourself
eTest.ie

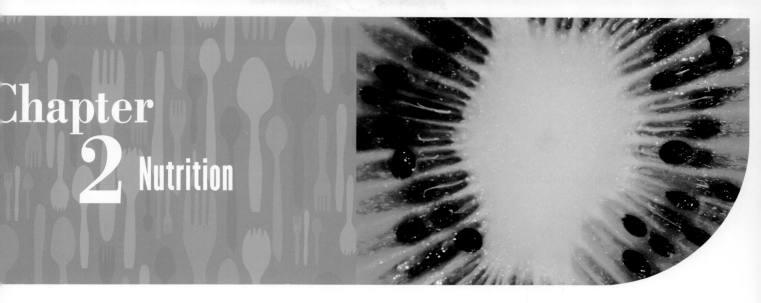

# Chapter
## 2 Nutrition

All food is made from chemical substances which are called **nutrients**.

**Nutrition** is the study of the nutrients in food and how the body uses them to keep us healthy.

## There are six groups of nutrients.

| | |
|---|---|
| *Macronutrients* (needed in large amounts) | Proteins <br> Carbohydrates <br> Fats |
| *Micronutrients* (needed in small amounts) | Vitamins <br> Minerals <br> Water |

*(Strictly speaking, water is not a nutrient, but it is essential for the digestion of food.)*

## Variety is the spice of life

Most foods contain several nutrients. Milk, for example, is a nutritious food which contains nutrients from each group.

However, no single food contains all the nutrients in the **correct proportion for the needs of the body**. This is why we must eat a **good variety of foods** if we are to stay healthy.

### Nutrition Glossary

| | |
|---|---|
| **Nutrients** | these are chemicals (e.g. protein) which make up food. They are broken down during digestion into simpler substances which are then absorbed and used by the body (e.g. to help it grow). |
| **Composition of nutrient** | this refers to the structure of each nutrient, i.e. how the elements in it are arranged. |
| **Composition of food** | the amount of each nutrient in a food, usually shown as a percentage. |
| **Source** | foods that contain a nutrient, particularly those that provide a good supply. |
| **Function** | the job a nutrient does in the body, e.g. calcium builds strong bones. |
| **Recommended daily allowance (RDA)** | (sometimes called recommended daily amount) – the amount of a nutrient the body needs each day to keep it in good health and prevent disease. |
| **Deficiency diseases** | diseases caused by lack of a nutrient. |

# Protein

Protein is the most important nutrient. It is essential for every body cell. Protein is needed to make new cells (growth) and to repair old ones. Once the body takes what it needs for growth and repair, the rest of the protein is used to supply heat and energy to the body.

❖ *Protein chain*

❖ *Separated amino acids*

## Composition

1. Protein contains the elements **carbon**, **hydrogen**, **oxygen** and **nitrogen**.
2. It is the only nutrient that contains nitrogen, which is responsible for growth.
3. The elements are arranged into small units called **amino acids**, which are linked together like beads in a necklace to form chains of protein.
4. During digestion, the protein chains are broken down into single amino acids, which are easily absorbed into the blood.
5. These are then used to make new cells, for example in a growing baby, or to repair damaged cells, e.g. in a wound.

## Classification and sources of protein

Some of the amino acids in protein can only be taken into the body in the foods that we eat: these are called **essential amino acids**.

Proteins are classified into two groups according to the amount of essential amino acids in them.

**High biological value (HBV) proteins** contain more essential amino acids. **Low biological value (LBV) proteins** usually contain fewer essential amino acids and are cheaper to produce. We should get half our daily protein from each group.

✢ *HBV foods*

✢ *LBV foods*

HBV proteins (mostly animal sources) – meat, fish, eggs, milk, cheese, yoghurt, soya beans, TVP/soya protein.

LBV proteins (mostly plant foods) – pulses (peas, beans), cereals (wheat, oats), nuts, bread, pasta.

## Functions of protein

1. Growth of body cells, e.g. blood, skin, bone.
2. Repair of damaged cells.
3. Heat and energy production.
4. Production of important body chemicals such as hormones and enzymes.

## RDA

Adults require 1g of protein for each kg of body weight: for example, a person weighing 70kg requires about 70g of protein daily. Growing children and teenagers need more protein than adults.

**ACTIVITY**

1. Calculate how much protein you need.
2. Make a list of the foods you ate yesterday. Circle those that contained HBV protein; underline those that contained LBV protein. Are you eating enough protein? Are you eating 50% of each type? Collect some food packaging. Look up the protein content of each food. Tabulate your answer according to the amount of protein present. Which food contains the most protein, and which contains the least?

Refined food, page 41

## Carbohydrates

Carbohydrates are found only in plant foods.* They are important in the diet as they are a cheap and plentiful source of energy. Most staple foods such as bread and rice consist mainly of carbohydrate. Many carbohydrate foods are refined or processed during manufacture. Unprocessed carbohydrates such as whole cereals and brown bread are healthier.

### Composition

1. The basic unit of a carbohydrate is a single sugar unit, e.g. **glucose**.
2. When several sugar units join, they form a carbohydrate: e.g. lots of glucose units joined makes starch, a common carbohydrate.
3. During the digestion of starch, the chains are broken down into glucose units, which are used by the body cells to provide energy.

(a) glucose unit

(b) starch

(c) starch after digestion

### Classification and sources of carbohydrate

Carbohydrates are placed in three groups:

| | | |
|---|---|---|
| 1 | **Sugars**\*\* | Sugar, honey, cakes, jam, fruit (fresh and dried), sweets, soft drinks. |
| 2 | **Starches** | Cereals, pasta, flour, bread, potatoes. |
| 3 | **Dietary fibre** | Whole cereals e.g. brown rice, oatmeal, wholemeal bread, fruit and vegetables. |

Low-sugar diet, page 45

*Plants make their food by a process called **photosynthesis**. A green colouring pigment (chlorophyll) in the leaves converts sunlight to energy; this is used to make food (glucose) in the plant.

\*\*Although sugar supplies energy, it is not essential in the diet. As it contains no other nutrients it is said to provide only 'empty kilocalories'. Starchy, high-fibre foods such as bread and potatoes are a healthier source of energy.

## Functions of carbohydrates

1. They supply heat and energy.
2. Excess carbohydrate is stored as fat, which helps to insulate the body.
3. Dietary fibre helps move food through the intestines; this prevents bowel disease.

## Dietary fibre

Dietary fibre is a substance that is plentiful in the outside layers of fruit and vegetables and the husks of grain. It is not digested or absorbed by the body but moves food quickly through the intestine, then passes out as waste.

The average person needs 30g of dietary fibre each day. In Ireland, we eat too little dietary fibre; nutritionists recommend a 50% increase in the amount of fibre in the average diet.

**ACTIVITY**

List four ways in which you could change your diet to increase the fibre content.

❖ *High-fibre foods*

High-fibre diet,
page 41

## Fats/oils (lipids)

These are the main source of energy in the diet. They are called **fats** when they are solid at room temperature (e.g. butter, margarine), and **oils** when they are liquid at room temperature (e.g. olive oil). The body stores any extra fat we eat. Eating too much fat can lead to obesity. Fat in some food is visible – the food looks greasy. Watch out for invisible fats which may be hidden in foods such as biscuits, pastry, sausages and snacks.

## Classification and sources of fats

| Saturated | Unsaturated |
| --- | --- |
| *(mainly animal sources)* | *(mainly vegetable sources)* |
| Meat fat (suet, lard, dripping), butter, cream, full fat cheese, egg yolk, hard margarines. | Many vegetable oils, e.g. corn and olive oil, oily fish, nuts, cereals, polyunsaturated margarines, e.g. Flora. |

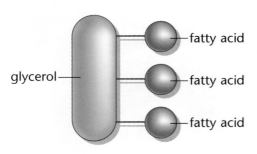

*❖ Structure of fats*

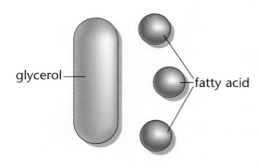

*❖ Fats after digestion*

Obesity, page 46

Coronary heart disease, page 43

## Composition

❶ Fats are made up of carbon, hydrogen and oxygen.

❷ These elements are arranged to form glycerol and three fatty acids.

❸ The fatty acids and glycerol link together to form a fat.

❹ During digestion the links break, separating the glycerol from its three fatty acids and allowing them to be absorbed into the blood.

## Functions

❶ Fats are a concentrated source of heat and energy.

❷ They protect delicate organs, e.g. the kidneys.

❸ They prevent heat loss by forming an insulating layer under th skin.

❹ They are a source of fat-soluble vitamins A, D, E and K.

❺ As fats stay a long time in the stomach, they give a feeling of fullness for longer.

## Fats in the diet

Fats contain twice as much energy as proteins or carbohydrates. Excess energy is stored as adipose tissue (body fat), therefore eating too much fatty food will cause a person to put on weight.

Too much fat may lead to:

✦ obesity

✦ heart disease/strokes

✦ some cancers.

Nutrition experts recommend that we reduce our daily intake of fat from 40% to 30% of the total energy in the diet, and change from saturated to unsaturated fats so that we eat about half of each.

1. Look up the food tables on pages 28–30. List the six food that contain the highest proportion of fat.

2. Find out six foods that contain no fat, and suggest a recip which you could use all six.

# Vitamins

Vitamins are **micronutrients**, i.e. they are needed in very small amounts. Vitamins are essential for good health; lack of any vitamin can cause a **deficiency disease**. The main source of vitamins is food, but some vitamins are also made in the body (B and K) and by sunlight on the skin (D). Vitamins are available as food supplements, e.g. in tablet form, but a good mixed diet should provide all the vitamins needed by the body.

## Classification

- Fat-soluble vitamins – A, D, E, K.
- Water-soluble vitamins – B group, C.

Fat-soluble vitamins are stored in body fat and can build up to toxic levels if too many vitamin supplements are taken. Water-soluble vitamins are not stored in the body, therefore care must be taken to eat foods rich in these vitamins each day. Water-soluble vitamins are destroyed by heat and careless cooking; follow the guidelines at the end of this section to prevent vitamin loss from food.

## Fat-soluble vitamins

| Vitamin | Sources | Functions | Deficiencies |
|---|---|---|---|
| A<br><br>Carotene (changes to vitamin A in the body) | Fish liver oils, e.g. cod liver oil, oily fish, offal, margarine, eggs<br>Carrots, peppers, oranges, tomatoes, dark green vegetables | 1 Growth<br>2 Healthy eyes<br>3 Healthy skin and lining membranes, e.g. mouth, throat | 1 Retarded growth<br>2 Night blindness<br>3 Dry lining tissues |
| D | Sunshine, fish liver oils, oily fish, milk, margarine, liver, eggs, cheese, breakfast cereals | Healthy bones and teeth | Bone diseases, e.g. rickets (children), osteoporosis (adults) |
| E | Margarine, egg yolk, vegetable oils, spinach, nuts | Healthy red blood cells Acts as an antioxidant | Anaemia in the newborn |
| K | Made in bowel by bacteria Green vegetables, cereals, liver | Helps blood to clot | Clotting problems |

## Water-soluble vitamins

| Vitamin | Sources | Functions | | Deficiencies | |
|---|---|---|---|---|---|
| B group | Meat, fish, eggs, cheese, nuts, pulses, cereals, wholemeal bread | 1 2 3 | Energy release Healthy nerves Growth | 1 2 3 | Tiredness Beriberi (nerve disease) Pellagra (disease of skin and tongue) |
| C (Ascorbic acid) | Fruit and vegetables, e.g. blackcurrants, citrus fruits, peppers, green vegetables, potatoes | 1 2 3 4 | General health Skin, gums Blood vessels Iron absorption | 1 2 3 4 | Feeling 'run down' Scurvy Slow healing (e.g. wounds Anaemia (indirectly) |

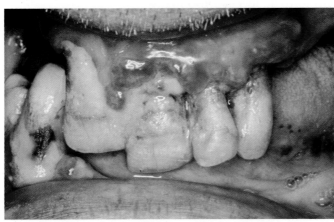

✥ *The mouth of someone suffering from scurvy*

## Vitamin C and scurvy

Hundreds of years ago, many sailors who spent a lor time at sea died from a disease called scurvy. Their gums and tongue became swollen and cracked; their teeth fell out and their skin cut and bruised easily. About 200 years ago it was discovered that citrus frui such as oranges and limes cured the disease. Captain Cook ordered that all sailors on his voyages be given ration of lime juice to prevent the dreaded scurvy. Before long, British sailors were known as limeys (they still sometimes are today). It took over a centur for scientists to discover the miracle ingredient which saved so many lives. It was vitamin C.

## Minerals

Mineral elements, like vitamins, are **micronutrients**, i.e. **they are required by the body in very small amounts**. Minerals are essential for good health. There are man minerals in food, but nutrition surveys have shown that the two most often lacking in the diet in this country, particularly that of females, are calcium and iron.

Calcium is the mineral that makes the bones of the skeleton hard. Calcium-rich foods must be eaten regularly to keep the bones strong. If there is not enough calciur or vitamin D in the diet, the bones become soft and pliable. This causes rickets (see below) in children and osteomalacia (softening of the bones) in adults.

Calcium is particularly important in the diet of pregnant and nursing mothers, babies, children and adolescents – in fact anyone whose bones are growing. The best sources of calcium are milk, yoghurt and cheese. Low-fat dairy products retain their calcium after the fat is removed, and enriched/fortified milks such as Supermilk contain extra calcium.

The most important minerals in food are:

| | | | |
|---|---|---|---|
| calcium | potassium | phosphorus | sodium |
| iron | chlorine | iodine | fluorine |

## Calcium

| Sources | Functions | Deficiency diseases |
|---|---|---|
| Milk, cheese, yoghurt, tinned fish (e.g. salmon), hard water, flour, green vegetables | Healthy bones and teeth (together with phosphorus and vitamin D) | Rickets (children), osteoporosis (elderly people), dental decay |

## Rickets

Calcium and vitamin D work together to build strong bones. If either is lacking in the diet of babies they are likely to suffer from rickets. **Children with rickets have badly deformed bones**, e.g. bow legs and bent spines. Rickets was common in industrial cities at the beginning of the twentieth century because smog prevented sunshine (a source of vitamin D) from getting through, and diets were poor. Today, rickets is rare.

## Osteoporosis (brittle bone disease)

As people get older, **their bones lose calcium and become thinner**. In some people, the bones become **porous and fragile and break very easily**. This is known as **osteoporosis**. It is much more common in women than in men, partly because women's bones are thinner than men's and partly due to calcium loss during pregnancy. While little can be done once it occurs, it can be prevented by:

- eating foods rich in calcium and vitamin D from an early age
- taking regular exercise from an early age
- avoiding smoking.

Preventative medicine, page 249

## Iron

| Sources | Functions | Deficiency diseases |
|---|---|---|
| Offal, red meat, dark green vegetables, cereals, wholemeal bread | Necessary to form haemoglobin in the blood | Anaemia (due to too little haemoglobin) |

Iron is necessary for healthy blood. It helps form the pigment haemoglobin in the red blood cells, which carries oxygen to every cell of the body.

If the body lacks haemoglobin, less oxygen gets to the cells and the body feels tired and weak. This is called anaemia.

### Anaemia

Anaemia is caused by lack of iron. Symptoms: feeling 'run down', tiredness, dizziness, pale skin, poor appetite.

### Vitamin C helps the body to absorb iron

A person could eat iron-rich foods and still become anaemic if their diet lacked vitamin C. Women of child-bearing age need to have a good intake of both iron and vitamin C to make good the iron they lose due to menstruation (periods) and childbirth. During pregnancy, iron intake needs to be increased to provide for the needs of the growing baby. Growing children and adolescents also need extra iron.

## Other minerals

| Mineral | Sources | Functions | Deficiency diseases |
|---|---|---|---|
| Phosphorus | Most foods, particularly meat, fish, cheese, eggs, green vegetables | With calcium, forms bones and teeth, regulates body pH | Weak bones |
| Iodine | Sea fish, seaweed, cereals, vegetables grown near sea | Necessary for thyroid gland (this controls metabolism) | Goitre (enlarged thyroid gland) Metabolism slows down, leading to obesity |
| Fluorine | Fish, drinking water, toothpaste | Helps prevent tooth decay | Dental caries (decay) |
| Potassium | Most foods. Soya beans, nuts, fish, bacon | Maintains muscles, nerves and heartbeat | Rare, except in starvation Weakness, kidney damage |
| Sodium* | Salt added at table and when cooking Bacon, cheese, snack foods | Controls water balance of body | Muscle cramps (loss of salt may be caused by vomiting, diarrhoea) |

Low-salt diet, page 44

*Too much salt in the diet is associated with high blood pressure and strokes.*

## Saving micronutrients

Vitamins and minerals are easily destroyed by careless food preparation. To retain maximum nourishment:

- All foods eaten should be as fresh as possible.
- Eat fruit and vegetables raw, if possible.
- Avoid peeling or soaking fruit and vegetables.
- Use the least possible amount of cooking water; avoid overcooking.
- Serve food at once; avoid keeping food warm for long periods.
- Antibiotics have a damaging effect on certain vitamins, so avoid overuse of them. People taking antibiotics should take vitamin supplements.
- Never add bread soda when cooking green vegetables.
- Smokers need extra vitamin C.

# Water

Water ($H_2O$) contains the elements hydrogen and oxygen in the ratio 2:1.

## Properties

- Pure water is colourless, odourless and tasteless.
- It boils at 100°C and freezes at 0°C.
- It evaporates easily – at 100°C it changes to vapour (steam).
- It dissolves certain substances easily, e.g. salt, sugar.

Water is essential for life. About 70% of the body is made of water – it is the main constituent of every cell. The amount of water in the body is carefully controlled. The body loses about 2 litres of water each day through perspiration and as urine via the kidneys. This loss must be replaced or the body will become dehydrated. Dehydration is common when severe food poisoning causes prolonged vomiting and diarrhoea. If water and salts are not replaced, death may occur.

## Sources of water

Most foods contain water – many fruit and vegetables contain over 90% water. Dry foods contain much less water, e.g. biscuits contain 2% water.

Rehydrating: The water evaporated from dried foods such as fruit and vegetables is replaced during soaking.

| Food | Drinks |
|---|---|
| Fruit and vegetables, soup | Tap water, mineral water*, soft drinks, milk, beverages such as tea and coffee, alcoholic drinks |

## Functions of water

1. Essential part of all body tissues – cells, muscles, etc.

2. Major part of all body fluids – blood, saliva, digestive juices.

3. Transports important substances – oxygen, nutrients, hormones.

4. Helps digestion and absorption by dissolving substances.

5. Assists removal of waste – kidneys filter urine from the blood.

6. Helps control body temperature through perspiration and evaporation from the skin.

## Recommended daily amounts (RDA)

| | |
|---|---|
| Protein | 1g for each kilo body weight |
| Fat | Relates to activity – no more than 30% of energy intake ($\frac{1}{2}$ saturated; $\frac{1}{2}$ unsaturated) |
| Carbohydrate | Relates to activity |
| Fibre | 30g |
| Vitamin A | 700-900 micrograms |
| Vitamin B group | Varies from vitamin to vitamin in the group |
| Vitamin C | 60-75mg |
| Vitamin D | 5 micrograms |
| Calcium | 1,000–1,200 mg |
| Iron | 10–15mg |
| Sodium | 1.5-2g |

*True mineral waters come from natural springs. Many bottled waters are ordinary water to which carbon dioxide has been added. Remember that many drinks contain substances such as caffeine, flavourings, sweeteners and sugar. Check the label.

# Energy

Every single cell in the body requires a constant supply of energy. Food is the fuel that supplies energy to the body. Much like petrol in a car, the food is burned in the body cells and, in the process, heat and energy are released. Because **oxygen is needed to burn the food**, this process is known as **oxidation**. The oxygen for cell activity is breathed in through the lungs.

## The functions of energy

Our bodies need energy:

1. to keep vital organs such as the heart and lungs working
2. for muscle movement and activity
3. for nerve function
4. for cell activity (e.g. oxidation) and cell growth
5. to maintain body temperature at 37°C.

## Energy requirements

The body needs a basic amount of energy to stay alive – to keep vital organs such as the heart and digestive organs working. This is known as the **basal metabolic rate (BMR)**. Extra energy is required for the activities we do, such as walking or running. The more active the body, the more energy is used.

## Factors that influence energy requirements

1. Activity – active people use more energy than less active people.
2. Size – smaller people use less energy than larger people.
3. Gender – females, because they have a lower muscle ratio, require less energy than males.
4. Age – a child or adolescent needs more energy for its size than an adult. Young people are more likely to be active than older people.
5. Pregnancy – extra energy is needed for growth, during pregnancy and during breast feeding.
6. Climate – in cold climates more energy is needed to keep warm.

The more active you are, the more energy you use.

| kcal/hour | Activity |
|---|---|
| 70 | Sleeping |
| 85 | Sitting/reading/watching TV |
| 90/100 | Standing/writing/studying |
| 185 | Normal walking |
| 200/300 | Light/heavy housework |
| 400 | Cycling |
| 500 | Dancing/tennis |
| 600 | Swimming/squash |
| 800/900 | Football/fast running |
| 950 | Walking upstairs |

## Measuring energy

Food energy is measured in **kilocalories or kilojoules (kcal/kJ)**.

1 kilocalorie = 4.2 kilojoules

Remember, a kilocalorie is not a nutrient.

 A kilocalorie is a measurement of the energy provided by a nutrient.

## Energy value of nutrients

Almost every food is a source of energy – some supply more than others.

The amount of energy we get from a food depends on the nutrients it contains.

> 1g of pure protein releases 4 kcal of energy.
>
> 1g of pure carbohydrate releases 4 kcal of energy.
>
> 1g of pure fat releases 9 kcal of energy.
>
> Vitamins, minerals and water supply little or no energy.

It follows that foods that are high in fat are high in kilocalories and are 'fattening'; those containing large amounts of water, such as fruit or green vegetables, are low in kilocalories. Few foods contain just one nutrient; they usually contain several. It would take a long time to work out the amounts of nutrients in and energy provided by different foods, so food tables provide us with this information (see pages 28–30). The nutrients/kilocalories in a food may be shown by the unit, e.g. in one apple, or by weight, e.g. per 100g.

**ACTIVITY** Study the food tables on pages 28–30 and list four high-energy and four low-energy foods.

Food packaging often displays food tables showing nutrition information about a product.

* This simplifies the planning of meals and diets.
* It helps those with allergies to avoid certain food additives.

## Nutrition Information

| | per 100g | per 37.5g serving |
|---|---|---|
| Energy | 1439kj | 540kj |
| | 339kcal | 127 kcal |
| Protein | 11.5g | 4.3g |
| Carbohydrate | 67.3g | 25.2g |
| (of which sugars) | (4.7g) | (1.8g) |
| Fat | 2.7g | 1.0g |
| Fibre | | |
| Soluble | 3.2g | 1.2g |
| Insoluble | 7.7g | 2.9g |
| Sodium | 0.3g | 0.1g |
| Vitamins | | |
| Thiamine ($B_1$) | 1.2mg/85%RDA | 0.4mg/32%RDA |
| Riboflavin ($B_2$) | 1.4mg/85%RDA | 0.5mg/33%RDA |
| Niacin | 15.3mg/85%RDA | 5.7mg/32%RDA |
| Folacin (Folic Acid) | 170.0µg/85%RDA | 63.8µg/32%RDA |
| Iron | 11.9mg/85%RDA | 4.5mg/32%RDA |

**ACTIVITY** This is a label from a cereal product.

1. What is the energy value of a serving of the product?
2. List four important nutrients in the product.
3. What is the total amount of fibre in a serving?
4. Name two foods you could serve with this product in order to improve its food value.

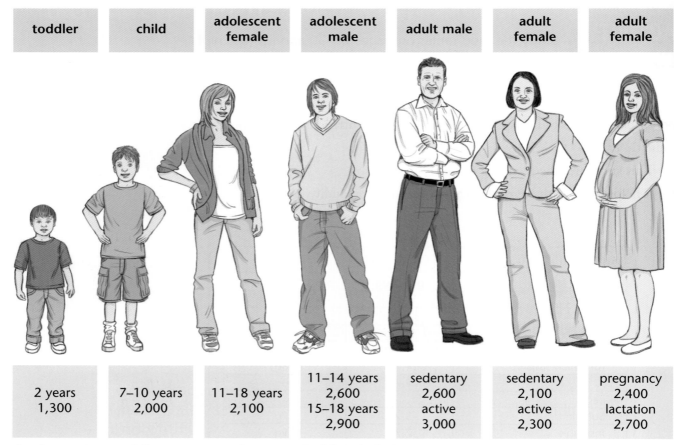

| toddler | child | adolescent female | adolescent male | adult male | adult female | adult female |
|---|---|---|---|---|---|---|
| 2 years 1,300 | 7–10 years 2,000 | 11–18 years 2,100 | 11–14 years 2,600 15–18 years 2,900 | sedentary 2,600 active 3,000 | sedentary 2,100 active 2,300 | pregnancy 2,400 lactation 2,700 |

❖ *Approximate daily energy requirements (in kilocalories)*

**ACTIVITY** Work out a day's menu for an adolescent girl. Use the food tables to check kilocalories.

Obesity, page 46

### Energy balance

**To maintain correct body weight, our energy intake (what we eat) must equal energy output** (activities, etc.). If a balance is not maintained, the result will be either weight gain or weight loss.

To lose weight, energy intake (food) must be reduced and energy output (activity/exercise) increased.

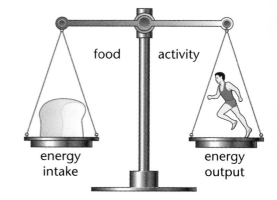

**REVISION QUESTIONS**

1. What is a nutrient? Name six nutrients.
2. Proteins contain nitrogen, which is essential for _____.
3. Explain the terms 'amino acid' and 'high biological value'.
4. Classify proteins and name two good sources of each type of protein.
5. Name two functions of protein.
6. During digestion, proteins break down into _____ _____.
7. Classify carbohydrates. Name a nourishing source of each type of carbohydrate.
8. Carbohydrates are made up of units of _____.
9. Name two functions of dietary fibre.
10. Fats contain the elements _____, _____ and _____.
11. Name three foods that contain unsaturated fat.
12. Name three functions of fat.
13. Explain the term 'adipose tissue'.
14. Name two diseases associated with too much saturated fat in the diet.
15. Name two fat-soluble vitamins and two water-soluble vitamins.
16. Name one vitamin required to prevent each of the following: scurvy, night blindness, beri beri, rickets.
17. What is meant by a deficiency disease?
18. What is the function of iron in the body?
19. Name two functions of vitamin C.
20. Name two diseases caused by lack of calcium.
21. Name two functions of B vitamins.
22. Food energy is measured in _____.
23. Name four factors that influence the amount of energy we need. What is meant by 'energy balance'?
24. What are the functions of energy in the body?
25. Explain the term 'oxidation'.
26. Name three properties of water.
27. What is the main function of haemoglobin in the body?
28. List the functions of water in the body.

# Chapter
## 3 Digestion of Food

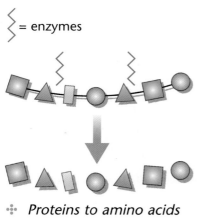

= enzymes

❖ *Proteins to amino acids*

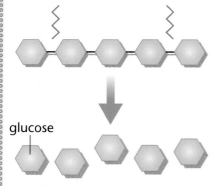

glucose

❖ *Carbohydrates to simple sugars*

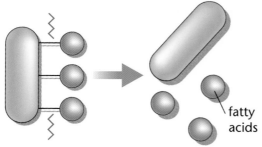

fatty acids

❖ *Fats to fatty acids and glycerol*

**❶ Digestion is the process that changes large nutrient molecules, e.g. protein, into smaller molecules, in order that they can enter the bloodstream and be used by body cells.**

**❷** Some changes are **physical** – e.g. the food is churned about and breaks up into small pieces.

**❸** Other changes are **chemical** – the food is changed into different, simpler substances by chemical substances called enzymes:

- ➤ proteins to amino acids
- ➤ carbohydrates to simple sugars such as glucose
- ➤ fats to fatty acids and glycerol.

(Vitamins, minerals and water do not need to be digested.)

Enzymes are chemicals that bring about chemical changes without themselves changing.

Enzymes break the chemical bonds that hold large food molecules together. Each enzyme works on only one nutrient, e.g. pepsin works only on proteins – it won't work on fats.

Nutrients are broken down in stages, e.g. from long chains to shorter chains and finally to single, small units which can be absorbed through the cell walls and travel to the body cells that need them.

# The alimentary canal

This is the passage through which material travels from the time food enters the mouth until the waste leaves the body.

It consists of the:

- mouth
- oesophagus (gullet)
- stomach
- small intestine
- large intestine.

## How food is digested

1. **Mouth:** the teeth break up the food; the tongue mixes it with saliva to moisten it. These are physical changes. Saliva contains an enzyme, salivary amylase, which changes cooked starch to maltose. (Chemical change.)

2. **Oesophagus:** This is a 25cm-long muscular tube that passes from the mouth to the stomach. The muscles move the food down to the stomach in a wave-like movement called **peristalsis**. (Physical change.)

3. **Stomach:** This is a muscular bag situated in the top left of the abdomen, beneath the diaphragm. The stomach churns the food around, changing it into a liquid called **chyme**. (Physical change.) Gastric juice is released from the lining of the stomach. This contains a strong acid called hydrochloric acid, which kills bacteria. It also contains two enzymes: **pepsin**, which changes proteins into peptides (smaller chains); and **rennin**, which curdles milk. The liquid food gradually leaves the stomach and enters the duodenum (the first part of the small intestine).

4. **Small intestine:** This is a tube 6 metres long coiled up in the centre of the abdomen. Its walls are made of muscle, and move the food along by peristalsis. Three important digestive juices enter the small intestine:
   (a) **pancreatic juice** from the pancreas – a gland under the stomach
   (b) **bile** from the liver, which forms an emulsion with fats, making them easier to digest
   (c) **intestinal juice**, which is produced by the lining of the intestine.
   The enzymes in the juices change:
   - proteins and peptides into **amino acids**
   - sugars into simple sugars, such as **glucose**
   - fats into **fatty acids and glycerol**.

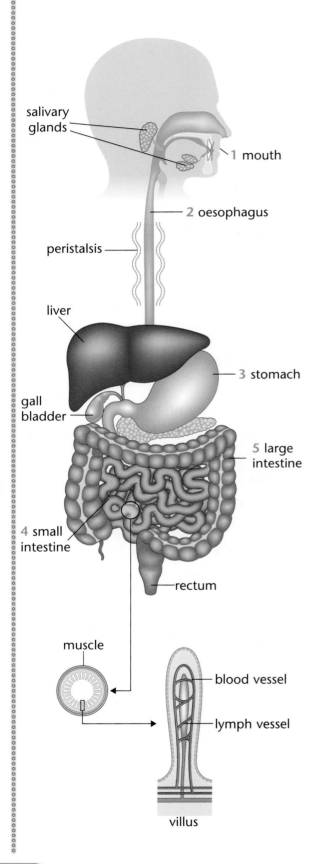

salivary glands
**1** mouth
**2** oesophagus
peristalsis
liver
**3** stomach
gall bladder
**5** large intestine
**4** small intestine
rectum
muscle
blood vessel
lymph vessel
villus

### Absorption

All foods have been broken down and are now ready to be absorbed. The lining of the small intestine is covered in tiny hair-like projections called **villi**. Each villus contains a tiny blood vessel and a lymph vessel into which the nutrients pass.

- Amino acids and glucose go directly into the blood.
- Fats pass through the lymph system to the blood.

The digested nutrients travel in the blood to each cell, where they are used to provide energy and make new cells.

5. **Large intestine:** This is a continuation of the small intestine, and is also called the **colon** or **bowel**. Most of the nutrients have been absorbed by the time food reaches the large intestine, and the food is quite liquid. Water is reabsorbed into the bloodstream, making the waste food (now called **faeces**) more solid. The faeces are pushed through the intestine by peristalsis; a high-fibre diet helps this movement by making the waste more bulky. The last few centimetres, called the rectum, contains strong muscles which expel the faeces from the body. Some vitamins (B group and K) are manufactured in the large intestine.

## Summary of digestion

| | |
|---|---|
| Mouth | Teeth break down food; it is mixed with saliva. |
| | Salivary amylase changes cooked starch to maltose. |
| Stomach | Food is churned into chyme. |
| | Hydrochloric acid kills bacteria. |
| | Pepsin changes proteins to peptides. |
| | Rennin curdles milk. |
| Small intestine | Bile emulsifies fats. |
| | Peptides are changed to amino acids. |
| | Fats are changed to glycerol and fatty acids. |
| | Starch/maltose are changed to glucose. |
| Absorption | Amino acids pass through villi into blood capillaries |
| | Glucose passes through villi into blood capillaries. |
| | Glycerol and fatty acids pass through lymph vessels to blood. |
| Large intestine | Waste is eliminated (removed). |
| | Water is reabsorbed from food into the blood. |
| | Vitamins B and K are manufactured. |

**REVISION QUESTIONS**

1. Describe a physical change and a chemical change that occur during digestion.
2. The enzyme in saliva is called _____.
3. What is an enzyme? What is its function in digestion?
4. Explain the term 'peristalsis'.
5. Name the acid in the stomach. What is its function?
6. What is the duodenum?
7. What is the purpose of bile?
8. Complete this sentence:
   At the end of digestion, proteins have changed into _____, carbohydrates have changed into _____ and fats have changed into _____.
9. What are villi?
10. List the functions of the large intestine.
11. Why is white fish more digestible than oily fish?

## Composition of Foods (per 100 g)

| FOOD | Inedible waste % | Energy kcal | kJ | Protein g | Fat g | Carbohydrate (as monosaccharide) g | Water g | Calcium mg | Iron mg | Vitamin A (retinol equivalent) µg | Vitamin B Group† | Vitamin C mg | Vitamin D µg |
|---|---|---|---|---|---|---|---|---|---|---|---|---|---|
| **Milk** | | | | | | | | | | | | | |
| Cream, double | 0 | 449 | 1848 | 1.8 | 48.0 | 2.6 | 47 | 65 | 0 | 420 | L | 0 | 0.28 |
| Milk, liquid, whole | 0 | 65 | 274 | 3.3 | 3.8 | 4.8 | 88 | 120 | 0.1 | 44 | L | 1 | 0.05 |
| Milk, condensed, sweetened | 0 | 322 | 1361 | 8.2 | 9.2 | 55.1 | 28 | 290 | 0.2 | 112 | L | 3 | 0.09 |
| Milk, dried, skimmed | 0 | 352 | 1498 | 36.0 | 0.9 | 53.3 | 5 | 1260 | 0.5 | 4 | M | 10 | 0 |
| Yogurt, low-fat, natural | 0 | 53 | 224 | 5.0 | 1.0 | 6.4 | 86 | 180 | 0.1 | 10 | L | 0 | 0.02 |
| Yogurt, low-fat, fruit | 0 | 96 | 410 | 4.8 | 1.0 | 18.2 | 75 | 160 | 0.2 | 10 | L | 1 | 0.02 |
| **Cheese** | | | | | | | | | | | | | |
| Cheese, Cheddar | 0 | 412 | 1708 | 25.4 | 34.5 | 0 | 37 | 810 | 0.6 | 420 | L | 0 | 0.35 |
| Cheese, cottage | 0 | 114 | 480 | 15.3 | 4.0 | 4.5 | 75 | 80 | 0.4 | 27 | L | 0 | 0.02 |
| **Meat** | | | | | | | | | | | | | |
| Bacon, rashers, cooked | 0 | 447 | 1852 | 24.5 | 38.8 | 0 | 32 | 12 | 1.4 | 0 | M | 0 | 0 |
| Beef, average | 17 | 226 | 940 | 18.1 | 17.1 | 0 | 64 | 7 | 1.9 | 0 | M | 0 | 0 |
| Chicken, roast | 0 | 148 | 621 | 24.8 | 5.4 | 0 | 68 | 9 | 0.8 | 0 | M | 0 | 0 |
| Ham, cooked | 0 | 269 | 1119 | 24.7 | 18.9 | 0 | 54 | 9 | 1.3 | 0 | M | 0 | 0 |
| Kidney, average | 11 | 89 | 375 | 16.2 | 2.7 | 0 | 79 | 9 | 6.0 | 300 | M | 12 | 0 |
| Lamb, roast | 0 | 291 | 1209 | 23.0 | 22.1 | 0 | 54 | 9 | 2.1 | 0 | M | 0 | 0 |
| Liver, fried | 0 | 244 | 1020 | 24.9 | 13.7 | 5.6 | 56 | 14 | 8.8 | 6000 | H | 20 | 0.75 |
| Luncheon meat | 0 | 313 | 1298 | 12.6 | 26.9 | 5.5 | 52 | 15 | 1.0 | 0 | M | 0 | 0 |
| Pork, average | 15 | 330 | 1364 | 15.8 | 29.6 | 0 | 54 | 8 | 0.8 | 0 | H | 0 | 0 |
| Sausage, pork | 0 | 367 | 1520 | 10.6 | 32.1 | 9.5 | 45 | 41 | 1.1 | 0 | M | 0 | 0 |
| Steak and kidney pie | 0 | 304 | 1266 | 13.3 | 21.1 | 14.6 | 51 | 37 | 5.1 | 126 | M | 0 | 0.55 |
| **Fish** | | | | | | | | | | | | | |
| Cod; haddock; white fish | 40 | 76 | 321 | 17.4 | 0.7 | 0 | 82 | 16 | 0.3 | 0 | L | 0 | 0 |
| Cod, fried in batter | 0 | 199 | 834 | 19.6 | 10.3 | 7.5 | 61 | 80 | 0.5 | 0 | M | 0 | 0 |
| Fish fingers | 0 | 178 | 749 | 12.6 | 7.5 | 16.1 | 64 | 43 | 0.7 | 0 | L | 0 | 0 |
| Herring | 37 | 234 | 970 | 16.8 | 18.5 | 0 | 64 | 33 | 0.8 | 45 | L | 0 | 22.20 |
| Salmon, canned | 2 | 155 | 648 | 20.3 | 8.2 | 0 | 70 | 93 | 1.4 | 90 | M | 0 | 12.50 |
| Sardines, canned in oil | 0 | 217 | 906 | 23.7 | 13.6 | 0 | 58 | 550 | 2.9 | 30 | M | 0 | 7.50 |
| **Eggs** | | | | | | | | | | | | | |
| Eggs, fresh | 12 | 147 | 612 | 12.3 | 10.9 | 0 | 75 | 54 | 2.1 | 140 | L | 0 | 1.50 |
| **Fats** | | | | | | | | | | | | | |
| Butter | 0 | 731 | 3006 | 0.5 | 81.0 | 0 | 16 | 15 | 0.2 | 995 | 0 | 0 | 1.25 |
| Lard; cooking fat; dripping | 0 | 894 | 3674 | 0 | 99.3 | 0 | 1 | 0 | 0 | 0 | 0 | 0 | 0 |
| Low-fat spread | 0 | 365 | 1500 | 0 | 40.5 | 0 | 57 | 0 | 0 | 900 | 0 | 0 | 8.00 |
| Margarine | 0 | 734 | 3019 | 0.2 | 81.5 | 0 | 15 | 4 | 0.3 | 900 | 0 | 0 | 8.00 |
| Oils, cooking and salad | 0 | 899 | 3696 | 0 | 99.9 | 0 | 0 | 0 | 0 | 0 | 0 | 0 | 0 |
| **Preserves, etc.** | | | | | | | | | | | | | |
| Chocolate milk | 0 | 578 | 2411 | 8.7 | 37.6 | 54.5 | 0 | 246 | 1.7 | 6.6 | L | 0 | 0 |
| Honey | 0 | 288 | 1229 | 0.4 | 0 | 76.4 | 23 | 5 | 0.4 | 0 | L | 0 | 0 |
| Jam | 0 | 262 | 1116 | 0.5 | 0 | 69.2 | 30 | 18 | 1.2 | 2.0 | | 10 | 0 |
| Sugar, white | 0 | 394 | 1680 | 0 | 0 | 105.0 | 0 | 1 | 0 | 0 | 0 | 0 | 0 |

Food

| | Inedible waste % | Energy kcal | kJ | Protein g | Fat g | Carbohydrate (as monosaccharide) g | Water g | Calcium mg | Iron mg | Vitamin A (retinol equivalent) µg | Vitamin B Group† | Vitamin C mg | Vitamin D µg |
|---|---|---|---|---|---|---|---|---|---|---|---|---|---|
| ables | | | | | | | | | | | | | |
| canned in tomato sauce | 0 | 63 | 266 | 5.1 | 0.4 | 10.3 | 74 | 45 | 1.4 | 50 | L | 3 | 0 |
| broad | 75 | 69 | 293 | 7.2 | 0.5 | 9.5 | 77 | 30 | 1.1 | 22 | M | 30 | 0 |
| runner | 14 | 23 | 100 | 2.2 | 0 | 3.9 | 89 | 27 | 0.8 | 50 | L | 20 | 0 |
| ot, boiled | 20 | 44 | 189 | 1.8 | 0 | 9.9 | 83 | 30 | 0.7 | 0 | L | 5 | 0 |
| s sprouts, boiled | 0 | 17 | 75 | 2.8 | 0 | 1.7 | 92 | 25 | 0.5 | 67 | L | 41 | 0 |
| ge, green, raw | 30 | 22 | 92 | 2.8 | 0 | 2.8 | 88 | 57 | 0.6 | 50 | L | 53 | 0 |
| ge, green, boiled | 0 | 15 | 66 | 1.7 | 0 | 2.3 | 93 | 38 | 0.4 | 50 | L | 23 | 0 |
| s, old | 4 | 23 | 98 | 0.7 | 0 | 5.4 | 90 | 48 | 0.6 | 2000 | L | 6 | 0 |
| ower | 30 | 13 | 56 | 1.9 | 0 | 1.5 | 93 | 21 | 0.5 | 5 | L | 64 | 0 |
| | 27 | 8 | 36 | 0.9 | 0 | 1.3 | 94 | 52 | 0.6 | 0 | L | 7 | 0 |
| potato | 0 | 533 | 2222 | 6.2 | 35.9 | 49.3 | 3 | 37 | 2.1 | 0 | M | 17 | 0 |
| ber | 23 | 9 | 39 | 0.6 | 0 | 1.8 | 96 | 23 | 0.3 | 0 | L | 8 | 0 |
| dry | 0 | 295 | 1256 | 23.8 | 0 | 53.2 | 12 | 39 | 7.6 | 6 | M | 0 | 0 |
| e | 20 | 8 | 36 | 1.0 | 0 | 1.2 | 96 | 23 | 0.9 | 167 | L | 15 | 0 |
| oms | 25 | 7 | 31 | 1.8 | 0 | 0 | 92 | 3 | 10 | 0 | L | 3 | 0 |
| s | 3 | 23 | 98 | 0.9 | 0 | 5.2 | 93 | 31 | 0.3 | 0 | L | 10 | 0 |
| s | 26 | 49 | 210 | 1.7 | 0 | 11.3 | 83 | 55 | 0.6 | 0 | L | 15 | 0 |
| resh or frozen, boiled | 0 | 49 | 208 | 5.0 | 0 | 7.7 | 80 | 13 | 1.2 | 50 | L | 15 | 0 |
| anned, processed | 0 | 76 | 325 | 6.2 | 0 | 13.7 | 72 | 27 | 1.5 | 67 | L | 0 | 0 |
| s, green | 16 | 14 | 59 | 0.9 | 0.2 | 2.2 | 94 | 9 | 0.4 | 42 | L | 91 | 0 |
| es, raw | 27 | 76 | 324 | 2.1 | 0 | 18.0 | 78 | 8 | 0.7 | 0 | L | 8–30* | 0 |
| es, boiled | 0 | 80 | 339 | 1.4 | 0 | 19.7 | 81 | 4 | 0.5 | 0 | L | 4–15* | 0 |
| chips, fried | 0 | 236 | 1028 | 3.8 | 9.0 | 37.3 | 48 | 14 | 1.4 | 0 | L | 6–20* | 0 |
| es, roast | 0 | 111 | 474 | 2.8 | 1.0 | 27.3 | 64 | 10 | 1.0 | 0 | L | 6–23* | 0 |
| orn, canned | 0 | 79 | 336 | 2.9 | 0.8 | 16.1 | 73 | 3 | 0.1 | 35 | L | 4 | 0 |
| es, fresh | 0 | 12 | 52 | 0.8 | 0 | 2.4 | 93 | 13 | 0.4 | 117 | L | 20 | 0 |
| s | 16 | 18 | 74 | 0.8 | 0 | 3.8 | 93 | 59 | 0.4 | 0 | L | 25 | 0 |
| | | | | | | | | | | | | | |
| | 20 | 46 | 197 | 0.3 | 0 | 12.0 | 84 | 4 | 0.3 | 5 | L | 5 | 0 |
| s, dried | 0 | 182 | 776 | 4.8 | 0 | 43.4 | 15 | 92 | 4.1 | 600 | L | 0 | 0 |
| as | 40 | 76 | 326 | 1.1 | 0 | 19.2 | 71 | 7 | 0.4 | 33 | L | 10 | 0 |
| rrants | 2 | 28 | 121 | 0.9 | 0 | 6.6 | 77 | 60 | 1.3 | 33 | L | 200 | 0 |
| erries | 1 | 27 | 116 | 0.9 | 0 | 6.3 | 87 | 22 | 0.4 | 30 | L | 40 | 0 |
| ruit | 50 | 22 | 95 | 0.6 | 0 | 5.3 | 91 | 17 | 0.3 | 0 | L | 40 | 0 |
| s | 60 | 7 | 31 | 0.3 | 0 | 1.6 | 91 | 8 | 0.1 | 0 | L | 50 | 0 |
| | 40 | 23 | 97 | 0.8 | 0 | 5.2 | 94 | 16 | 0.4 | 160 | L | 25 | 0 |
| es | 30 | 35 | 150 | 0.8 | 0 | 8.5 | 86 | 41 | 0.3 | 8 | L | 50 | 0 |
| e juice, canned, | 0 | 47 | 201 | 0.8 | 0 | 11.7 | 87 | 10 | 0.4 | 8 | L | 40 | 0 |
| ncentrated | | | | | | | | | | | | | |
| s, fresh | 13 | 36 | 156 | 0.6 | 0 | 9.1 | 86 | 5 | 0.4 | 83 | L | 8 | 0 |
| s, canned (incl. syrup) | 0 | 88 | 373 | 0.4 | 0 | 22.9 | 74 | 4 | 1.9 | 41 | L | 4 | 0 |
| fresh | 25 | 41 | 175 | 0.3 | 0 | 10.6 | 83 | 8 | 0.2 | 2 | L | 0 | 0 |
| ple, canned (incl. syrup) | 0 | 76 | 325 | 0.3 | 0 | 20.0 | 77 | 13 | 1.7 | 7 | L | 8 | 0 |
| | 8 | 32 | 137 | 0.6 | 0 | 7.9 | 85 | 12 | 0.3 | 37 | L | 3 | 0 |
| , dried | 17 | 161 | 686 | 2.4 | 0 | 40.3 | 23 | 38 | 2.9 | 160 | L | 0 | 0 |
| rries | 0 | 25 | 105 | 0.9 | 0 | 5.6 | 83 | 41 | 1.2 | 13 | L | 25 | 0 |
| b | 33 | 6 | 26 | 0.6 | 0 | 1.0 | 94 | 103 | 0.4 | 10 | L | 10 | 0 |
| erries | 3 | 26 | 109 | 0.6 | 0 | 6.2 | 89 | 22 | 0.7 | 5 | L | 60 | 0 |
| as | 0 | 249 | 1064 | 1.7 | 0 | 64.7 | 18 | 52 | 1.8 | 0 | L | 0 | 0 |

| | Inedible waste % | Energy kcal | kJ | Protein g | Fat g | Carbohydrate (as monosaccharide) g | Water g | Calcium mg | Iron mg | Vitamin A (retinol equivalent) µg | Vitamin B Group† | Vitamin C mg | Vitamin D µg |
|---|---|---|---|---|---|---|---|---|---|---|---|---|---|
| **Nuts** | | | | | | | | | | | | | |
| Almonds | 63 | 580 | 2397 | 20.5 | 53.5 | 4.3 | 5 | 247 | 4.2 | 0 | M | 0 | 0 |
| Coconut, desiccated | 0 | 608 | 2509 | 6.6 | 62.0 | 6.4 | 3 | 22 | 3.6 | 0 | L | 0 | 0 |
| Peanuts, roasted | 0 | 586 | 2428 | 28.1 | 49.0 | 8.6 | 5 | 61 | 2.0 | 0 | M | 0 | 0 |
| **Cereals** | | | | | | | | | | | | | |
| Barley, pearl, dry | 0 | 360 | 1531 | 7.7 | 1.7 | 83.6 | 11 | 10 | 0.7 | 0 | L | 0 | 0 |
| Biscuits, chocolate | 0 | 497 | 2087 | 7.1 | 24.9 | 65.3 | 3 | 131 | 1.5 | 0 | L | 0 | 0 |
| Biscuits, cream crackers | 0 | 471 | 1985 | 8.1 | 16.2 | 78.0 | 4 | 145 | 2.2 | 0 | L | 0 | 0 |
| Biscuits, plain | 0 | 431 | 1819 | 7.4 | 13.2 | 75.3 | 3 | 126 | 1.8 | 0 | L | 0 | 0 |
| Biscuits, rich, sweet | 0 | 496 | 2084 | 5.6 | 22.3 | 72.7 | 3 | 92 | 1.3 | 0 | L | 0 | 0 |
| Bread, white | 0 | 251 | 1068 | 8.0 | 1.7 | 54.3 | 39 | 100 | 1.7 | 0 | L | 0 | 0 |
| Bread, wholemeal | 0 | 241 | 1025 | 9.6 | 3.1 | 46.7 | 38 | 28 | 3.0 | 0 | L | 0 | 0 |
| Cornflakes | 0 | 354 | 1507 | 7.4 | 0.4 | 85.4 | 2 | 5 | 0.3 | 0 | M | 0 | 0 |
| Crispbread, Ryvita | 0 | 318 | 1352 | 10.0 | 2.1 | 69.0 | 6 | 86 | 3.3 | 0 | L | 0 | 0 |
| Flour, white | 0 | 348 | 1483 | 10.0 | 0.9 | 80.0 | 13 | 138 | 2.1 | 0 | L | 0 | 0 |
| Oatmeal | 0 | 400 | 1692 | 12.1 | 8.7 | 72.8 | 9 | 55 | 4.1 | 0 | M | 0 | 0 |
| Rice | 0 | 359 | 1531 | 6.2 | 1.0 | 86.8 | 12 | 4 | 0.4 | 0 | L | 0 | 0 |
| Spaghetti | 0 | 364 | 1549 | 9.9 | 1.0 | 84.0 | 12 | 23 | 1.2 | 0 | L | 0 | 0 |
| **Beverages** | | | | | | | | | | | | | |
| Chocolate, drinking | 0 | 397 | 1683 | 5.5 | 6.3 | 84.8 | 3 | 5 | 2.8 | 2 | L | 0 | 0 |
| Coffee, ground | 0 | 0 | 0 | 0 | 0 | 0 | 4 | 0 | 0 | 0 | M | 0 | 0 |
| Cola drink | 0 | 46 | 195 | 0 | 0 | 12.2 | 90 | 0 | 0 | 0 | 0 | 0 | 0 |
| Squash, fruit, undiluted | 0 | 122 | 521 | 0.1 | 0.1 | 32.2 | 63 | 16 | 0.2 | 0 | 0 | 1 | 0 |

† Average values: High (H), Medium (M), Low (L)
* Higher figure = fresh/new potatoes

# Chapter 4 Balancing the Diet

A balanced diet is a diet that contains all necessary nutrients in the correct proportion for the needs of the body.

As it is difficult to work out exactly how much of each nutrient we eat, even at one meal, nutritionists have made it easier by grouping foods of similar food value.

There are four main food groups:

- the protein/meat group
- the milk/cheese group
- the fruit/vegetable group
- the cereal/bread/potato group.

To make it easier, the groups are shown on a food pyramid. This represents the groups in a way that helps us remember which we should be eating more of and those we should eat in smaller quantities. We should eat more of the foods shown at the bottom, where the pyramid is wider. It narrows towards the top, and we should eat less of the foods shown at the top.

*The healthy diet pyramid*

**Others** *(eat sparingly)*
Sugar, sugary snack foods, e.g. sweets
Oils and fats, fatty snack food, e.g. biscuits (use oil sparingly – spread fats thinly)
Alcohol: moderately, preferably with meals

**The protein group**
*(for body-building and repair)*
Adults and children – 2 servings daily
Pregnancy – 3 servings daily
- 2 eggs
- palm-sized piece of meat or fish
- 50g cheese (preferably low-fat)
- 6 tablespoons cooked peas or beans
- 75g nuts

**The milk/cheese group**
*(rich in calcium, protein, vitamins A and B)*
Adults and children – 3 servings daily
Adolescents – 4 servings daily
Pregnancy/breast feeding – 5 servings daily
- glass of milk
- carton of yoghurt
- 25g hard cheese
- bowl of milky pudding (low-fat products are preferable, except for young children)

**The fruit/vegetable group**
*(vitamins, minerals, fibre)*
4 or more servings daily
- small glass of unsweetened fruit juice
- at least two tablespoons of cooked vegetable or salad
- one medium-sized fruit
- small bowl of vegetable soup
- two tablespoons of cooked unsweetened fruit

**The cereal/bread/potato group**
*(this should be our main source of energy – choose unrefined foods for fibre and B vitamins)*
Adults – 6 servings daily
Children – 4 servings daily
*(active people need larger amounts)*
- 25g unsweetened wholegrain breakfast cereal
- 25g slice of wholemeal bread
- heaped tablespoon of cooked rice/pasta
- 1 medium potato – boiled or baked

- *indicates one serving*

**ACTIVITY**

1.  (a)  Make a list of the foods you ate yesterday.
    (b)  Group them according to the healthy diet pyramid.
    (c)  Are you eating the correct amount from each group?
2.  Using the diet pyramid, plan a healthy eating day, possibly at the weekend.

❖ *Manual workers require more energy food than sedentary workers*

## Balanced eating

A well-balanced diet, as already mentioned, will supply nutrients in the proportion needed by the body ($\frac{1}{6}$ protein; $\frac{1}{3}$ fat; $\frac{1}{2}$ carbohydrates). However, because people differ a lot allowances must be made for:

-   age and size – young people need more nutrients for their size than adults
-   growth – babies, children, adolescents, and pregnant and nursing mothers require more protein, iron, calcium and energy foods than others
-   activity – active people such as manual workers require more energy foods than sedentary people (those who spend most of the day sitting down)
-   health – those with certain conditions such as allergies or diabetes may have to restrict their diet.

Eating a balanced diet gives you the best possible chance of being healthy and fit. Although we have a greater selection of food than ever before, many people today make bad food choices.

Diseases associated with a poor diet include:

-   coronary heart disease
-   high blood pressure/strokes
-   cancer, particularly of the bowel
-   obesity.

### Prevention is better than cure

In most cases, food-related diseases can be prevented by eating correctly. A change in eating patterns can often improve an existing condition.

# Dietary needs

## Babies

1. Babies should be **breast fed** if possible for the first six months of life, because:
   - the nutrients in breast milk are more suitable for a baby's needs
   - breast milk is at the correct temperature
   - immunity to certain illnesses is passed from mother to child
   - it helps mother–child bonding.

2. If a dried milk formula is used, follow measuring and sterilising instructions carefully.

3. **Skimmed milk is not suitable** for children, as it lacks fat and fat-soluble vitamins.

4. **Weaning takes place at 4–6 months – the baby is gradually introduced to solid foods.** These should be puréed or finely mashed, at first. Avoid adding salt or sugar to foods. Hard foods such as crusts are needed for teething.

5. Babies are born with enough **iron** to last 6 months. After that, iron-rich foods such as liver and dark green vegetables must be introduced. Vitamin C drinks are also needed.

6. By their first birthday, **infants should be eating the same fresh foods as the rest of the family**: these foods should be puréed or finely chopped. Avoid over-use of convenience foods.

## Children

1. Feed children a wide variety of fresh foods. **Restrict fats, sugar, salt and unhealthy snack foods**.

2. Children need plenty of **protein and vitamin A** for growth, and **calcium and vitamin D** for bones. Whole milk should remain their main drink.

3. Vegetables will supply **iron, vitamin C and fibre**. Large amounts of fibre, e.g. bran, are not necessary.

4. Make sure **energy foods** suit their activity. Serve starchy rather than sugary foods. Instead of sweet puddings, serve fresh fruit.

5. Take care to serve **healthy packed lunches**.

6. Children have small appetites: serve food in **attractive, small portions.**

7 Develop **good eating habits** by having meals at regular times. Avoid snacks between meals.

8 Children may become 'faddy' or refuse to eat. Making a fuss only makes this worse. Keep **mealtimes relaxed** and make sure that tempting, healthy food is available when they are hungry.

9 **Parents should set an example** of healthy eating.

## Adolescents

1 There is a rapid growth spurt in early adolescence. Teenagers require lots of **protein, iron, calcium and vitamins to cater for growth**.

2 **Energy requirements vary.** Some teenagers are extremely active and others are 'couch potatoes'. Teenage males have higher energy needs than any other group. Failure to balance energy intake (eating) with energy output is likely to result in weight gain or loss.

3 For maximum health, fitness and concentration, keep to a nourishing diet. Include lots of **whole cereals, fruit, vegetables and milk/cheese (low-fat dairy foods retain their protein, calcium and vitamins A and D)**.

4 **Females need to take iron-rich foods**, such as red meat and green vegetables, as they are often anaemic due to menstruation. Calcium-rich foods are necessary to prevent osteoporosis. (Surveys show that both these minerals are lacking in teenage girls.)

5 To keep skin clear, **avoid greasy foods** such as fried foods, pastries and chocolate. Eat lots of salads (without dressing) and fresh fruit, and **drink lots of water**.

6 Teenagers need three good meals a day. Snacks between meals are acceptable for young people who are active, but they should choose healthy foods such as fruit, salads and high-fibre rolls rather than chocolate bars or rich pastries.

## Adults

1 Nutrient intake varies according to age and size. All adults should follow a well-balanced diet, keeping to the healthy eating guidelines.

2 Intake of **protein can be reduced slightly**, as it is needed only for repair. Choose vegetable proteins such as cereals rather than animal sources as they have less saturated fat and more fibre.

3　**Balance energy intake with activity.** Sedentary workers require fewer kilocalories than those who are active. As people age (over 25), their kilocalorie requirements reduce; failure to reduce kilocalorie intake may lead to obesity. Starchy, high-fibre carbohydrates are a healthier source of energy than the empty kilocalories in sugary foods.

4　Keep to a **high-fibre** diet in order to prevent bowel disorders; this is also a means of keeping weight down.

5　**Keep fat intake low**: use low-fat dairy products. Choose vegetable oils and spreads rather than animal fats to reduce cholesterol and prevent heart disease.

6　**Restrict salt intake** to help prevent high blood pressure and strokes.

7　Women in particular should have a good intake of **iron to prevent anaemia and of calcium to prevent osteoporosis**.

8　Keep **alcohol intake to a minimum** – alcohol is a source of empty kilocalories.

## Pregnant and breast-feeding women

1　During pregnancy the baby depends on the mother for its nutrients and health. Failure to follow a healthy diet may cause deficiency diseases in mother and baby. While it is not necessary to 'eat for two', foods should be a concentrated, well-balanced source of nutrients.

2　**Proteins are essential for the growth of the foetus; calcium and vitamin D for its bones; and iron for its blood.**

3　**All other minerals and vitamins** are important, particularly vitamin C to help the absorption of iron.

4　**Energy intake should be increased slightly**, but care must be taken not to gain too much weight at this time.

5　Pregnant women should **avoid**:

- strong tea and coffee
- rich, spicy or fatty foods
- soft-cooked eggs (danger of salmonella)
- unpasteurised cheeses, cook-chill foods, commercially prepared salads (danger of listeria)
- liver, shellfish
- alcohol, smoking and drugs of any description, unless on prescription.

LINK-UP

Food poisoning, page 69

## Elderly people

1. Some elderly people may have problems that affect their diet:
   - they may live on low incomes
   - they may have poor digestion
   - they may have disabilities such as arthritis, poor mobility, weak eyesight or dental problems, any of which may interfere with shopping, cooking and eating.

2. Elderly people must be particularly conscious of the healthy eating guidelines: they should eat **less sugar, less fat, less salt and more fibre**.

3. As elderly people often have **small appetites, nutrients should be concentrated**. They should eat three nourishing meals a day and avoid snacks between meals.

4. **Protein is important for repair**: choose proteins that are easy to digest, such as white fish and chicken.

5. Old people **need less energy** and are less active. Choose high-fibre carbohydrates rather than processed or sugary foods – these are more filling and less fattening.

6. Dairy products such as milk, cheese and yoghurt contain **calcium and vitamins A and D** to maintain bones and prevent osteoporosis. Choose low-fat varieties to avoid weight gain.

7. To prevent heart disease, **keep high-cholesterol foods such as butter and eggs to a minimum**. Choose oil instead of hard fats for cooking. Cut down on salt to prevent high blood pressure.

8. Eat **plenty of fruit**, **vegetables and brown bread** to supply vitamins, minerals and fibre. Elderly people often lack vitamin C, which is important for iron absorption and general health.

## Invalids/convalescents

1. People who are ill or recovering from illness need **nourishing, easy-to-digest food that is not too bulky**, e.g. white fish, chicken breast, custard, fruit juices. Liquid foods such as milk and broths are easy to digest when a patient is unable to eat solid food. Invalids and convalescents should take:
   - **protein** to repair damaged cells
   - **vitamin C** to help healing and fight infection
   - **iron** to replace any blood loss and prevent anaemia
   - **smaller amounts of energy foods**, as less energy is used during illness.

**2** **Fluids** are important during fever, when high temperatures may lead to dehydration.

**3** Serve **small portions** of best quality fresh food.

**4** Hygiene is very important: everything used for cooking and serving should be spotlessly clean.

**5** Boiling, steaming, stewing and baking are suitable cooking methods: avoid fried, reheated and rich or spicy foods.

**ACTIVITY**

1. Find out the differences in composition between breast milk and cow's milk. Present the information in a chart:

| Milk | Protein | Carbohydrate | Fat | Vitamins | Minerals | Water |
|------|---------|--------------|-----|----------|----------|-------|
| Human | | | | | | |
| Cow's | | | | | | |

2. Make a list of rules to be followed when bottle-feeding a baby. Find out and explain how to sterilise a bottle correctly.

3. List the reasons you think teenagers develop bad eating habits. Suggest a meal plan for one day for an active teenage girl. Explain your choice of dishes.

4. Plan a day's menu for a pregnant woman, using the healthy eating guidelines.

5. Work out five two-course lunches that you could cook and deliver to an elderly person as part of a 'Meals on Wheels' scheme in your area.

6. Working in twos, plan a day's menu for a convalescent child. Give reasons for your choice of main foods. Compare your menu with others in your class. Which is most suitable?

**REVISION QUESTIONS**

1. Define a 'balanced diet'.
2. Name the four food groups. From which two groups should we get most of our food?
3. Name three diseases associated with an unhealthy diet.
4. About what age is a baby weaned? Suggest three foods suitable for a baby who is being weaned.
5. Why is skimmed milk unsuitable for babies?
6. Name two foods rich in iron and two rich in vitamin C that are suitable for a baby.
7. Make a list of foods you would include in a lunch box for an active 10 year old.
8. Plan a low-kilocalorie day for a teenage girl. Include breakfast, lunch and dinner.
9. Describe two wholefood snacks you could pack for after a school football match. What healthy drink would you include?
10. Write a menu for a sit-down lunch suitable for a group of women, which would be a good source of iron and calcium and not too high in kilocalories.
11. What is meant by a 'sedentary person'? What foods must be restricted by a sedentary person?
12. List four nutrients that are particularly important for pregnant women. List some foods they should avoid.
13. What cookery methods are most suitable for those who are ill or recovering from illness?
14. State the proportions of (a) protein and (b) fat which should be included in a well-balanced diet.

*Test Yourself*

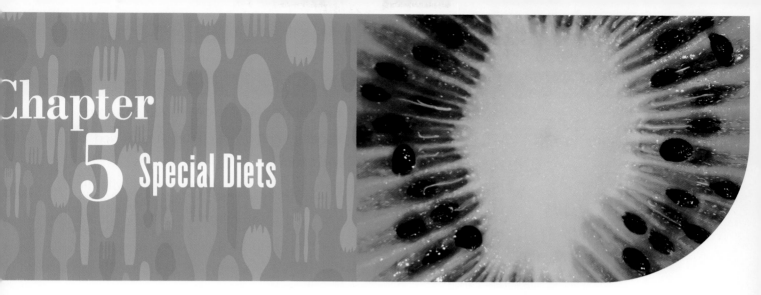

# Chapter 5 Special Diets

## Vegetarian diets

**A vegetarian does not eat meat or fish.** There are two types of vegetarian.

- **Lactovegetarians,** who **do not eat meat, poultry or fish but do eat products from animals,** such as milk, cheese and eggs.
- **Vegans,** who are strict vegetarians – **they do not eat any animal product.** They live entirely on plant foods such as cereals, nuts, fruit and vegetables.

People become vegetarians for many reasons:

1. because they think it is morally wrong to kill or harm animals
2. because they think it is healthier not to eat meat – they may worry about hormones in meat and diseases such as bird flu
3. because they believe it is environmentally wasteful to fatten animals on land that can produce plant food more cheaply
4. for religious reasons – certain religions don't eat meat, e.g. Hindus are mainly vegetarian because they disapprove of the violence involved in killing animals.

## Advantages of vegetarianism

Vegetarians are less likely to suffer from bowel disorders, due to the high fibre content of a vegetarian diet.

They are less likely to suffer from heart disease or high blood pressure because their diet is lower in saturated fat.

They are less likely to be overweight.

Plant foods are cheaper than animal foods.

## Disadvantages of vegetarianism

As meat is the main dietary source of iron and vitamin $B_{12}$, vegetarians may lack these nutrients.

## Vegetarian foods

| Protein | Carbohydrates | Fats/oils | Minerals/vitamins |
|---------|---------------|-----------|-------------------|
| Cereals, nuts, peas, beans, soya beans, soya protein (TVP)*, tofu (bean curd), soya milk | Whole cereals, wholemeal bread, pasta, cereals, potatoes, root vegetables | Vegetable oil, margarine, nuts, olives, avocado | Fruit, fresh/dried vegetables, nuts, yeast (vitamin B), sunshine (vitamin D), dark green vegetables (iron) |

### Guidelines for vegetarian diets

1. A good knowledge of nutrition is necessary to make sure that the diet is balanced.
2. Include vegetable protein foods such as pulse vegetables (e.g. lentils), and cereals and nuts.
3. Use unprocessed cereals and grains for extra vitamins and fibre.
4. Use vegetable stock only.
5. Vegans should use only vegetable fats or oil, no butter.
6. Vegans should use soya milk as a substitute for milk.
7. Read labels carefully to make sure that convenience foods contain no animal products.

## Case study

Pat and Irene are a young married couple. Irene is a lactovegetarian. Pat was planning to cook something similar to bacon quiche for dinner.

Suggest two ingredients he could substitute for the bacon in order to make the dish suitable for Irene.

Suggest accompaniments to the main course.

Suggest what you would serve as another course to make a two-course meal.

**\*Soya protein or textured vegetable protein (TVP)**
This is a meat substitute made from soya beans or another vegetable protein source. The bean is ground down, carbohydrate is removed for flour, and the pulp is flavoured, dried and shaped into either chunks or mince to look and taste like meat.

TVP has a similar food value to meat, except it contains only a small amount of fat (polyunsaturated) and has more calcium.

## Vegetarian dishes

### Lactovegetarian dishes

| | Breakfast | Lunch | Dinner |
|---|---|---|---|
| | Fruit juice | Salads | Avocado |
| | Cereal | Omelettes | Soup |
| | Porridge (made with water) | Milk puddings | Quiche |
| | Toast | Fruit | Pizza |
| | Tea | Cakes | Macaroni cheese |
| | | | Stir fries |
| | | | Vegetarian pasta dishes |
| | | | Vegetarian curries |
| | | | Stewed fruit |
| | | | Custard |
| | | | Yoghurt |
| | | | Cheese |

## Vegan dishes

| | Breakfast | Lunch | Dinner |
|---|---|---|---|
| | As above | Wholewheat bread | Curried TVP |
| | | Marmite | Noodle dishes |
| | | Soup | Risottos |
| | | Nuts | Stir fries |
| | | Raisins | Pasta dishes |
| | | Juice | Salads |
| | | | Vegetables |
| | | | Fruit |

# High-fibre diet

**Dietary fibre is found only in plant foods**. It consists mainly of **cellulose**, which forms the structural framework of the plant. It is **most plentiful in the outer skin of vegetables and fruit and the husks of cereals**. (When cereals are refined or processed, the husks are removed and sold separately as bran.) Fibre is not digested but helps to move the food along by creating bulk in the intestine.

# Refined food

In the past, because fibre was considered to be rough on the intestines (in fact it was called roughage), manufacturers began to refine or process food. Processing removes

Vegetarian recipes, page 179

Carbohydrates, page 10

Cereals, page 101

the outer layers from cereals, etc. so that there is little fibre left. Processing also removes valuable minerals and vitamins, particularly vitamin B. For these reasons unprocessed foods are now recommended in the diet.

## Advantages of dietary fibre

1. **Fibre absorbs water in the bowel**, making the waste soft and bulky. As a result, the **waste passes quickly through the bowel**, **preventing constipation and other bowel disorders** such as diverticulitis and irritable bowel syndrome.

2. It is thought that, because the waste is eliminated quickly, **chemicals that may cause bowel cancer are prevented from acting** on the lining of the bowel.

3. Unlike starch and sugar, dietary fibre does not provide kilocalories. This makes it useful for weight-watchers. Also, because fibre absorbs lots of water in the stomach, it **gives a feeling of fullness, so that we eat less**.

4. A high-fibre diet can help in **reducing cholesterol** levels.

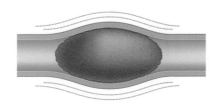

*(a) Fibre absorbs water, making waste bulky – this stimulates the walls of the intesine and moves waste along*

*(b) A low-fibre diet results in waste that is hard and causes constipation*

## Guidelines for a high-fibre diet

1. Change to **whole cereals** – breakfast cereals such as Weetabix and muesli, wholemeal bread, wholewheat pasta, brown rice, etc.

2. Increase the amount of **fruit and vegetables** in the diet. Eat unpeeled fruit and vegetables, as most fibre is in or just under the skin.

3. Eat more **salads and vegetarian dishes** in the diet.

4. Choose **high-fibre products** for lunches and between-meals snacks, e.g. prunes, raisins, nuts.

5. **Avoid highly processed foods** – most are low in fibre and high in fat and sugar.

6. **Drink lots of water.** As fibre absorbs large amounts of water, more water must be taken in order to prevent dehydration.

Food

## Foods rich in fibre (per 100g)

| | | | |
|---|---|---|---|
| Bran* | 62.0g | Muesli | 8.0g |
| Brown rice | 4.8g | Cooked potato | 2.5g |
| All-Bran | 27.5g | Peanuts | 8.0g |
| Brown bread | 4.5g | White bread | 2.5g |
| Fresh/frozen peas | 9.0g | Baked beans | 7.0g |
| Raw carrot | 3.0g | Bananas/raisins | 2.0 g |
| Wholemeal bread | 8.7g | Sweetcorn | 5.7g |
| White rice | 2.8g | Apples/oranges (approx.) | 2.0g |

## Low-fat/low-cholesterol diet

Most people in this country eat too much fat – health experts recommend that we reduce the amount of fat we eat to a maximum of a third of our calorie intake. The recommended maximum daily intake for an average male is 95g and for an average female 70g.

A high-fat diet can cause:

- **coronary heart disease**
- **high blood pressure**
- **obesity** (overweight)

and aggravate other diseases such as **cancer** and **diabetes**.

⁜ *A healthy artery*

## Coronary heart disease

Heart disease is one of the main causes of death in the Western world and is Ireland's biggest killer, accounting for 36% of all deaths (Irish Heart Foundation).

It occurs when the main arteries of the heart become hard and blocked with a substance called cholesterol. Experts believe that eating too much fat, particularly saturated fat, builds up cholesterol in the blood vessels.

⁜ *An artery blocked by cholesterol*

This narrows the diameter of the vessels and prevents blood from flowing freely, so that blood pressure rises. Eventually an artery may become totally blocked, causing a heart attack. In a similar way, blockage of an artery in the brain causes a stroke.

Bran is a good source of fibre, but large amounts can reduce the amount of minerals, such as iron and zinc, that are absorbed. Children and pregnant women should avoid too much bran: they can obtain fibre from whole cereals, wholemeal bread, fruit and vegetables.

| Factors that increase risk of heart disease: | To reduce risk: |
|---|---|
| 1. Heredity | 1. Eat a low-fat/low-cholesterol diet |
| 2. Overweight/diet high in saturated fat | 2. Avoid becoming overweight |
| 3. Smoking | 3. Avoid smoking |
| 4. Stress | 4. Avoid stress |
| 5. Lack of exercise | 5. Take lots of exercise |
| 6. Abuse of alcohol | 6. Drink alcohol only in moderation |
| | 7. Eat five or more portions of fruit and vegetables daily |
| | 8. Eat oily fish twice weekly |
| | 9. Have regular blood pressure checks |

## Guidelines for reducing fat

1. Avoid fried food – boil, grill, bake or microwave instead.*
2. Choose low-fat proteins such as white fish, chicken, turkey and pulses.
3. Trim visible fat from meat; cut down on red meat.
4. Use fat sparingly – spread thinly on bread, add less in cooking.
5. Choose low-fat products – low-fat milk, yoghurt, cheese, mayonnaise.
6. Switch to unsaturated oil, e.g. olive oil.
7. Avoid fatty snack foods such as crisps, biscuits, pastries and chocolate.
8. Cut down on high-cholesterol foods:

| Cut down on high-cholesterol foods: | Choose instead: |
|---|---|
| Butter/hard margarine | Unsaturated spreads, oils |
| Suet, lard, dripping | White and oily fish |
| Fatty meats e.g. bacon, sausage, pâté | Chicken, turkey, pulses |
| Cheese, cream | Cottage cheese, low-fat yoghurt |
| Eggs, particularly egg yolk | Fruit, vegetables, high-fibre cereals |

*Cooking food in fat increases kilocalories: the more food is cut up and exposed to fat, the more fat it absorbs.

## Low-salt diet

Salt controls the amount of fluid in the body. We require about 2g of salt each day. People in Western countries often eat up to 10 times that amount. Only those living in hot climates or those who perspire a lot due to work or sport require extra salt as salt is lost in sweat.

## Dietary problems caused by salt

Too much salt in the diet causes **hypertension** (high blood pressure), which can lead to heart disease, strokes and kidney damage; so reducing salt intake would reduce the number of deaths caused by these conditions. People are not born with a liking for salt – we develop a taste for it as children, when salt is added to our food.

## To reduce salt intake

1. Parents should **avoid adding salt to children's food** or giving them salty snack foods.

2. **Avoid adding salt during cooking**; use flavourings such as onions, garlic and herbs instead.

3. **Keep salt off the table**, or at least taste food before you add salt.

4. **Read labels carefully**; look out for the chemical name for salt (sodium chloride) or the symbol NaCl. Monosodium glutamate, found in many snack foods, is also a type of salt.

5. Instead of eating high-salt foods e.g. bacon, cheese, butter, **change to low-salt versions**.

6. **Avoid the foods listed below**, particularly convenience foods and salty snack foods.

## These foods have a high level of salt:

- Snack foods such as crisps, popcorn and salted nuts.
- Most processed foods, e.g. smoked and salted fish.
- Processed meats such as bacon, salami, corned beef.
- Packet and tinned soups and sauces.
- Stock cubes.
- Many breakfast cereals.
- Butter, margarine, cheese.

## Low-sugar diet

Sugar is a source of energy in the diet. The problem is, it contains nothing else – no vitamins, no minerals, simply 'empty kilocalories'. Because it is a source of energy, many people think sugar is necessary in the diet. It is not. Other energy foods are far more nourishing, e.g. fruit, pasta, rice.

Many people in the Western world have a sweet tooth. Our liking for sugar begins in childhood, e.g. when parents reward good behaviour with sweets. Sugar is added to many foods by manufacturers to encourage us to eat it. It is found even in savoury foods such as tomato ketchup and baked beans.

## Dietary problems caused by sugar

1. **Type 2 diabetes** (non-insulin-dependent diabetes) can be brought on by excess sugar in the diet over a prolonged period.

2. Too much sugar can cause weight problems or even **obesity** (see next section).

3. Sugar is the main cause of **dental decay**.

### To reduce sugar intake

1. **Cut out sugar in tea and coffee**; this is best done gradually to prevent cravings.

2. **Don't add sugar** to foods such as breakfast cereals. Add less sugar during cooking.

3. **Cut down on foods that contain a lot of sugar** – sweets, biscuits, cakes, pastries, soft drinks, breakfast cereals with added sugar, convenience foods. Develop a taste for savoury foods instead. Choose sugar-free soft drinks: an average can of fizzy drink can contain 8 teaspoons of sugar.

4. **Eat healthier low-sugar snacks** such as fruit, nuts, popcorn, yoghurt, fruit juices and low-calorie drinks.

5. Check food labels; look for labels such as 'no added sugar'. Check for hidden sugars in savoury foods. Remember that glucose, fructose, sucrose and honey are all forms of sugar.

A high-sugar snack food

Modifying a recipe, page 162

# Obesity

**'Obesity' means being more than 20% above maximum healthy weight for a person's height.** While it is occasionally caused by a hormone disorder, obesity is most often caused by eating more food than the body needs. The excess is stored by the body as fat. An estimated 300,000 Irish children are obese (*Irish Times* 2008), while almost 20% of the overall population suffers from the condition.

## Problems caused by obesity

1. It increases the risk of **serious diseases** such as:
   - heart disease
   - high blood pressure/strokes
   - diabetes.

2. Shorter life expectancy.

3. Poor self-image.

4. Joint problems resulting from carrying excess weight.

5. Liver disease.

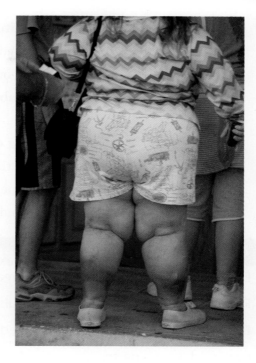

5 Gout (joint pain caused by the build-up of crystals that form an acid).

7 Sleep problems, e.g. stopping breathing during sleeping (apnoea).

8 Problems in surgery and childbirth.

## Reasons why people gain weight

1 Eating more than the body needs.

2 Insufficient exercise – people are less active than they were in the past. Many children spend an average of 3 hours every day in front of a TV or computer screen.

3 Ignorance about nutrition.

4 Poor self-image, which may lead to 'comfort eating' and bulimia.

5 Poor eating habits, e.g. snacking constantly.

## Guidelines for losing weight

A person who is overweight has probably been eating incorrectly. The aim in a low-kilocalorie or slimming diet should not be instant weight loss, but a change to healthier eating on a long-term basis. Special slimming foods are expensive and unnecessary.

1 **Reduce energy intake** (food) and **increase energy output** (activity/exercise).

2 **Avoid crash diets**; gradual weight reduction is safer and more permanent.

3 **Don't skip meals**; eat three proper meals a day.

4 **Avoid snacking** but if it is necessary, eat healthy foods such as fruit.

5 **Choose low-kilocalorie** protein foods, such as white fish, chicken, cottage cheese.

6 **Cut down on fats**; use low-fat products and spread fats thinly.

7 **Cut down on sugary foods** such as biscuits and pastries.

8 **Eat high-fibre** carbohydrate foods such as brown bread, potatoes and root vegetables – these swell in the stomach, giving a feeling of fullness.

9 **Eat plenty of green vegetables and salad vegetables** such as tomatoes, peppers and cucumber for vitamins and minerals.

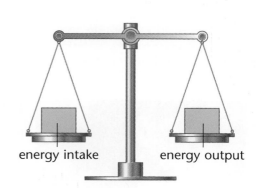

energy intake    energy output

❖ *A balanced diet*

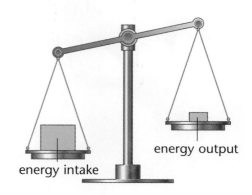

energy output

energy intake

❖ *Weight gain*

10. **Sugar substitutes and low-calorie drinks** can be used, but it is probably better to break the addiction to sweetness by avoiding them. Drink lots of water instead.
11. Keep an eye on **portion sizes**: large portions are a major factor in weight gain.
12. **Read food labels carefully** to check for sugar and fat, which contribute to weight gain
13. **Avoid eating out regularly**; instead, try to eat food that has been prepared at home where the ingredients can be controlled.
14. Limit the time spent in front of the TV, computer, etc. **Enjoy regular activities** as a family and make them fun.

| Avoid: | Restrict: | Eat plenty of: |
| --- | --- | --- |
| Fats, e.g. butter, margarine | Bread, potatoes | Lettuce, tomato, cucumber |
| Fried and roast foods | Pulses | Green vegetables, cauliflower |
| Fatty meat, e.g. bacon | Red meats | Chicken, white fish |
| Cream, desserts, pastry | Breakfast cereals | Low-fat dairy products |
| Sugar, jam, honey, nuts | Rice, pasta | Citrus fruits, apples |
| Biscuits, sweets, cakes | Full-fat milk (use skimmed) | Fresh fruit juice, clear soup |
| Tinned fruit, soft drinks | Skimmed milk cheese | Low-fat (cottage) cheese |
| Alcohol, high-fat cheese | Low-fat yoghurt, fruit | Low-calorie drinks |

# Eating disorders

It is important that losing weight does not become an obsession. Too much emphasis on thinness and slimming diets can lead to eating disorders.

## Anorexia nervosa

Anorexia is an inability to eat due to a loss of appetite. It is a psychological condition. People see themselves as overweight when in fact they are too thin. People who suffer from anorexia (who are usually young and female) tend to have a poor self-image. They refuse to eat food and, if they are forced to eat it, will often make themselves vomit to get rid of it. Eventually they suffer serious vitamin deficiencies, their periods stop and they may, in time, die slowly of starvation, and/or organ failure.

Specialised treatment is required, usually in hospital, which consists of a supervised eating regime with psychological counselling.

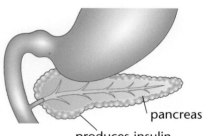

## Bulimia

This is a similar disease, but it takes the form of binge eating followed by vomiting and sometimes the use of laxatives to eliminate the food. People with bulimia are not always thin, and they may be older than anorexia sufferers. Treatment can take the form of counselling and help from support groups such as Bodywhys.

## Other special diets

Certain people may require a special diet, due to illness, allergies or other factors.

## Diabetes

**Type 1 diabetes (insulin-dependent diabetes) is a condition in which the pancreas does not make enough of the hormone insulin.** (Insulin is necessary to control the level of sugar (glucose) in the blood.) If the blood sugar level rises (usually because the patient has not kept to the strict diet required), or if it falls (usually due to a long fast), the patient may become weak and may lapse into a coma.

**Type 2 diabetes (non-insulin-dependent diabetes) usually occurs in older people who are likely to be overweight. The pancreas makes insulin, but the insulin doesn't work**. This form of diabetes may be helped by losing weight and/or following a diabetic diet.

Symptoms of diabetes: excessive urine production; thirst; weight loss; tiredness.

pancreas
produces insulin

## Treatment

Mild diabetes may be treated by diet alone. Otherwise insulin must be injected daily in sufficient amounts to control the blood sugar level. The doctor will prescribe a diet and exercise plan along the following lines.

1. Follow a low-sugar diet.
2. Eat high-fibre/starchy foods.
3. Eat often – never go too long without food. Small frequent meals are best.
4. Artificial sweeteners may be used to replace sugar. Special diabetic foods such as jam and chocolate are available. Glucose sweets should be carried to provide a quick sugar boost when it is needed.
5. Lose weight if necessary. Exercise helps to balance energy and maintain weight.
6. Avoid alcohol.

LINK-UP

Low-sugar diet,
page 45

LINK-UP

High-fibre diet,
page 41

## Coeliac disease

People with coeliac disease **cannot digest gluten, a protein that is found in wheat and some other cereals**. The gluten is not broken down into amino acids but is absorbed in large molecules which damage the delicate lining of the small intestine. As a result, absorption of other foods is affected and the patient suffers from pain and diarrhoea and often becomes thin and anaemic.

## Treatment

Coeliacs must avoid all foods containing gluten. These include the following foods:

| |
|---|
| All wheat products, e.g. bread, cakes, pastry, biscuits, pasta |
| Many convenience foods – many of these are thickened with flour |
| Sausages, pies, stuffings |
| Many breakfast cereals |
| Anything coated in breadcrumbs or batter |
| Many snack foods |
| Packet soups and sauces |

Check all food labels for wheat-based products, as well as those containing oats, barley and rye.

## Gluten-free foods

- Fruit and vegetables, including potatoes.
- Uncoated meat and fish.
- Chicken.
- Eggs.
- Dairy products such as butter, milk and cheese.
- Rice.
- Soya products.
- Cornflour, which can be used for thickening.
- Gluten-free flour and products such as bread and biscuits are available.

The gluten-free symbol

**TIVITY**

1. List two foods which would supply each of the nutrients below in a vegan diet.

| Protein | Carbohydrate | Fat | Vitamin A | Vitamin B | Calcium | Iron |
|---|---|---|---|---|---|---|
|  |  |  |  |  |  |  |
|  |  |  |  |  |  |  |

2. Visit your local supermarket or health food shop and make a list of foods available that are suitable for (a) people with diabetes and (b) people with coeliac disease.

| Diabetes (sugar-free) | Coeliac disease (gluten-free) |
|---|---|
|  |  |
|  |  |

3. List (a) four ways in which you could modify your diet to increase fibre, and (b) four ways to reduce sugar. In each case, plan meals for a day that would put these changes into practice.

4. Plan a week's main meals for a middle-aged man who has a high cholesterol level. List four changes, other than diet, that he could make to his lifestyle in order to prevent a heart attack.

5. Plan menus for five days, to include five breakfasts and five two-course dinners, for a person on a low-kilocalorie diet. List four other lifestyle changes that would help to reduce weight safely.
Lifestyle changes: _____

| | Monday | Tuesday | Wednesday | Thursday | Friday |
|---|---|---|---|---|---|
| Breakfast |  |  |  |  |  |
| Dinner |  |  |  |  |  |

1. Name two types of vegetarian. What are the advantages of being a vegetarian?

2. Explain the term TVP. Name two vegetarian dishes that could be made from TVP.

3. How does a high-fibre diet help keep weight down? Name two foods which are good sources of fibre.

4. What is meant by 'refined' food? How is a refined food 'fortified'?

5. Explain how heart disease occurs. What factors increase the risk of heart disease?

6. Too much salt is likely to cause _____. Give three ways of cutting salt intake.

7. Why is sugar called a source of empty kilocalories? Name two problems caused by excess sugar in the diet. Give three good ways of reducing sugar in the diet.

8. Define obesity. What ill-effects result from obesity?

9. What is diabetes? Describe the usual form of treatment by diet.

10. What is gluten? How does coeliac disease affect the body?

11. Name three foods that must be avoided by coeliacs. Name three gluten-free products.

12. Name four foods that have a high salt content.

13. Give two guidelines which may be followed in order to reduce the risk of heart disease.

*Test Yourself* eTest.ie

# Chapter 6 Meal Planning

A healthy diet requires a certain amount of planning and organisation. By spending some time planning menus, shopping, preparing and cooking, you waste less time and the work is done more efficiently.

## Advantages of weekly meal planning

It is a good idea to plan meals for about a week at a time, for the following reasons.

1. It is easier to make meals nutritionally well balanced.
2. Weekly planning provides a basis for weekly shopping.
3. It is easier to vary the menu from week to week.
4. Planning and preparation save time in the long run and avoid confusion.
5. Waste is reduced and leftovers are catered for.
6. One can save time by doubling up the cooking, e.g. 'cook two and freeze one'.
7. Money is saved as there will be fewer 'emergencies' such as takeaways and convenience foods.

### Meal planning guidelines

When deciding on a meal it may be necessary to balance your priorities (see below). Consider the following.

1. **Food value:** the meal should be nutritious and well balanced.

2. **Cost:** how much can you afford to spend? Consider the cost of food and fuel.

3. **Type of meal:** breakfast, lunch or dinner; formal or informal; a special occasion? Number of courses – two, three or four? Each situation will have its own priorities.

4. **Time available** for preparation and cooking will influence what you choose – a stew is unsuitable when time is short; a grill or salad is quicker. Meals may have to fit in with family commitments such as shiftwork or sports fixtures. A school cookery assignment may be restricted to 1 or $1\frac{1}{2}$ hours.

5. **The number eating:** you must know how many are eating in order to plan quantities and shopping. Certain foods, such as omelettes, are unsuitable for large numbers.

6. **Cooking methods/contrast:** vary cooking methods – each course should contrast with the next. There should also be contrasts in colour, flavour and texture between courses, e.g. chewy meat and crunchy salads; hot and cold; spicy and bland.

7. **Restrictions/preferences:** check whether there are restrictions due to health or a special diet, e.g. a vegetarian diet. Consider the likes and dislikes of those eating, within reason.

8. **Time of year:** cold dishes such as salads are popular in summer but not as suitable in winter, when a hot casserole would be more appreciated. Seasons influence the choice and cost of fresh fruit and vegetables – certain fresh food may be in or out of season.

9. **Equipment available:** check that essential equipment, such as scales and knives, is available before starting to cook a recipe; a food processor or deep fat fryer may be recommended but alternatives can be used.

10. **Skills:** beginners should start with easy dishes. They can try more advanced recipes as they gain skills and experience.

## Priorities

People in different circumstances have different meal planning priorities. One often has to balance between cost and time: some low-cost meals such as a casserole and baked potatoes take a long time. Those with a job and a home to run may have to make more expensive choices which will cook more quickly. Convenience foods are quick but more costly. Health should always be a priority – follow the healthy eating guidelines and always include at least one raw fruit or vegetable at every meal, to supply vitamins, minerals and fibre.

## Arrangement of meals

Daily meals usually consist of the following.

1. Breakfast is the first meal of the day. It may be served early or, more usually, at about 7.30–8.00. At weekends it may be more substantial and served later, at around 12 noon or 1 p.m., and known as 'brunch'.

2. Lunch may be a light or medium-sized meal, served in the middle of the day. For schoolchildren and many workers it often takes the form of a packed lunch.

3. Dinner is the main meal of the day, usually eaten in the evening between 6 and 8 p.m.

4. If lunch is the main meal of the day, the evening meal is usually called tea or supper.

5. Snacks are often eaten between meals, for example at mid-morning or mid-afternoon. Snacks should be small, nourishing and low in kilocalories so as not to spoil the appetite for main meals.

# Menus

**A menu is a list of all the dishes served at a meal.** In a restaurant, a menu may be:

- **table d'hôte** – this is a **set menu** which usually consists of between 2 and 5 courses, each with some choices. There is a set price for the meal, regardless of the number of courses eaten. It is usually cheaper than an à la carte menu.

- **à la carte** – a long list of dishes, grouped into courses, each with its own price. Individual dishes can be ordered separately.

**Table d'hôte Menu**

Minestrone
Seafood cocktail
Bruschetta
Warm chicken salad

Poached sole in white wine
Roast duck in orange sauce
Chicken stir fry
Vegetarian lasagne
Baked ham and Cumberland sauce

Selection of vegetables

Bread and butter pudding
Pavlova
Orange and lemon ice cream
Chocolate gateau
Fruit salad in port

Tea or coffee

Price €22.95

**À la Carte Menu**

| *Appetisers* | |
|---|---|
| Cream of cauliflower soup | 5.00 |
| Garlic mushrooms | 4.00 |
| Egg mayonnaise | 4.00 |
| Melon in crème de menthe | 5.00 |
| Prawn salad | 6.00 |

| *Main course* | |
|---|---|
| Grilled salmon hollandaise | 12.00 |
| Roast pork and apple sauce | 11.00 |
| Beef casserole | 12.00 |
| Vegetarian risotto | 9.00 |
| Cheese omelette with selection of vegetables | 9.00 |

| *Sweets and puddings* | |
|---|---|
| Apple tart à la mode | 4.00 |
| Tiramisu | 5.00 |
| Summer pudding | 5.00 |
| Stewed apricots | 4.00 |
| | |
| Cheese board | 5.00 |
| Tea or coffee | 2.00 |
| Cappuccino | 3.00 |

# Courses

Meals are usually divided into courses.

**1** The appetiser or starter. Examples: salad, soup.

**2** The main course. Meat and fish are traditional main course dishes. Today, vegetarian and egg dishes are also popular. Accompaniments are usually served with the main course, e.g. a carbohydrate food, such as potato, rice or pasta, vegetables, salad and suitable sauces.

**3** The pudding or dessert. A dessert is a usually a cold dish. Puddings are more substantial and often hot. Alternatively, cheese and biscuits may be served.

**4** Tea or coffee.

1. Why do you think accompaniments are served with food?
2. Name two accompaniments that you would serve with each of the following:

| | | |
|---|---|---|
| Roast pork | Vegetarian lasagne | Chicken curry |
| Fried fish | Pizza | Omelette |

## Writing a menu

There is a correct way to write a menu (see page 57).

- It is written down the centre of the page.
- Courses are written in the order in which they are eaten.
- Leave a line between courses.
- The main dish of each course is written first. Underneath this are written the accompaniments, such as vegetables, salads and sauces.
- Be specific. Write the type, cut and cooking method of dishes, e.g. 'Pan-fried medallions of pork' or 'Roast rib of beef'. (Don't just say, e.g., 'Chops and potatoes'.)

## Menu card

When planning a menu for school assignments and examinations, follow the meal planning and menu guidelines above. Make an attractive menu card from a folded sheet of stiff paper, write the menu neatly by hand or type and print on a computer, and decorate if wished.

Study the meal planning guidelines on pages 53–4, then, following the healthy eating guidelines, plan and write menus for the following meals.

1. An economical summer-time lunch menu for four.
2. An attractive three-course meal for eight friends.
3. A dinner for two which you could prepare in 30 minutes.
4. A three-course dinner for four vegans.
5. Meals for a day for an elderly female on a low income.

# Sample menus

**Breakfast**
Grapefruit
Muesli and yoghurt
Brown toast and honey
Tea or coffee

**Lunch**
Mushroom quiche
Green salad
Wholemeal roll (optional)
Brown rhubarb crumble
Cream or custard

Special points: Light main course, therefore more substantial pudding. Lots of fibre. Quiche and crumble baked at same temperature.

**Winter Dinner**
Crudités and yoghurt dip
Pork casserole
Baked potatoes
Red cabbage with apple
Caramel custard

Special points: Cooking is all done in the oven. Raw vegetable starter for vitamins and minerals.

**Breakfast**
Orange juice
Scrambled egg on toast
Wholemeal bread, marmalade
Tea or coffee

**Lunch**
Sweet and sour salad
Chicken stir fry
Boiled rice
Tea/coffee

Special points: Low-kilocalorie meal. Quick – made in 40–50 minutes. Oven not used.

**Summer Dinner**
Cold cucumber salad
Lasagne
Garlic bread
Green salad
Summer pudding
Crème fraiche

Specal points: Cucumber, salad and fruit in season. Only one hot dish. Little cooking.

# Table setting

Table and tray settings should be arranged for the convenience of those eating the meal. Consider the menu and arrange settings accordingly. You should follow the general points for a table layout if you are asked to set the table in the practical exam.

1. Make sure everything required is present and clean, and bring it all to the table.
2. Tablecloth, mats, china, cutlery, flowers, etc. should blend or complement each other.
3. Cutlery is arranged in order of use, i.e. cutlery used first is placed on the outside of the setting.

Setting a breakfast tray, page 91

4. Allow 60cm for each place; cutlery should be about 3cm from the table edge.

5. Place knives to the right, with blades facing in, forks to the left, prongs upwards.

6. Place drinking glass(es) upright above the dinner knife.

7. Check that condiment (pepper, salt, mustard) vessels are filled and butter is in dishes. Fill the cold water jug last. A large table may require two sets of each.

8. Place heat-resistant mats in the centre of the table, with a serving spoon beside each.

9. Fold or roll napkins and place on the side plates.

10. When serving guests, serve food to the left of the diner; plates are removed from the right.

## Buffets

A buffet is the simplest way to entertain a crowd. Food should be easy to eat with a fork only or by hand. Arrange the food on the table so that guests can help themselves. Wrap cutlery in a napkin and place with dinner plates on the side of the table nearest the door, so that guests can pick up both as they enter and then help themselves. Serve drinks from a separate table.

❖ *A well-presented buffet table*

| Suitable buffet dishes | | |
| --- | --- | --- |
| Hot foods | Cold foods | Sweet foods |
| Curries and casseroles. Lasagne, pizza, sausage rolls, cocktail sausages, savoury rice, quiches. | Green, rice, potato and pasta salads. Coleslaw, meat and fish salads, curried chicken salad. | Gateaux and flans, mousses, summer pudding, trifle, fresh fruit salad and cream, cheesecakes, fruit tarts. |

## Food presentation

There is a proverb that says 'the eyes eat first'. The final step in preparing good food is to present it attractively. Well-presented food stimulates the appetite and encourages us to eat.

*A typical table setting*

## Presentation priorities

**Cleanliness:** Table, cutlery, napkins, etc. should be spotless. Wipe spills from dishes before serving, using damp kitchen paper.

**Appearance:** food should be attractively arranged. The colours of the food, dishes, sauces and garnishes should complement each other.

**Temperature:** Food should be served as soon as possible after cooking. Serve hot foods piping hot on heated dishes, and cold foods really cold. Certain foods, such as cheese, should be served at room temperature.

**Hygiene:** Never leave prepared foods in a warm room. They should be covered and stored in a very cold place, e.g. the refrigerator, until required.

Food hygiene,
page 69

**REVISION QUESTIONS**

1. List the six meal planning guidelines that you consider most important.
2. What are the advantages of planning meals a week at a time?
3. What is a menu? Name two types of menu available in a restaurant. Describe one of them.
4. Write a menu for a nourishing two-course dinner in winter.
5. Draw a simple diagram and explain how to set out a place setting for one, for your choice of dinner in question 4.
6. Name two hot and two cold dishes suitable for a buffet. Name two accompaniments you could serve at a buffet.

*Test Yourself*
eTest.ie

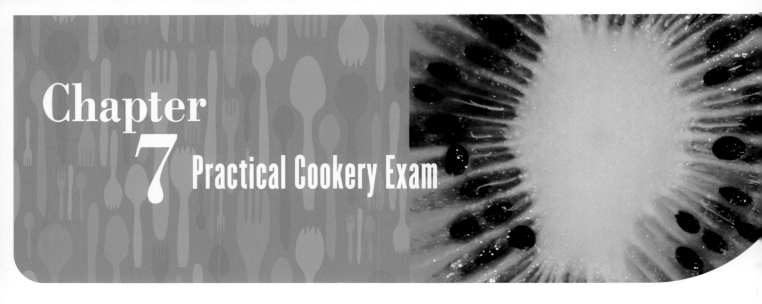

# Chapter 7 Practical Cookery Exam

## Food management

A **resource** is something that helps us in our lives, e.g. to achieve a goal or complete a task.

**Management** is the skilful use of resources in order to achieve a goal, e.g. making a plan to complete a task.

Management, page 292

### Resources involved in the practical exam

| Food | Knowledge/skills |
|---|---|
| Utensils, e.g. knives | Money |
| Equipment, e.g. cookers | Time |

### Planning

To achieve good results in any task it is necessary to plan what you are going to do. Careful planning when cooking helps use resources efficiently so there is less chance of running into problems, such as forgetting an ingredient or running out of time. A plan, such as a time plan, will help achieve this.

## Cookery brief

A **brief** is a problem to be solved or a task to be completed. To complete the brief, follow this step-by-step formula.

### Step by step to your goal

1 **Read the brief.** What am I being asked to do?

2 **Analyse the factors to be considered**, e.g. amount of time, money, level of skill etc.

3 **Do any necessary research/investigation.**

4 **Consider possible solutions** – and their effects.

5 **Decide on a solution.**

6 **Plan the assignment.**

7 **Action** – carry out practical work.

8 **Evaluate the result.** Did you achieve your goal?

## Cookery assignment

Plan and set out a menu for an economical two-course dinner for three female students, to be prepared, cooked and served in $1\frac{1}{2}$ hours. Serve the main course.

1. **Identify the brief** (see above).

2. **Analyse the factors to be considered** (aim for at least three).
Underline them on your brief: e.g. economical; two-course; dinner; three people; female; students; $1\frac{1}{2}$ hours.

3. **Research/investigation.**
Look up cookery books. Ask advice from teacher. Check shops for cheap seasonal foods. Use the internet.

4. **Consider possible solutions** – and their effects.
Think out recipes/menus, keeping the following factors in mind.
- Ingredients must be **cheap**.
- Two courses – will you choose a **starter** or a **pudding** with the main course?
- **Number eating** – three – most recipes cater for four. Quantities may have to be reduced slightly.
- What **nutrients** would particularly suit female students? (Remember the healthy eating guidelines.)
- Meal must be prepared and cooked **within 90 minutes** – a casserole would take too long.

5. **Decide on a solution.**
Decide on the menu that best fits the brief. Name the dishes and write them down in menu form. Give reasons for your choice if

asked. Suggestions include:
- cottage cheese salad with orange
- baked liver and bacon with apple stuffing
- boiled new potatoes with mint
- steamed broccoli.

**Reasons for choice:**
(a) Economical, nutritious.
(b) Contains good supply of calcium (cottage cheese) and iron (liver and broccoli).
(c) Not high in kilocalories.
(d) Good contrasts of colour, flavour and texture.
(e) Can be prepared, cooked and served within the time.

6. **Plan the assignment.**
**Write out:**
(a) List of factors.
(b) Possible solutions.
(c) Name of chosen dishes.
(d) Reasons for choice.
**Then:**
(a) Make a list of ingredients and cost them.*
(b) Make a list of equipment.**
(c) Make a time plan for preparation and exam.***
(d) Do shopping.

7. **Carry out practical work.**
Carefully follow time plan and recipe.
Tidy and clean up as you go. Put away equipment.
Present dishes attractively.

8. **Evaluation**
Examine the results under the following headings.

- **Colour:** correct for dish, nicely browned, attractive?
- **Presentation:** attractively arranged on clean hot/chilled dishes, well garnished?

- **Texture:** correct for the dish, i.e. crisp bacon, crunchy salad?
- **Taste:** appetising, well seasoned/flavoured, not too sweet or salty?
- **Properly cooked:** not overdone or underdone?
- **Was work done efficiently and time plan followed exactly?**
- **Did the dish/meal meet the brief?**
- **Would you make any changes to improve the results?**

\*    *Costing, see below*
\*\*   *Equipment, see page 63*
\*\*\* *Making a time plan, see page 63*

## \*Costing a recipe

1. List the main ingredients and the weight/amount you need.
2. Calculate and write down the cost of each.
3. Allow a few cents for fuel and small extras such as seasonings/herbs.
4. Allow the following quantities per person.

Meat/fish 150–250g        Uncooked pasta/rice 50–75g

Vegetables 100–150g       Soup/dessert/savoury recipes usually serve four.

| Apple stuffed liver and bacon | Cost |
|---|---|
| 300g lamb's liver | |
| 6 streaky rashers | |
| **Stuffing:** | |
| 50g breadcrumbs | |
| Chopped parsley/pepper/salt | |
| 1 dessertsp finely chopped onion | |
| $\frac{1}{2}$ cooking apple, finely chopped | |
| 1 tablespoon olive oil | |
| **Gravy:** | |
| 200ml brown stock | |
| Tomato ketchup, pepper, salt | |
| **Fuel**           **Total cost** | |

## Costing tips

- Most recipe ingredients are in multiples of 25g. To find the cost of 25g, divide 500g packs by 20 and 1kg packs by 40. Flour usually comes in 2kg packs – divide by 80. Divide a packet of block margarine by 9 to find out the approximate cost of 25g.

- For other calculations, divide the price by the total quantity and multiply by the amount you need.

- **Example of price calculation:**

  To work out the cost of 100g plain yoghurt @ 69c per 150g carton

  $$\frac{\text{Price of carton x weight used}}{\text{Total weight of carton}} = \frac{90 \times 100}{150} = \frac{900}{15} = 60c$$

## **List of equipment for assignment brief menu

| | |
|---|---|
| Foil (to cover liver/bacon) | Sharp knife |
| Chopping board | Processor |
| Measuring jug | Ovenproof dish |
| Teaspoon, tablespoon | Salad dishes (three) |
| Saucepan/lid | Steamer |

### Find out the cost of the following and keep in this book for reference.

| Full size | | Unit size | | | | Unit size (1 medium) | |
|---|---|---|---|---|---|---|---|
| 1l milk | ____ | 100ml milk | ____ | 500g potatoes | ____ | 1 | ____ |
| 2kg plain flour | ____ | 5g flour | ____ | 500g onions | ____ | 1 | ____ |
| 500g Cheddar | ____ | 25g Cheddar | ____ | 500g tomatoes | ____ | 1 | ____ |
| 453g (1lb) Flora | ____ | 25g Flora | ____ | 500g carrots | ____ | 1 | ____ |
| 500g rice | ____ | 25g rice | ____ | 500g lemons | ____ | 1 | ____ |
| 500g pasta | ____ | 25g pasta | ____ | 500g cooking apples | ____ | 1 | ____ |
| 1kg sugar | ____ | 25g sugar | ____ | 500g mushrooms | ____ | 50g | ____ |
| 1kg caster sugar | ____ | 25g caster sugar | ____ | 1l cooking oil | ____ | 15ml | ____ |

*Some products are not metricated to the nearest 5 or 10 units. Round up or down accordingly, e.g. 453g Flora: round down to 450 g.*

## ***Making a time plan

A **time plan** is a step-by-step written plan of how to prepare, cook and serve the dishes in a meal so that all of them are ready on time without being either undercooked or kept warm for too long. It is not as detailed as a recipe.

**MENU**

*Cottage cheese salad
with orange*

*Baked liver and bacon
with apple stuffing*

*Boiled new potatoes
with mint*

*Steamed broccoli*

With experience, you can work out a time plan in your head, but for cookery assignments it must be carefully worked out on paper.

You need to know:

**1** The time the meal will be served.

**2** The time it takes to prepare and cook each dish.

**3** The time required for serving up and garnishing.

**4** Work back to the time it takes to prepare, cook and serve the dish that takes the longest, e.g. a stew or soup. This is when you usually start.

**5** Allow time for preparing sauces and vegetables – about 30–40 minutes from the end – so they don't have to be kept hot for long. Salads can be made at any time and stored in the fridge.

**6** Gaps are filled with washing up, table setting, etc.

**Example, using the menu from the design brief**

- Salad takes 15 minutes to prepare.
- Baked liver takes 15 minutes to prepare (using a processor) and 30 minutes to cook.
- Medium potatoes take 5 minutes to prepare and up to 20 minutes to cook.
- Broccoli takes 5 minutes to prepare and 15 minutes to steam.

*Remember: 30 minutes' preparation time is given before the exam, and then you have 90 minutes during the exam*

## Time plan

**Starting time: 12.00**    **Serving time: 1.30**

| | |
|---|---|
| **12.00** | Wash lettuce, drain and set aside in fridge. Prepare orange. |
| **12.20** | Turn on oven. Make stuffing. Prepare liver and bacon. |
| **12.40** | Make up dish and place in oven. |
| **12.45** | Prepare potatoes. |
| **12.55** | Prepare broccoli. Put potatoes and broccoli on to cook. |
| **1.00** | Wash up and tidy up. |
| **1.10** | Arrange salad. Turn off oven. |
| **1.20** | Take liver out of oven. Dish up vegetables. |
| **1.25** | Garnish dishes. |
| **1.30** | Serve meal. |

# Garnishing and decorating food

**1** A simple, well-chosen garnish will improve the appearance of most dishes. The colour of the garnish should complement the food.

**2** Garnishes can be raw or cooked. Examples: lemon/lime slices, wedges or 'butterflies'; tomato slices or lilies; parsley and other herbs, in a sprig or finely chopped; edible flowers such as chives and nasturtiums; grated cheese; julienne strips of carrot, celery or pepper; grilled tomatoes or peppers.

**3** Sauces can do much to improve the appearance and flavour of food, and they can be placed either under or beside the food (e.g. a coulis), or used to coat the food (e.g. an 'au gratin' dish).

**4** Over-garnishing is the most common fault when decorating food: it can look fussy and untidy, it can cause hot food to cool, and the extra handling can deposit bacteria on the food.

✦ *Lemon or lime loop*

✦ *Spring onion tassel*

✦ *Carrot/leek julienne*

✦ *Fresh herbs*

✦ *Lemon/line twist*

✦ *Cream rosette*

✦ *Tomato lilies*

✦ *Strawberry fan*

**ACTIVITY**

**Sample assignment**
Using the design brief, plan and set out a day's meals for an elderly pensioner on a low income. Make a time plan for preparing, cooking and serving the main course (main dish and accompaniments).

# Shopping for food

Food shopping requires advance planning. (See 'Shopping', p. 234.)

**1** Plan menus/weekly shopping in advance so that there is time to make a shopping list.

**2** Check store cupboard and list foods required. Add to this a list of fresh foods required for menu(s).

3    Group food according to kind: dairy, meat, fish, fruit/vegetables, dry goods, etc. This makes it easier to find foods in the shop.

4    At the shop, keep to your list and budget. Buy essentials first – fresh, nutritious foods are a priority. Avoid unhealthy non-essentials such as biscuits, sweets and 'junk foods'.

5    Be price-conscious – shop around for good value. Look out for genuine bargains. Convenience foods such as ready meals are expensive.

6    Read labels carefully for weight, ingredients, nutrients and additives. Check expiry dates. Packaging and cans should be sealed and undamaged.

7    Perishables (meat, fish, milk, bread, fruit and vegetables, etc.) should be bought in small amounts. Buy fruit and vegetables in season – they are better quality and cheaper.

8    Dry goods can be bought in bulk (large sizes or 3 for the price of 2) if they are cheaper and you need them. Own brands may also be cheaper.

9    Avoid shopping when rushed, tired or hungry – you are likely to buy unwisely and buy more.

10    Shop only in clean, hygienic food shops/markets.

## On a limited budget?

- Decide what you can afford to spend and stick to it.
- Choose cheaper cuts of meat, e.g. shin of beef – they are just as nutritious. Whole chickens are much better value than chicken joints.
- Cheap fish include herring and haddock.
- Root vegetables are cheap, filling and nourishing.
- Vegetarian recipes using cereals and dried pulses are cheap, healthy and tasty.

**ACTIVITY**

1. You are having four friends around to watch a video. Prepare a simple main course and salad that you could eat beforehand. Follow the design brief sequence in this chapter and work out the design brief you would follow for making this meal. Cost the meal.

2. Work out: (a) the price of 150g tinned tomatoes if they cost 55c for 400g; (b) the price of 400g fish if it costs €3.50 per kilo.

ACTIVITY

3. (a) What is a time plan? What do you need to know before making a time plan for a meal?

(b) You are serving scrambled egg on toast with tea for breakfast. Pick a first course for this meal.

(c) Write out the menu and work out a time plan for the meal if it is to be served at 8 a.m.

4. Look at this shopping list and see what healthy changes you can make.

| Shopping list | Healthier alternative |
|---|---|
| White sliced pan | Wholemeal loaf |
| Whole milk | |
| Full fat cheese, e.g. Cheddar | |
| Sugar-coated cereals | |
| Butter | |
| 500g stewing steak/mince | |
| Cream | |
| Canned fruit | |
| Fruit squash | |
| Chips | |
| White flour/rice/pasta | |

REVISION QUESTIONS

1. Name four resources you might need in food management.

2. What is a design brief? List briefly the main sequence of a cookery design brief.

3. List three guidelines to follow when preparing a shopping list.

4. List four guidelines that might help you to shop for food.

5. Name five foods suitable for a person catering for a family on a low income.

# Chapter

## 8 Food Hygiene and Storage

### Food spoilage

Food has a limited life – after a certain time it will spoil and go bad. Food spoilage is caused by enzymes (chemicals) in the food and by micro-organisms such as moulds and bacteria – often called germs.

It is speeded up by carelessness in personal hygiene, lack of kitchen hygiene and incorrect storage. Lack of hygiene also leads to serious illness such as food poisoning.

❖ *Micro-organisms (sometimes called germs)*

### What causes food spoilage?

1. Enzymes. (Enzymes destroy food from inside.)
2. Micro-organisms. (Micro-organisms are inside and outside.)
3. Air (oxygen).

❶ **Enzymes** are chemicals present in food. They are involved in the ripening of fruit and vegetables: e.g. they cause bananas to go yellow, but eventually cause them to decay and rot – when they turn black. Enzymes work best at room temperature.

❷ **Micro-organisms** are living cells. They are found everywhere. They include:
- 🍴 **yeasts**, which cause fruit and jam to go off
- 🍴 **moulds**, which form a furry growth on fruit and bread in certain conditions
- 🍴 **bacteria**, which cause animal foods such as meat and fish to go off. Bacteria are also the main cause of food poisoning.

❸ **Oxygen** in the air causes fats to go off (become rancid) – this is why unwrapped fats such as butter or margarine develop 'off' flavours. Oxygen also reacts with enzymes, causing discoloration of food, e.g. apples going brown.

# Food poisoning

Food poisoning occurs when a person swallows food or drink that contains large numbers of pathogenic (disease-bearing) bacteria. When these enter our body, they multiply rapidly, making us sick.

Sometimes people ingest bacteria that make toxins or poisons in the food, which cause more serious food poisoning.

Often the food shows no signs of spoilage – there may be no change in colour, taste or smell.

**Symptoms:** nausea, abdominal pain, vomiting, diarrhoea, high temperature.

## Food poisoning bacteria

The following bacteria are among the most common causes of food poisoning.

1. **Salmonella** live in the intestines of most animals and humans. Raw meat, poultry and sometimes eggs can cause salmonella food poisoning. Flies and vermin can spread it to our food. It can also be caused by carelessness in bathroom hygiene; hands must always be washed after using the lavatory.

2. **Staphylococci** are often present in the nose, throat and skin of humans, where they can cause boils. They can enter the blood through cuts. By covering cuts with a waterproof dressing, we avoid infecting ourselves and the food we are handling.

3. **Listeria** multiply at lower temperatures than most other bacteria, e.g. in a fridge. They may be present in soft cheeses, mayonnaise, prepared salads and pâté. Healthy adults are not usually affected by listeria but they can cause food poisoning and serious side-effects in babies. Pregnant women and the vulnerable elderly should not eat these foods.

4. **Clostridium botulinum** multiplies in faulty cans of food. It causes serious poisoning, called **botulism**, and may result in paralysis and death. Examine cans before buying – they must not be rusted, leaking or bulging.

5. **E. Coli** lives in the intestines of cattle and sheep and can pass into the food chain through the faeces of these animals. It can also be present in contaminated water. Symptoms include stomach cramps with diarrhoea or blood in the diarrhoea. It can be fatal in some cases, because it damages the liver so badly.

# Food hygiene

Bacteria are tiny invisible living cells. They are found everywhere – in air, water, soil, animals and humans. Not all bacteria are harmful – some are used in the manufacture of yoghurt and cheese. However, many bacteria cause food poisoning. In small amounts, they do little harm – this is known as an acceptable level of contamination. In large amounts, however, they are dangerous. They multiply rapidly in the right conditions, causing disease and sometimes death.

## Conditions for growth of micro-organisms (e.g. bacteria)

1. **Food:** micro-organisms need food to survive. They like moist, high-protein food such as raw meat, poultry and fish. As these often contain large numbers of micro-organisms, they must be well cooked.

2. **Warmth:** most micro-organisms grow best at 30–40°C. Our body temperature (37°C) is within this range, which is why bacteria multiply in the human body and cause illness. Cold slows down their growth – this is why we store food at 4°C in a fridge; freezing (0°C or lower) stops them growing but does not kill them. Very high temperatures and disinfectants kill them.

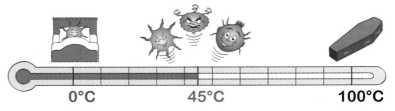

0°C          45°C          100°C

❖ *Bacteria like warmth*

3. **Moisture:** micro-organisms need moisture to multiply. They find this in kitchens and in food.

4. **Air** (usually): most micro-organisms need air to multiply, although some can multiply without air, e.g. in a can.

5. **Time** to multiply: a single micro-organism becomes two every 20 minutes. If food is used up quickly, there is less time for bacteria to multiply.

Food must be kept:
- ❀ cool  ❀ clean  ❀ covered.

A warm kitchen, particularly a dirty kitchen, provides perfect conditions for bacteria to grow. If we remove the favourable conditions they will not survive. For this reason we should keep the kitchen:
- ❀ cool (food storage areas)
- ❀ clean
- ❀ well ventilated, to remove moisture.

used to make yoghurt/cheese

cause food spoilage

cause food poisoning and disease

❖ *Not all micro-organisms are harmful*

❖ *One germ at noon*

❖ *2 million by 7 p.m.*

Food

# How is food infected with bacteria?

1. By **humans with bad hygiene habits**, e.g. not washing hands after using the lavatory, coughing and sneezing over food.

2. **Dirt and grease**: dirty kitchen surfaces, storage areas, cloths, utensils and equipment are breeding grounds for bacteria.

3. By **cross-contamination: storing or preparing raw food, e.g. meat, with food that will not be cooked**. For example, if a chicken is prepared on a surface, and without being well washed the same surface is used to prepare a salad, bacteria 'cross' from the raw chicken to the salad. This can result in food poisoning.

4. By **pets**, and **vermin** such as rats and mice.

5. By **insects**, such as flies. Flies feed on dirt and waste. They pick up bacteria on their legs, then land on uncovered food. They vomit and excrete on the food as they eat!

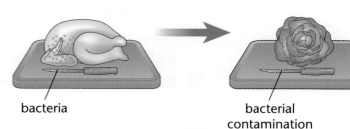

bacteria                  bacterial contamination

❖ *Cross-contamination*

# Hygiene in food preparation

## Food handlers

Humans carry bacteria in their nose, throat, skin and intestines. Bacteria can be transferred to food unless basic rules of personal hygiene are followed.

1. Wear a **clean apron** and **tie back or cover hair**.

2. **Wash hands** before handling food.

3. **Cover cuts**, etc. with a waterproof dressing.

4. Do not touch face or hair while cooking.

5. **Handle food as little as possible**; use tongs, etc.

6. Taste food using a **fresh spoon** each time. Never lick fingers.

7. **Never cough or sneeze** over food. People who are ill, e.g. with food poisoning, should not handle food.

## Food

1. Use the **freshest ingredients**, within the expiry date.

2. Keep **perishable food cool**; keep all food **clean and covered**.

3. Prepare food on a **clean work surface**, using **clean utensils**.

4. Cook meat, poultry, fish thoroughly, especially if it has been minced or chopped.

5. Keep **raw meat/fish separate** at all times from food that will not be cooked.

6. Place **leftovers** on a clean plate, cover, cool and place in fridge. **Reheat thoroughly**.

7. **Check fridge regularly** and use up leftovers and foods reaching their expiry date.

### Kitchens

A kitchen should be well designed to maintain hygiene. It should be well ventilated to remove heat and moisture. Surfaces should be easy to clean.

1. Kitchen surfaces, equipment and floors should always be kept **clean**.
2. Wash utensils and equipment in **hot soapy water** after use. Rinse and dry.
3. Keep cooker, fridge and sink clean; **disinfect** sink regularly.
4. Sweep floor daily; wash and disinfect regularly.
5. **Kitchen cloths** can be a breeding ground for bacteria, as they contain food particles and moisture. They should be changed daily, then washed, rinsed and dried. Disinfect regularly. Disposable cloths, e.g. 'J-cloths', are more hygienic if they are disposed of regularly. Use kitchen paper to mop up spills. Keep separate cloths for bathroom and kitchen use.
6. **Kitchen bins** should be kept covered. Always wrap food; empty daily; wash and disinfect regularly.
7. Keep kitchen free from smokers, pets and any source of bacteria.

# Food storage

Food spoilage can be delayed by storing food correctly. Badly stored food results in the growth of micro-organisms, food spoilage and waste.

## Good storage

- prolongs the life of food
- protects food from dust, flies, etc.
- makes it easier to find each food
- keeps the kitchen clean, hygienic and free from pests.

## Storage guidelines

1. The shelf life of food (how long it remains fit to eat) depends on the type of food and the conditions in which it is stored.
2. **Follow storage instructions** on packaging. Always use up food before its expiry date.
3. Use food in **rotation** – old before new.
4. **Keep cupboards clean**; tidy, wash and disinfect regularly.
5. Check food in the refrigerator daily and use up leftovers quickly. Wash the fridge regularly using warm water and bread soda. Check temperature occasionally – it should be 4°C or below – or keep a fridge thermometer in the fridge.
6. Store foods according to type, as follows.

- **Perishables**, e.g. **meat**, **fish**, **milk**, **cream** have the shortest shelf life and are most in danger of being contaminated. Use within three or four days. Eggs and cheese will keep longer. All should be covered and stored in the refrigerator at 3–4°C.
- **Bread, cakes, biscuits:** Store each separately in a cool place, in a bread bin or a tin.
- **Fruit and vegetables:** If washed, many can be stored in the vegetable drawer of the fridge. Root vegetables are stored in a vegetable rack in a cool dark part of the kitchen/utility room or in a ventilated food cupboard.
- **Frozen food:** Store sealed and wrapped in a freezer at –18°C or below.
- **Dry/non-perishable foods:** Store dry foods (e.g. flour, sugar, cereals) in the original package. Once opened, store in airtight, insect-proof containers. Store oil and canned, bottled and dried foods in a clean dry cupboard, keeping foods of the same type together. Many foods, e.g. tea and herbs, react to air and light – store them in a dark place.

**LINK-UP**

Refrigerators, page 318

Floor units are unsuitable for food storage. Why?

## Star markings for frozen foods and freezers

* food will keep for one week

** food will keep for one month

*** food will keep for three months

**** food will keep for up to one year

## Packaging materials

Many materials are available for cooking and storing food.

1. **Aluminium foil:** used to cover food in the fridge and oven; also for packed lunches. Foil containers are stronger and are used for foods that are stored in the freezer, then baked in the oven. Do not use foil in a microwave.
2. **Polythene bags:** useful for lunches and for storing many foods. Heavy-duty polythene is used for freezer bags.
3. **Covered polythene boxes:** ideal for storing food of all types.
4. **Clingfilm:** used for covering food for storage and for packed lunches. If possible, avoid direct contact with food, particularly fat.

5. **Roasting bags:** keep moisture in food when roasting and also keep oven clean.
6. **Greaseproof paper:** used to wrap cheese and line tins for baking.
7. **Baking parchment:** used to line tins for meringues, cakes, etc.
8. **Recycled containers:** well-washed margarine and ice cream tubs can be used for storing and freezing food.

**ACTIVITY**

Collect press cuttings on food poisoning/food hygiene, e.g. court cases for breaches of hygiene regulations in shops and restaurants. Stick them into your copybook.

**REVISION QUESTIONS**

1. What is meant by food spoilage?
2. Complete this sentence:
   To prevent spoilage, food must be kept c _____,
   c _____ and c _____.
3. Explain the term 'enzyme'.
4. Name three types of micro-organism.
5. What are the symptoms of food poisoning? Name two food-poisoning bacteria.
6. What is meant by 'acceptable levels of contamination'?
7. List the conditions required for multiplication of micro-organisms.
8. How is food infected by micro-organisms?
9. Complete this sentence:
   Bacteria grow best at _____°C. A single bacterium becomes two every _____.
10. List four rules to be followed by people handling food.
11. Explain the term 'cross-contamination'. Give one example.
12. List four rules to follow in order to keep a kitchen clean and hygienic.
13. Explain the terms (a) 'shelf life', (b) 'expiry date'.
14. Name four perishable foods. How should they be stored?
15. Name five packaging materials used for storage. Which would you consider best for use in a freezer? Why?
16. Explain what a four-star rating on a frozen product means.

Test Yourself
eTest.ie

# Chapter 9 Food Preparation

## Before you cook

- Tie back or cover hair and put on a clean apron.
- Wash hands before handling food; never lick fingers or touch face or hair.
- Read recipe through, following it step by step.
- Check that you have sufficient time to make the dish.
- Make sure work area and equipment are clean.
- Collect and weigh ingredients accurately. Place ingredients and cutlery on plates.
- Preheat oven and prepare tins/dishes.
- Tidy and wash up as you go: wash equipment in hot soapy water, rinse, dry and store.

LINK-UP

Food handlers, page 71

❖ *Put on apron*

❖ *Wash hands*

❖ **Check time available**

❖ *Weigh accurately*

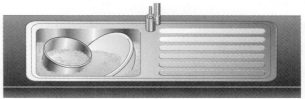

❖ *Wash up as you go*

## Kitchen safety

- Never handle electric equipment with wet hands.
- Do not overfill chip pan or leave unattended. Keep a lid nearby in case of fire.
- Keep saucepan handles turned away from edge of cooker.
- Never walk about when holding knives or hot saucepans.

**work top**

**shelf beneath**

❖ *Work area ready for cooking*

| | |
|---|---|
| 1, 2 | ingredient plates |
| 3 | jug |
| 4 | pot stand |
| 5 | cutlery on plate |
| 6 | mixing bowl |
| 7 | sieve |
| 8 | chopping board |
| 9 | basin/bin |
| 10 | tin |
| 11 | wire tray |
| 12 | serving plate |
| 13 | cloths |

*❖ Curl fingers inwards*

*❖ Use oven gloves*

- Never, ever run in a kitchen.
- Wipe up floor spills at once.
- Use oven gloves when removing hot tins from the oven.
- Use sharp knives; they cut more efficiently. Always use a chopping board.
- Hold food with fingers curled inwards to avoid cuts.

## Basic cookery resources

### 1 Recipes

Recipes consist of:

(a) a name

(b) a list of ingredients and the amount of each required

(c) the method – step-by-step instructions for making the dish.

Note particularly:

- the oven temperature required to cook the dish
- the length of cooking time.

### Apple cake

| | |
|---|---|
| 200g self-raising flour | 1. Place a circle of greaseproof paper on the base of a greased tin. |
| $\frac{1}{4}$ teaspoon cinnamon | |
| 75g margarine | 2. Sieve flour and cinnamon into a mixing bowl. |
| 100g caster sugar | 3. Rub in the margarine; stir in the sugar and raisins. |
| 50g raisins | 4. Peel, core and chop apples; stir into mixture. |
| 2 medium cooking apples | 5. Beat egg and mix in with a wooden spoon. Add milk only if necessary. |
| 1 egg | |
| 2 tablespoons milk | 6. Place mixture in tin, sprinkle with brown sugar and bake at 190°C/375°F/Gas 5 for 20–25 minutes until browned. |
| Brown sugar, to sprinkle | |

Serve hot or cold.

### 2 Weighing and measuring resources

Dry ingredients are measured in grams (g) and kilograms (kg or kilos). 1kg = 1,000g.

Grams are very small amounts, so cookery ingredients are usually measured in multiples of 25g, e.g. 50g, 75g, 100g, 250g.

In old cookery books the standard unit was the ounce – this is roughly equal to 25g.

Liquid ingredients are measured in millilitres (ml) and litres (l): 1l = 1,000ml.

Interestingly, a millilitre of water weighs a gram, therefore 00ml weighs 500g (useful if you don't have a measuring jug!).
,000g = 1 kilogram
,000ml = 1 litre

A normal bag of sugar weighs 1kg.
A bag of flour weighs 2kg.

## Weighing

or good results, ingredients should be weighed and measured accurately. Dry ngredients and fats are measured on a scales.

A spring scales has a pan to hold the ingredients. It has a dial which should be at 0 hen the pan is empty. Food is added until the dial points to the required measure, .g. 100g.

The balance scales has a pan on one side and weights are put on the other side. o weigh an ingredient, place the required weight in position, e.g. 200g. Carefully dd the ingredient to the pan. When the scale balances, you have the correct eight. If it goes down with a bang, you have too much.

❖ *Spring scales*

❖ *Balance scales*

## ats

lace greaseproof paper beneath fats to stop them ticking. Block margarine can be measured by narking in ten 'squares' as shown. Each square eighs 25g.

| 25g | | | | |
|-----|--|--|--|------|
| | | | | 50g |
| 25g | | | | |

## Measuring

. measuring jug is used to measure liquids. It is usually marked in 100ml divisions. lace the jug on a level surface and add liquid, reading it at eye level.

Measuring spoons are used to measure small amounts of dry or liquid ingredients.

They usually come in sets of four:

- 2.5ml ($\frac{1}{2}$ teaspoon)
- 5ml (1 teaspoon)
- 10ml (1 dessertspoon)
- 15ml (1 tablespoon)

heck whether the recipe requires a level or a eaped spoon – one is twice the other. When eliable recipe books refer to a teaspoon or ablespoon, they mean a level measuring spoon.

Measuring cups are used in some recipes.

❖ *Measuring jug*

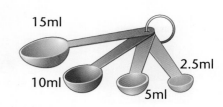

❖ *Measuring spoons*

## ∃ Utensils

Cooking utensils are an important resource. They last longer if well cared for – keep them clean, sharp and in good condition. Utensils are made from several materials.

| Utensils | Care and cleaning |
|---|---|
| **Delph/glass** | |
| Basins and bowls | Steep, if necessary. |
| Pie dishes | Wash in hot soapy water, rinse, dry. |
| Heat-resistant glass, e.g. Pyrex | Never place a hot dish on a cold surface or handle with a wet cloth. |
| **Wood** | |
| Chopping boards, rolling pins, wooden spoons, pastry brushes | Avoid steeping. Wipe off pieces of food and wash in warm soapy water using a brush. Rinse and dry well. |
| **Plastic** | |
| Chopping boards, jugs, bowls, spoons | Keep away from dry heat – most plastic melts although modern cooking tins are available in plastic that won't melt and can go into the oven. They do not require greasing. |
| Parts from processors, mixers, etc. | Some are unsuitable for dishwashers. |
| **Metals** | |
| Cast iron (casseroles) | Soak, if necessary. Wash in hot soapy water. |
| Stainless steel (cutlery, utensils, saucepans) | Rinse in hot water and dry well. Leave lids off saucepans. |
| Tin (tins, utensils) | Tin rusts easily; never leave damp. |
| Non-stick finishes (on tins and saucepans) | Never use abrasives. |

*Note: Some utensils may be cleaned in a dishwasher. Check instructions before doing so.*

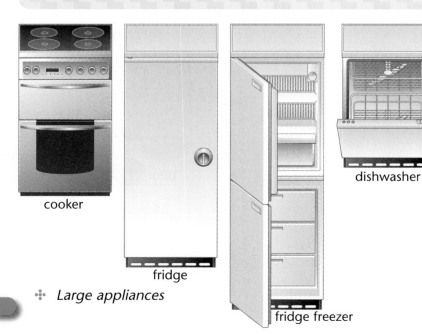

cooker

fridge

fridge freezer

dishwasher

❖ *Large appliances*

## 4 Equipment

This includes large appliances such as cookers, refrigerators, freezers and dishwashers, and smaller appliances such as food preparation machines, deep fat fryers and kettles.

LINK-UP

Electrical appliances, page 314
Cookers, page 316

## Oven management

Cookers are heated by gas, electricity or solid fuel. These can be dangerous – learn how to use them correctly.

1. **Shelf position.** Place shelves in position before you turn on the oven. Why?

2. **Lighting the oven**

   *Electric ovens:* turn the oven switch to the temperature required. A light usually comes on, and goes out when the correct temperature is reached. It may turn on and off during the cooking – this is normal.

   *Gas ovens:* modern ovens have push-button ignition. Older ovens may need to be lit with a match or gas lighter. Turn on oven, light flame, then set correct temperature.

3. **Preheating.** It takes 5–10 minutes for an oven to heat up. A fan oven heats up quickly. Switch on the oven in time, so that it has reached the correct temperature before you put in the food. This is particularly important when baking, e.g. bread and cakes.

4. **Temperature differences.** When you set the oven temperature, that is the temperature in the centre of the oven. Because hot air rises, the temperature is higher at the top of the oven than on the lower shelves (except in fan ovens, which have an even temperature throughout). A recipe may suggest a certain position; if not, place dish on the centre shelf. Never place anything on the oven floor.

5. **Thermostat.** A thermostat is a device that keeps an oven or other heating appliance at the correct temperature. It is usually based on a bimetal strip, which bends at a certain temperature, cutting off the electricity or gas supply.

✛ *Oven temperature*

✛ *Thermostat*

## Oven temperatures

| Description | C | F | Gas |
|---|---|---|---|
| Very cool | 110 | 225 | $\frac{1}{4}$ |
| | 120 | 250 | $\frac{1}{2}$ |
| Cool | 140 | 275 | 1 |
| | 150 | 300 | 2 |
| Very moderate | 160 | 325 | 3 |
| Moderate | 180 | 350 | 4 |
| | 190 | 375 | 5 |
| Moderate/fairly hot | 200 | 400 | 6 |
| Hot | 220 | 425 | 7 |
| | 230 | 450 | 8 |
| Very hot | 240 | 475 | 9 |

**6** **Oven temperatures.** It is very important to set the oven to the temperature stated in the recipe, e.g. 190°C/375°F/Gas 5. Modern electric cookers are measured in degrees Celsius; older cookers may use Fahrenheit; gas cookers use numbers. Only one system will apply to your cooker. Always note the time when you put something in the oven, and work out when it should be finished. You should start testing food for 'doneness' a little while before this.

## Cooker economy

- Avoid heating the oven for one item – cook two or more things at once.
- Dual rings and grills save fuel – use inner elements for small items.
- Avoid opening oven door unnecessarily. Cover saucepans.
- Heat only as much water as you need in saucepans, kettles, etc.

## Food preparation machines

Food processors and mixers are useful resources as they save time and energy.

| Mixers | Processors |
|---|---|
| Cream fat and sugar | Blend soups, sauces, batters, etc |
| Whisk eggs for sponges and meringues | Purée fruit and vegetables |
| Whip cream | Make breadcrumbs |

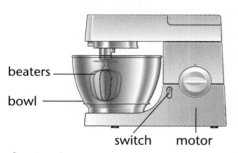

*A mixer*

beaters
bowl
switch    motor

Processors normally have a variety of attachments which allow them to carry out extra functions, e.g. slicing, grating, mincing.

Both types of machine are worked by a motor which turns the beaters or knives. This part should never be placed in water. To clean, simply unplug and wipe over with a damp cloth. Loose parts are removed and washed in hot soapy water, rinsed and dried or put into the dishwasher if appropriate. Don't reassemble the machine until it is completely dry.

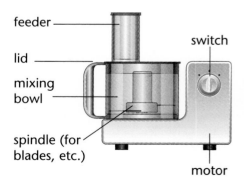

*A processor*

feeder
switch
lid
mixing bowl
spindle (for blades, etc.)
motor

## Using

- Follow manufacturer's instructions.
- Do not overfill.
- Use the correct speed.
- Do not allow to run too long – it will overheat.

## Cookery terms

**Any of the following definitions may appear on the written paper.**

| | |
|---|---|
| Au gratin: | Food which has been covered in a sauce, and often with cheese, and browned under the grill or in the oven. |
| Bake blind: | Bake a pastry case without a filling to prevent it collapsing when the filling goes in. |
| Baste: | Spoon hot fat over roast meat to stop it drying out. |
| Beat: | Mix quickly to introduce air. |
| Blanch: | Put into boiling water and then plunge into iced water. This is done, for example, to remove skins (of tomatoes), remove strong flavours (onion) or to retain the colour of food (e.g. green vegetables) before use. It is also used to destroy enzymes when freezing (see page 151). |
| Blend: | Mix a starchy powder with a cold liquid, so that it does not go lumpy, e.g. cornflour with cold water. |
| Bouquet garni: | A bunch of mixed herbs or a sachet of herbs added to foods such as soups and stews to give flavour. |
| Brine: | Salted water. |
| Chill: | Refrigerate. |
| Coat: | Cover with a protective layer such as batter or breadcrumbs, e.g. for frying. Sauces are used to 'coat' foods. |
| Consistency: | The thickness of a mixture. |
| Cream: | Mix fat and sugar together until pale and fluffy, e.g. Madeira mixture. |
| Croûtons: | Small dice of fried bread used to garnish soup. |
| Dough: | A soft or fairly stiff mixture of flour and liquid used to make bread, scones and pastry. |
| Dredge: | Sprinkle with sugar or flour. |
| Dredger: | Container for dredging. |
| Flan: | A shallow case of pastry or sponge which may be filled with a savoury or sweet filling. |
| Fold: | Incorporate lightly a dry ingredient, such as flour, into a whipped mixture using a metal spoon, in such a way that the air is not removed. |
| Garnish: | Decorate a savoury dish. |
| Glaze: | Brush egg or milk over foods to be baked; this gives them a shine. |
| Infuse: | To heat food in liquid to a very low temperature in order to extract the flavour. |
| Knead: | To work dough with the hands in order to make it elastic and smooth. |
| Liaison: | A thickening ingredient for soups, stews, sauces, e.g. flour, cornflour, roux. |
| Marinade: | A mixture of oil, acid and flavourings used to tenderise and flavour meat before grilling, baking or barbecuing. |
| Menu: | A list of foods available for a meal. |

| | |
|---|---|
| **Panard:** | A thick sauce used to bind ingredients together. |
| **Parboil:** | Partly cook by boiling. |
| **Poach:** | Cook gently in water well below boiling point. |
| **Purée:** | A soft, smooth mixture of fruit or vegetables or a thick smooth soup, usually blended in a food processor. |
| **Quiche:** | An open pastry case filled with a savoury custard and other ingredients. |
| **Raising agent:** | A substance such as baking powder added to baked foods such as bread to make them light and help them to rise. |
| **Roux:** | A mixture of flour and fat used to thicken sauces and soups. |
| **Rub in:** | Crumble fat into flour using the fingertips, e.g. scones, pastry. |
| **Sauté:** | Toss quickly in hot fat. |
| **Seasoning:** | Salt, pepper, herbs and spices used to add flavouring to savoury dishes. |
| **Shortening:** | Any fat used in baking, e.g. pastry making, that produces a brittle 'short' texture, e.g. margarine, butter, pastry fat. |
| **Simmer:** | Cook in liquid just below boiling point. |
| **Skim:** | Remove a substance from the top of a liquid, e.g. scum when boiling jam or oil from the top of sauces. |
| **Syrup:** | A solution of sugar and water. |
| **Whisk:** | Beat air into a mixture using a utensil called a whisk. |

**REVISION QUESTIONS**

1. Give four hygiene guidelines you would follow before starting to cook.
2. List four safety procedures to remember in a kitchen.
3. Why is efficiency important when you are cooking?
4. What is a recipe? Why should you read a recipe through before starting to cook?
5. How many grams are in a kilogram?
6. Describe briefly how a spring balance scale works.
7. List three guidelines to follow when caring for and cleaning metal utensils.
8. What is meant by preheating an oven? Why is it important?
9. Describe what is meant by a thermostat.
10. Name the two temperature measurements found on cookers today.
11. List three guidelines for using a food processor.
12. Explain the following cookery terms:
    - baking blind
    - blanch
    - consistency
    - flan
    - infuse
    - roux.

# Chapter 10 Cooking Food

## Reasons for cooking food

Some foods, such as fruit and vegetables, can be eaten raw. However, we usually cook food, for the following reasons.

1. Heat kills harmful bacteria, making food safer to eat.
2. Heat helps preserve food so that it lasts longer.
3. Cooking makes many foods easier to digest, e.g. starchy foods such as pasta.
4. Cooking improves the appearance, colour and flavour of many foods.
5. Cooking adds variety, by developing new flavours.

## Heat causes changes in food

|   |  | Examples |
|---|---|---|
| 1 | Protein coagulates and hardens the food. | Eggs, cheese |
| 2 | Some foods lose water and shrink. | Meat, fish |
| 3 | Starch absorbs liquid and swells. | Rice, pasta, thickened sauces |
| 4 | Some foods soften and break up. | Potatoes, apples |
| 5 | Fat melts. | Butter, meat fat |
| 6 | Colour changes. | Meat, bread |
| 7 | Some nutrients are lost. | Vitamins B and C, and minerals |

Overcooking causes:

- greater loss of nutrients
- loss of colour, flavour and texture
- toughness and indigestibility, e.g. meat, cheese
- waste of fuel.

## Heat travels to food in three ways

### Conduction

Heat passes from molecule to molecule.
Example: shallow and stir frying. The heat passes from the hot pan into the food.

### Convection

Heat travels in convection currents through water/air/oil. These heat the food, e.g. in oven baking, deep frying. Moist cookery methods are based on convection of water or steam, which is heated at the heat source, rises, then falls as it cools. *Note:* fan ovens use forced convection.

### Radiation

Heat travels to the food in straight rays.
Grilling cooks by radiation; the outside is heated by rays from the grill, and the heat then passes into the food by conduction. Microwave ovens cook by radiation; heat travels within food by conduction.

❖ Conduction

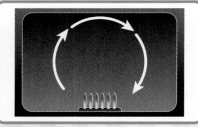

❖ Convection

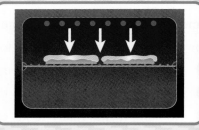

❖ Radiation

# Methods of cooking

The cooking method you choose depends on several factors:

- the type of food, e.g. fish or apples, tough or tender meat
- the shape and size of the food
- the time available, e.g. stewing takes a long time
- the equipment available
- the result you want – soft, moist, crisp, low-fat, etc.

## Moist cooking methods

| Method | Description | Equipment | Suitable foods | Guidelines |
|---|---|---|---|---|
| Boiling at 100°C | Cooking food in boiling liquid | Covered saucepan | Fresh or salt meat<br>Most vegetables<br>Rice<br>Pasta | Immerse food in boiling water. When it returns to the boil, time it, reduce to a simmer and cover. Fresh meat is placed in boiling water to seal surface, then simmered. Salt meat is started in cold water to draw out the salt. Use stock, seasoning and herbs to improve flavour. |

steam — bubbles — water

| Method | Description | Equipment | Suitable foods | Guidelines |
|---|---|---|---|---|
| Poaching | Cooking in water which is barely bubbling | Saucepan Poacher | Eggs Fish | Never allow water to boil. Lift delicate foods carefully. |
| Stewing/ casseroling | Long, slow cooking in a little liquid in a tightly closed vessel | Covered saucepan or casserole | Tough meat, fish Vegetables Fruit | Keep temperature low; never boil. Cook stew on hob; casserole in oven. Fruit – Cover pot to reduce evaporation. Use stock, herbs, etc. to improve flavour. Slow but economical method of cooking. |
| Steaming | Cooking in steam rising from boiling water | Saucepan and plates Steamer Covered bowl | Fish Chicken fillets Vegetables Puddings | Steamed food lacks flavour: season well or serve with sauce. Puddings – keep water on the boil. Covered bowl – replenish with boiling water. Cover tightly to prevent heat loss. Food retains nutrients; digestible. |
| Pressure cooking | Cooking in steam, under pressure | Pressure cooker, a heavy saucepan with a sealed lid | Stock, soups, stews, bacon Root vegetables | Foods cook quickly; don't overcook. Let steam build up before adding food. Time carefully. Steamed puddings – use correct amount of water. Preserves e.g. jam – follow manufacturer's instructions. Opening cooker – steam must be released before opening. |

❖ *Plates over saucepan*  ❖ *Steamer*  ❖ *Covered bowl*

**Principle of pressure cooking**

The sealed pressure cooker causes a controlled build-up of pressure. Steam under pressure reaches a higher temperature and cooks the food faster.

## Cooking methods using fat or oil

| Method | Description | Equipment | Suitable foods | Guidelines |
|---|---|---|---|---|
| Roasting | Cooking food in hot fat in the oven (convection) | Roasting tin Roasting bags | Tender meat joints Poultry and game Vegetables, e.g. potatoes, onions | Use high temperature; preheat oven Meat may be open roasted or covered; the latter takes longer. Weigh meat to work out cooking time. Baste with hot fat to prevent drying. Let meat stand for 10 minutes before carving. |
| Frying* (Shallow, deep or stir frying) | Cooking in fat at a high temperature, i.e. 180°C | Frying pan Deep fat fryer Wok | Thin cuts of tender meat or poultry Eggs Fillets/cutlets of fish Reheated food, chips, fritters Vegetables, e.g. onions | Fat must be hot before adding food. Dry food before frying. To ensure crispness, do not cover or overcrowd the pan. Drain fried food to avoid greasiness. Frying adds kilocalories to foods, so eat fried foods sparingly. |

**\*Danger! Frying is a dangerous way of cooking:**
1. Never overheat oil.
2. Never move frying pan while oil is hot.
3. Never leave frying pan unattended.
4. Keep a lid/fire blanket nearby in case of fire.

**Fried food may be coated in breadcrumbs or batter:**
1. To give an attractive crisp coating.
2. To prevent it breaking up.
3. To protect it from hot fat.
4. To prevent food flavours getting into fat.

## Dry cooking methods

| Method | Description | Equipment | Suitable foods | Guidelines |
|---|---|---|---|---|
| Grilling | Food cooks quickly by rays of heat from the hot grill | Gas or electric grill or barbecue Grill pan and grid | Thin, tender meat e.g. steak, chops, burgers Small fish, fish fillets, cutlets, fingers, cakes Mushrooms, tomatoes, toast Au gratin dishes. | Food cooks quickly. Use only tender meat. Preheat grill. Season with salt/pepper. Brush food and grid with oil. Grill quickly on both sides to seal. Use a tongs; piercing food with a knife causes juices to escape. |

| Method | Description | Equipment | Suitable foods | Guidelines |
|--------|-------------|-----------|----------------|------------|
| Baking | Cooking food in dry heat in an oven | Baking tins<br>Cake tins<br>Pyrex dishes | Bread, cakes, buns, etc.<br>Pastry dishes, e.g. pies<br>Fruit, e.g. apples<br>Puddings | Preheat oven to correct temperature.<br>Place food in correct position.<br>Do not overcrowd – allow air to circulate.<br>Avoid opening oven door unnecessarily.<br>Make full use of oven when it's on. |

Food

## Microwave cooking

### Principle

Microwave ovens send energy waves about 5cm into the food. These cause friction between the molecules of food, which makes them heat up. The heat then travels into the food until it is cooked. The outside of the food does not brown in a microwave, unless it has a built-in grill element.

❖ *Dispersal of rays inside a microwave*

### Microwave ovens

A microwave oven is small enough to place on the worktop. It is plugged into a normal socket. Power is measured in watts; the higher the wattage, the faster it cooks. Most are in the 600–800W range. Controls include an on/off pushbutton or dial, power control and timing control. It has a sealed door which cuts off the cooking when it is opened. Most models have a turntable which revolves during cooking. Optional features are a fan, a temperature probe, a browning element and a memory for programmed cooking.

### Suitable foods

- Microwave ovens cook most fresh foods, preferably in small amounts.
- They are very suitable for fish and vegetables.
- They defrost frozen food.
- They reheat food.

### Unsuitable foods

- Whole tomatoes
- Whole eggs
- Pastry
- Foods requiring browning (if this option is not available).

### Cooking by microwave

1. Follow instruction book.
2. Note size, thickness and density of food for calculating cooking time. Large amounts of separate foods such as potatoes take longer than small amounts, in contrast to normal ovens. Solid foods such as meat take longer than light foods.

3 Cover most foods with a plate or microwave film. This speeds up cooking and prevents soiling of the oven.

4 Prod egg yolks and food with skins, such as sausages and potatoes, to prevent bursting.

5 Arrange food such as potatoes in a circle; foods such as chicken legs, broccoli and fish fillets should have the thickest side facing out.

6 Turn dishes and food for even cooking; stir if possible to distribute heat.

7 Allow 'standing time'. During this time the food continues to cook.

## Suitable cooking materials

- Microwave cookware.
- Ceramic, glass and certain plastics.
- Microwave clingfilm.

Never use metal containers or aluminium foil. Metal damages the microwave oven.

## Care and cleaning

1 Follow the manufacturer's instructions for use, care and cleaning.

2 Never use metal containers or foil for cooking food.

3 Never switch on when empty.

4 Wipe up spills at once and clean regularly.

## Cleaning:

- Unplug.
- Remove loose parts, e.g. turntable dish, and wash separately.
- Wash interior with hot, soapy water; rinse and dry.
- Repeat with outside.
- Avoid using abrasives – a cream cleaner may be used if necessary.

## Methods of cooking

Different methods of cooking have different advantages and disadvantages.

| Advantages | Disadvantages |
| --- | --- |
| Quick/easy | Slow |
| Little preparation | Troublesome to prepare |
| Food stays moist | Food dries out |
| Adds flavour/tasty | Loss of flavour/flavourless |
| Retains nutrients | Loses nutrients |

Food

| | |
|---|---|
| Clean/not greasy | Dirty/greasy |
| Low kilocalorie | Adds kilocalories |
| Digestible | Indigestible |
| Good texture, e.g. crisp | Soft/lacks texture |
| Economical – food/fuel/wash up | Expensive meat must be used |
| Needs little attention | Constant attention required |
| Safe for beginners | Can be dangerous |

**ACTIVITY**

List several methods that could be used to cook these basic foods:

- fish fillet
- a potato
- 500g minced beef
- 2 eggs.

For each food, circle the method you think conforms most closely to dietary guidelines. Give reasons for your answer.

**REVISION QUESTIONS**

1. Give four reasons why food is cooked.
2. How does heat affect (a) protein foods, (b) fat, (c) starchy foods?
3. Name the vitamins likely to be destroyed by cooking.
4. Name four moist cooking methods.
5. List some guidelines to follow when grilling food. Give one advantage and one disadvantage of grilling.
6. List some safety procedures to follow when frying.
7. What cookery method do you consider the healthiest? Give two reasons for your answer.
8. What cookery method do you consider the least healthy? Give two reasons for your answer.
9. List four guidelines to follow when cooking with a microwave.
10. Give three advantages of microwave cooking. List three materials suitable for microwave cooking. Explain 'standing time'.
11. What is poaching? Name three foods that could be poached.
12. List four guidelines for baking and name four different foods suitable for baking.
13. What is stewing? Name two methods of stewing.
14. List the effects of overcooking.

Test Yourself
eTest.ie

# Chapter 11
## Breakfasts and Packed Meals

*'Breakfast like a king, lunch like a prince and dine like a pauper'*

Breakfast is a very important meal: when blood sugar is low after the long overnight fast, it 'breaks the fast' and supplies the body with fuel for the new day. Many people go to school or work without eating – this deprives the body of nutrients when they are most needed.

Research shows that people who skip breakfast are more accident-prone, work less efficiently and find it difficult to concentrate. They are also more likely to overeat during the day.

## Choose your breakfast from the following

| Fruit | Cereal | Main course | Bread | Drink |
|---|---|---|---|---|
| (Fruit/veg group) | (Cereal + milk group) | (Protein + milk group) | (Cereal group) | (Milk group) |
| Fresh fruit, e.g. grapefruit | e.g. porridge, muesli, All-Bran, Weetabix, bran flakes, Shredded Wheat, cornflakes | Eggs: poached, boiled, fried, scrambled, omelette | Wholemeal | Tea |
| Fruit juice, e.g. orange, apple | | Grilled bacon, sausages pudding, kidneys, tomatoes, mushrooms | Toast | Coffee |
| Segments, e.g. grapefruit, orange | | French toast | White | Milk |
| Stewed fruit, e.g. prunes | | Grilled kippers | Wholemeal scones | Chocolate |
| | | Cold: cheese, yoghurt, cooked meat | Savoury Croissants | |
| | | | Bagels | |

# Breakfast guidelines

**1** Include food from each food group.

**2** Avoid fries; grill instead.

**3** Fats on bread, e.g. butter, low-fat or unsaturated spreads, should be used sparingly.

**4** Use high-fibre cereals and avoid sweetened varieties; the milk on cereals provides calcium and protein.

**5** Food should be quick and easy to prepare.

**6** Avoid rushing; get up in time to prepare breakfast and sit down to eat it.

LINK-UP

Sample menus, page 57

Food

# Setting a breakfast tray

**1** Collect everything you need: tray, cutlery, glass and delph should be really clean.

**2** Choose small dishes, teapot, etc. so that they fit on the tray.

**3** Place items on tray in logical order, e.g. teapot and milk beside cup – see diagram.

**4** Make sure to include cutlery for each item, e.g. grapefruit, cereals. Don't forget condiments and a napkin.

**5** Cover cooked food to keep it warm.

**6** It should look attractive, with co-ordinated colours on delph, napkin, etc. A small flower will give it a nice finish.

1 toast rack
2 butter
3 marmalade
4 orange juice
5 milk jug
6 main course
7 sugar

**ACTIVITY**

Plan a winter breakfast for schoolgoing children from the selection on page 90.
Write the menu down and work out a time plan for the breakfast.

**REVISION QUESTIONS**

1. Why is it important to have a good breakfast?
2. Plan a low-fat/high-fibre breakfast.
3. Plan a breakfast for a diabetic (see page 49).

# Packed meals

Packed meals include lunches for people at work and school, picnics, and meals for those travelling. For many people, they are not just a snack but a midday meal. Like all meals, they should be nutritious and follow the healthy eating guidelines. Avoid high-kilocalorie snacks such as crisps, chocolate bars and sugary drinks.

❖ *A healthy packed lunch*

## Planning packed meals

❶ The meal should be nutritious and tasty.

❷ Pack sufficient food for the dietary needs of each person, depending on age, etc. and the amount of time until the next meal.

❸ Include unprocessed carbohydrate, fruit and salads for fibre and vitamin C.

❹ Avoid too many sweet or fatty foods.

❺ Food should keep well and stand up to packing, e.g. banana sandwiches or a cream slice are not a good idea. (Why?)

❻ For freshest sandwiches, pack ingredients separately and make them up on the spot. Bring buttered rolls, tomatoes, ham, mini cheeses, etc. Don't forget knives.

❼ Wrap different foods separately in secure packaging; pack heaviest foods at the bottom.

## Suggested foods

| | |
|---|---|
| **Cereal group** | Wholemeal or white sandwiches/rolls/baps/scones (spread butter thinly). Rice, pasta or potato salads. Popcorn. |
| **Fruit/vegetable group** | Fresh whole fruit, e.g. apple, mandarin orange, small bunch grapes, banana. Green, vegetable and fruit salads; soups; fruit or vegetable juice (e.g. carrot juice); sticks of celery and carrot, with a dip (optional). |
| **Meat group** | Cold meat, e.g. chicken pieces, ham; hard-boiled or Scotch eggs; meat pies or pasties; sausage rolls; meat or fish in mayonnaise, e.g. prawn cocktail. |
| **Milk group** | Cheese; a wide selection of individually wrapped cheeses is available. Yoghurt and yoghurt drinks; chilled milk or milk shakes; hot chocolate. |
| **Sweet treats** | Homemade biscuits, raisins, cereal bars. |

## Packaging for packed meals

Plastic lunch boxes, aluminium foil, empty margarine tubs, polythene bags, foil cartons, insulated (freezer) bags, clingfilm, plastic bottles, insulated picnic box, greaseproof paper, vacuum flasks.

## Making sandwiches

Sandwiches are easy to make, to carry and to eat. They can be made the night before and stored in the fridge. A huge number of variations can be made, as each of the three parts of a sandwich can be varied – the bread, the spread and the filling.

## Bread

Choose between wholemeal and white sliced pan or soda bread, rolls, tortilla wraps, baps, pittas or crispbreads.

## Spread

This provides a waterproof layer and prevents moist foods making the bread soggy. It also adds flavour, especially if seasoning, herbs, mustard, etc. are added before spreading.

Choose from spreadable butter, soft margarine and low-fat spread.

## Filling

Vary colour, texture and flavour. Combine crisp lettuce with soft foods. Moisten dry fillings with mayonnaise or savoury sauce. For example:

- thinly sliced beef or ham, lettuce and garlic-flavoured mayonnaise
- flaked tinned salmon, tuna or sardine with cucumber, lemon juice and mayonnaise
- chicken or turkey with chopped apple and curry-flavoured mayonnaise
- smoked fish (salmon, kipper), bean sprouts, cream cheese and lemon juice.

## Top ten sandwich types

1. Single – two slices of bread and one filling.
2. Double decker – three slices of bread and two complementary fillings.
3. Club – four or more slices of bread and three or more fillings.
4. Submarine ('sub') – large crisp rolls or French bread with fillings and optional dressing. Remove some of the inside of a crusty roll and fill with chopped chicken, lettuce, tomato.
5. Toasted – filled sandwiches, lightly buttered on the outside and toasted in a sandwich toaster or under a grill. Fillings such as lettuce are unsuitable.
6. BLT – hot crisp bacon rashers, lettuce and tomato moistened with mayonnaise. May or may not be toasted.

7 Pitta pockets – halved and filled with hot or cold filling, e.g. smoked chicken, lettuce, chutney, mayonnaise.

8 Rolled – crustless, thinly sliced bread, spread with thin filling such as pâté, ham or smoked salmon, then rolled up and chilled.

9 Pinwheels – as for rolled, then chilled and sliced like a Swiss roll into tasty mouthfuls.

10 Open – one layer of buttered firm bread or toast with tasty combinations of food on top. Example: brown soda bread, buttered, a leaf of lettuce and a slice of ham on top, garnished with a little mayonnaise and cucumber pieces.

**ACTIVITY**

1. Plan a menu for a packed lunch for a schoolchild in winter. Give reasons for your choices.

2. Plan a substantial menu for a summer picnic for four teenagers. It should be cheap, nourishing and contain no sandwiches.

3. Design a sandwich suitable for a school lunch for a vegan. What foods would you add to her lunch box in order to make this a balanced meal?

4. You have been asked to make open sandwiches for a fund-raising tea for 25 people. Using the design brief sequence, design five open sandwiches that you would make. They must be tasty and attractive but economical.

**REVISION QUESTIONS**

1. List four guidelines for making a successful packed meal.

2. Name two foods from each food group which you would include in a packed lunch for an active schoolboy.

3. Name six different forms of packaging used for packed meals.

4. There are three parts to a sandwich: (a) _____, (b) _____, (c) _____.

5. Name five different types of sandwich. Which do you like best? In one sentence, explain why.

Test Yourself
eTest.ie

# Chapter 12 Soups and Sauces

## Soups

Soups may be served as an appetiser at the beginning of a meal, as the main part of a lunch or as a warming snack at any time of the day.

### Stock

 Stock is a well-flavoured basis for soups, stews and sauces.

Meat stock is made by simmering bones, meat and flavouring vegetables such as onions, carrot and celery in water for $1-1\frac{1}{2}$ hours. Fish and vegetable stock are never cooked for more than half an hour. The stock is then sieved, cooled and stored in the fridge. It should be used within three days.

Stock cubes are made from concentrated, dried stock. As they are highly seasoned and usually contain additives, they are best kept for emergencies.

### Food value of soup

This can vary a lot, depending on the ingredients. A meat soup made with stock can be a good source of protein; thick vegetable soup can be a valuable source of vitamins, minerals and fibre as long as it is not overcooked. As a rule, the more liquid the soup, the lower the food value. Convenience soups, such as dried soups, are not as nourishing as fresh soups.

### Characteristics of a good soup

It should be:

- well flavoured, tasting of the main ingredient, e.g. tomato
- the correct consistency – thick or thin, with no floury lumps
- a good colour
- free from grease
- piping hot (unless it is a cold soup).

## Classification (types) of soup

Thin soups – clear soups and broths.

Thick soups – purées and thickened soups.

1. Clear soups, e.g. consommé, are based on a rich stock. They are thin and transparent.

2. Broths, e.g. chicken broth, are clear soups containing finely chopped meat and vegetables. A wholegrain cereal such as barley or rice is used to thicken the broth.

3. A purée is thickened by sieving or blending its ingredients. Most vegetable soups, e.g. mushroom, tomato, are purées. Starchy thickeners such as potato may be used.

4. Thickened soups are not sieved. The meat/vegetables are finely chopped before cooking and the soup is thickened towards the end with blended flour, a roux or pasta. Examples: mixed vegetable soup, minestrone, chowder.

## Thickening soups

Use 25g of one of the following to thicken a litre of soup.

1. Starch, e.g. flour or cornflour, is usually added towards the end of cooking. Blend with cold liquid, then stir into the soup and cook for at least 5 minutes.

2. After sautéing ingredients in 25g fat/oil, an equal quantity of flour is added to form a roux. The stock is then added. Used in thickened soups and purées.

3. Whole cereals, e.g. pearl barley, rice; as these take some time to cook, they are added near the beginning of cooking broths and some thickened soups. Pasta may also be used, but it is added about 20–30 minutes from the end.

## Guidelines for making soup

1. Use a heavy saucepan with a well-fitting lid.
2. Use the correct proportion of fresh ingredients.
3. Use a good stock, and sauté ingredients to improve flavour.
4. Slice or chop ingredients to release more flavour.
5. Use cold water and bring slowly to the boil. Cover and simmer gently to extract nutrients and flavour.
6. A pressure cooker speeds up cooking time; a processor speeds up preparation and puréeing.

## Convenience soups

These are useful in emergencies or when time is short, as they are easy to use and they cook quickly. However, these soups may contain added sugar, salt and other additives, so their use should be limited. There is a wide variety of types and flavours.

- Dried soup – both regular and instant versions are available. Cheap.
- Canned soup – medium priced.
- Chilled, in a carton – expensive but good flavour.

## Garnishes for soup

Soups are usually served in warm individual soup bowls accompanied by brown bread, a roll or Melba (very thin) toast. They may be garnished with:

- croûtons (diced bread, fried in hot oil)
- finely chopped herbs
- a swirl of cream
- grated cheese.

## Sauce

A **sauce is a well-flavoured liquid**. It may be hot or cold, thick or thin, savoury or sweet.

Sauces are usually served as an accompaniment to food. They may also form part of a food, e.g. a casserole, or be used to coat a food, e.g. cauliflower cheese.

Sauces are served with food:

- to improve the appearance of food
- to add flavour
- to moisten food
- to improve digestibility
- to add variety and sometimes colour
- in some cases, to improve food value (but many sauces add kilocalories!)
- in some cases, to offset the richness of the food, such as apple sauce with pork and orange sauce with duck.

## Food value of sauces

The food value of a sauce depends on the ingredients used. If milk is used, as in a white sauce, the food value will be higher than if water is the main liquid.

## Classification

Most sauces fit into one of four groups.

Roux sauces:   White sauce, cheese sauce, brown stewing sauce.

Custard, page 175

**Egg sauces:** Custard sauces, hollandaise sauce.

**Fruit sauces:** Stewed, flavoured fruit, e.g. apple or cranberry sauce, raspberry coulis.

**Cold sauces:** Mint sauce, salad dressings, mayonnaise.

These are the sauces used most often and the food they are usually served with:

| | |
|---|---|
| béchamel (white sauce) | lasagne |
| bread | chicken |
| apple | pork |
| mint | lamb |
| custard | desserts |
| pesto | pasta |
| tomato | pizza |
| hollandaise | salmon |
| béarnaise | steak |
| tartare | fish |
| butterscotch | ice cream |
| fruit sauce (coulis) | desserts |
| sweet and sour | Chinese dishes |
| barbecue | ribs |
| horseradish | beef |

## Roux sauces

**A roux consists of equal quantities of fat and flour cooked to form a paste.** The liquid is added slowly and then the sauce is boiled for 5 minutes. The consistency (thickness) depends on the amount of liquid added. Milk is used for white sauces, and stock for dark sauces e.g. tomato or brown sauce.

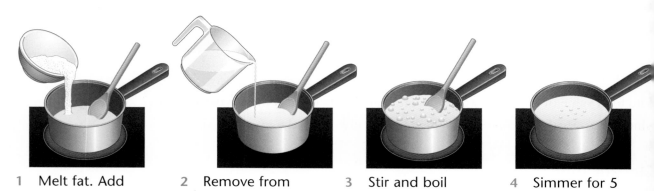

1 Melt fat. Add flour

2 Remove from heat and add milk

3 Stir and boil

4 Simmer for 5 minutes

| asic roux sauces | Fat | Flour | Liquid (milk/stock) |
|---|---|---|---|
| ouring | 25g | 25g | 500ml |
| tewing | 25g | 25g | 375ml |
| oating | 25g | 25g | 250ml |
| inding | 25g | 25g | 125ml |

## Variations on a white roux sauce

| Type of sauce | To every 500ml of pouring sauce add: | Goes well with: |
|---|---|---|
| Parsley | 1–2 tbsp chopped parsley | Bacon, ham, fish |
| Mustard | 1 tsp made mustard, 2 tsps vinegar | Fish |
| Onion | **Method** Sauté 1 medium finely chopped onion in fat before adding flour. | Bacon, vegetables |
| Mushroom | Sauté 50g mushrooms in fat, then remove while making sauce. Return for final simmer. | Grills, roasts |
| Cheese | 50g grated cheese, $\frac{1}{4}$ tsp made mustard. Add mustard and finish cooking the sauce. Stir in cheese; allow to melt without cooking. | *Fish, vegetables, cauliflower, lasagne, macaroni, other pasta |
| Béchamel | Put 2 cloves, pinch of nutmeg, 1 bay leaf and a slice of onion in milk and infuse for 15 minutes. Use this milk to make white sauce. | Stuffed vol-au-vents or pancakes |
| Velouté | A white sauce using stock instead of milk. | Chicken |

*May form part of the dish, as in fish pie, macaroni cheese or vegetable cheese.

## Guidelines for making a roux sauce

1. Follow recipe accurately.
2. Cook roux gently but thoroughly before adding liquid.
3. Take saucepan off the heat when adding the liquid.
4. Add the liquid very slowly, stirring all the time to prevent lumping. Return to the heat.
5. Make sure to cook the sauce fully to prevent a floury taste.
6. Unless otherwise stated, add seasonings and flavourings near the beginning, so that they cook into the sauce.
7. Taste at the end and correct seasoning, if necessary.

*Tip:* To keep sauce hot without a skin forming, place a circle of damp greaseproof paper on the surface of the sauce and cover with a lid.

LINK-UP

Recipes: macaroni cheese, page 179

Characteristics of
a good soup,
page 95

## Characteristics of a good sauce
These are the same as for soups.

## Convenience sauces
Dried, canned and bottled sauces are quick and easy to use.
A wide variety is available, including pasta sauces and
Oriental sauces. They help to shorten the preparation and
cooking time of a complicated recipe. The standard of canned
and bottled sauces is quite high, but check for chemical
additives, added sugar and salt.

**REVISION QUESTIONS**

1. What is stock? Name three types of stock.
2. Classify soups into four types, and name one of each type.
3. Name two ways in which soups may be thickened.
4. What are the advantages and disadvantages of convenience soups?
5. Name two pieces of equipment that speed up soup-making.
6. Name four ways in which sauces can be used.
7. Why are sauces served with food?
8. What sauce is traditionally served with (a) pork (b) beef (c) lamb (d) chicken (e) salmon?
9. What is a roux sauce? Give four ways in which it can be varied.
10. List four guidelines for making a roux sauce.
11. Give two benefits of using stock when making soup.

# Chapter 13 The Cereal Group

Most of the food we eat should come from this food group.

**Cereals/bread/potatoes: Eat 6 portions daily.**

## Cereals

**Cereals are the seeds or grains of cultivated grass plants.** They include wheat, rice, oats, maize (corn), barley and rye. Cereals are a staple food in many countries, because they are:

- easy to grow
- nutritious
- cheap and filling
- easy to prepare and cook.

## Food value

**Carbohydrate** is the main nutrient in cereals and cereal products; it is present in the form of starch and fibre. (Fibre content is reduced by processing.)

**Protein:** Cereals are a good source of vegetable protein – up to 13%.

**Fat:** Cereals contain a little fat – mainly in the germ.

**Vitamins/minerals:** Unprocessed cereals are a good source of B vitamins. Cereals also contain iron and calcium.

**Water** content is low, therefore cereals store well. Water is absorbed during cooking, e.g. rice.

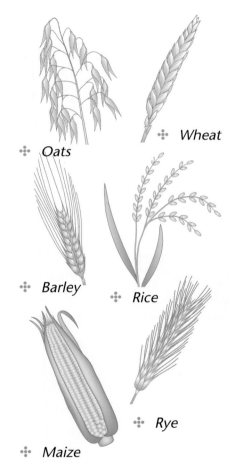

❖ *Oats*

❖ *Wheat*

❖ *Barley*

❖ *Rice*

❖ *Maize*

❖ *Rye*

## Average composition of cereals

| Protein | Carbohydrate | Fat | Vitamins | Minerals | Water |
|---------|--------------|-----|----------|----------|-------|
| 12% | 74% | 2% | B group | calcium and iron | 12% |

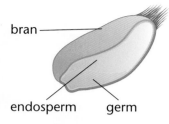

bran

endosperm    germm

❖ *A wheat grain*

## Structure of cereals

Here is a drawing of a wheat grain. Other cereals have a similar structure.

**A.** **The bran layer:** This is a good source of fibre, vitamin B and iron. It is removed when cereals are processed.

**B.** **The endosperm (85% of the grain):** This is mainly starch. It also contains the protein gluten. (See page 105.)

**C.** **The germ:** This is the most nutritious part of the grain. It contains protein, fat and vitamin B. It is removed in the manufacture of white flour and is sold as a health food called wheat germ.

## Processing cereals

Cereals in their natural form are difficult to digest, as they have a strong protective layer of bran around them. They must be broken down to release the starch. This crushing of cereal grains is called **milling**.

**1** The grain is washed, dried, then passed through metal rollers to break open the grain. If the milling is stopped at this stage, the product is wholemeal flour.

**2** To make white flour, the wheat continues through a series of rollers and sieves until it is smooth and white. Unfortunately, the 20–25% of grain that is removed contains the germ and bran, which contain much of the cereal's protein, iron, vitamin B and fibre.

High-fibre diet,
page 41

**Processed** or **refined** describes a product which has gone through this or a similar process. **Unprocessed** or **unrefined** foods have had the minimum amount of processing. These are usually healthier, and contain more nutrients, particularly fibre. Certain whole cereals such as rice and barley have just the bran removed to help them keep longer. They are then called 'polished rice' and 'pearl barley'.

## Fortified foods

Certain processed foods, such as white flour and breakfast cereals, have some of the vitamins and minerals that were removed during processing put back into the product. Alternatively, **extra vitamins or minerals may be added to any food. This is called 'fortifying' the food.**

## The effects of cooking on cereals

Every small starch cell in each cereal grain has a strong wall of cellulose which is difficult to digest. Cooking breaks this down, releasing the starch.

**1** Cellulose is softened and starch becomes **digestible**.

**2** Heat causes starch grains to **swell and burst** (e.g. popcorn, pastry).

**3** The grains **absorb liquid** (e.g. white sauce) or fat (e.g. pastry).

Collect empty packages from as many breakfast cereals as possible. Copy down the nutrient information on each packet. Compile a chart of the nutrients in each, using the following headings:

| Cereal | Protein | Carbohydrate | Fat | Vitamins | Minerals | Water | kcal |
|---|---|---|---|---|---|---|---|
|  |  |  |  |  |  |  |  |

1. Which cereal has the highest content of (a) protein, (b) fibre, (c) sugar?
2. Which do you consider to be the healthiest breakfast cereal? Give three reasons why.

## Cereal products and their uses

**WHEAT**
wholemeal
flour/bread
brown flour/bread
white flour/bread
pasta, semolina
noodles, couscous
breakfast cereals, e.g.
Weetabix, All-Bran
cakes and biscuits
wheat germ, bran

**OATS**
pinhead oatmeal
and rolled oats
for porridge
breakfast cereals,
e.g. muesli,
Ready Brek

**MAIZE**
breakfast cereals,
e.g. cornflakes
cornflour,
cornmeal
corn oil, popcorn
eaten as a
vegetable, e.g.
sweetcorn, corn on
the cob

**BARLEY**
pearl barley
barley water
whiskey
malt
beer

**RYE**
rye flour
rye bread
crispbread,
e.g. Ryvita
rye whiskey

## Rice

Most rice is produced in the Far East, the USA and Italy. The main types of rice are as follows.

● Long grain rice – used in savoury dishes and as an accompaniment, e.g. for curry. Easy-cook rice has been steamed to help the grains stay separate during cooking. Boil-in-the-bag rice has been partially cooked and sealed in a bag. It cooks quickly as small holes in the bag allow the water to penetrate the rice. Fully cooked microwaveable rice is also available.

Recipes: cooking rice, page 177

2. Medium grain rice – also used for savoury dishes, particularly risotto.
3. Short grain rice – cooks to a stickier consistency and is used for sweet dishes, e.g. rice pudding.
4. Brown rice – rice with only the outer husk removed. Takes longer to cook and has a chewier, nuttier texture. Contains more protein, fibre and B vitamins. Used for savoury dishes.
5. Ground rice – used for milk puddings and shortbread.

## Rice products

These include:

- puffed rice, e.g. Rice Krispies
- rice flour: used in certain cakes and biscuits
- rice cakes: eaten as a snack
- rice noodles: thin white noodles used in Oriental dishes
- rice paper: edible paper, can be found on the bottom of certain baked goods, e.g. biscuits
- rice milk: used as an alternative for people who are lactose intolerant (cannot drink cow's milk)
- rice wine: a sweet wine used in Asian cooking
- rice vinegar

## Pasta

A special wheat called durum wheat is used to make pasta. It is ground down to a coarse flour, then mixed with water, and usually egg, to form a dough. This is rolled, then cut into various shapes and dried. 'Fresh' pasta is dried for a short time; it must be used within a few days. 'Dried' pasta is dried for longer and keeps for up to a year. Wholewheat pasta is made from brown flour. Tomato and spinach flavoured pastas are also available: they are coloured red and green respectively.

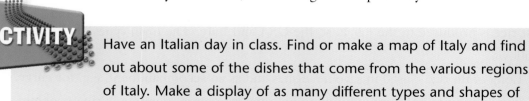

**ACTIVITY**

Have an Italian day in class. Find or make a map of Italy and find out about some of the dishes that come from the various regions of Italy. Make a display of as many different types and shapes of pasta as you can collect; use Italian colours and decorations.

Plan and cook a selection of pasta recipes using different pastas.

# Flour

Although flour can be made from many products, including rice, rye, corn and soya, the main flour we eat in this country is wheat flour.

## Types of flour

1. **Wholemeal flour** – 100% whole grain; this consists of the whole crushed grain of wheat. Nothing is added or taken away.
2. **Brown flour** – 85% grain; the rough outer layers of germ and bran are removed.
3. **White flour** – 73% grain; consists mainly of starchy endosperm and some gluten. White flour is fortified with calcium, iron and B group vitamins.
4. **Self-raising flour** – white flour with a raising agent added.
5. **Strong flour** – a high-gluten flour for using with yeast.
6. **Gluten-free flour** – most of the gluten* is removed; this flour is used to make bread, etc. for coeliacs.

❖ *Gluten-free symbol*

**ACTIVITY**

Put a heaped tablespoon of flour in a piece of cloth. Secure it with a rubber band, then rinse under cold water for a minute or two to wash out the starch. Open the cloth, and what is left is mostly gluten. Feel it. How would you describe it?

Coeliac disease, page 50

# Bread

Bread is one of our staple foods. It is available in many forms: brown and white, in yeast loaves, soda bread, sliced pan, French sticks, etc.

Bread dough can also be made into rolls, baps and buns. Different types of bread are eaten in different countries.

- Ireland: soda bread
- France: baguettes
- Greece, Turkey: pitta bread
- India: naan bread, chapatis
- Germany: pumpernickel
- Mexico: tortilla
- USA: cornbread

*Gluten is a protein found in wheat flour. It is activated when moistened and becomes very elastic. During baking, when gases expand in the oven heat, the elastic dough rises. Bread made from flours without gluten, such as cornflour, cannot rise. Coeliacs cannot eat gluten because they cannot digest it.*

# Home baking

Home-made bread and cakes are tastier, cheaper and more nutritious than many of th
bought products available.

## Baking guidelines

1. **Prepare:** line tins, arrange oven shelves and preheat oven to correct temperature.
2. **Be accurate:** weigh correct proportions of fresh ingredients; be particularly careful with raising agents and liquids. Read recipe through and follow it exactly.
3. **Oven management:** set oven and time baking accurately. Avoid opening the oven door unnecessarily. Test that food is cooked before removing.

## Raising agents

A **raising agent** is **a substance that makes bread and other foods rise**. It produces gas in the dough which expands and rises when heated, raising the dough and making it spongy and light.

There are 4 raising agents:

1. air
2. bread soda
3. baking powder
4. yeast.

✤ *$CO_2$ bubbles in dough expand in the heat of the oven*

1. **Air.** In all baked foods, it is important to get lots of air into the mixture. Air will expand when heated and make the food light. In some dishes, such as batters and sponges, it is the only raising agent. Air is introduced into a mixture by:
   - sieving the flour (bread, cakes, pastry)
   - rubbing fat into flour, high over the bowl (scones, pastry, plain cakes)
   - creaming or beating fat and sugar (Madeira cakes, batters)
   - whisking eggs and sugar (sponges, meringues, soufflés).

**Chemical raising agents: bread soda and baking powder**

Acid + alkali + liquid = carbon dioxide

- **Bread soda** is an alkali. When it is mixed with an acid (e.g. buttermilk) and a liquid is present, it makes carbon dioxide.
- **Baking powder** is a mixture of bread soda and an acid (cream of tartar). When this is moistened, e.g. by eggs or milk, carbon dioxide is produced.
- **Yeast** is a micro-organism which produces carbon dioxide in dough. Yeast is the raising agent used in most commercial breads.
*Note:* Raising agents are used in very small amounts, but it is important to measure them accurately. If too much is used, the dough will blow up too quickly and then collapse like a balloon. If too little is used the product will be hard and flat.

## Methods of mixing bread and cakes

1. **The rubbing-in method:** this is used in plain doughs which do not have a lot of fat, e.g. breads, scones and pastry. The fat is rubbed into the flour high over the bowl using the fingertips, until the mixture looks like breadcrumbs. The liquid is added last.

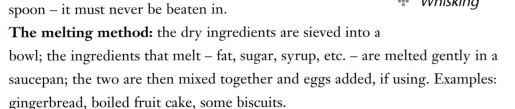

❖ *Rubbing in*　　❖ *Creaming*

2. **The creaming method:** this is used for richer mixtures, such as Madeira cake. The fat and sugar are beaten well together, until pale and creamy, using a mixer or wooden spoon. Eggs are added gradually, then flour is folded into the mixture.

3. **The whisking method:** this method is used for fatless sponges. The eggs and sugar are whisked together until very pale and thick. The flour is then folded in with a metal spoon – it must never be beaten in.

❖ *Whisking*

4. **The melting method:** the dry ingredients are sieved into a bowl; the ingredients that melt – fat, sugar, syrup, etc. – are melted gently in a saucepan; the two are then mixed together and eggs added, if using. Examples: gingerbread, boiled fruit cake, some biscuits.

❖ *Melting*

5. **The all-in-one method:** this quick method can be used for several types of cake, e.g. Madeira. All the ingredients are put in a bowl, then beaten for up to one minute. Soft, easy creaming margarine must be used. All-in-one pastry can also be made in a food processor.

6. **Cake mixes:** these usually consist of a mixture of flour, raising agent, dried fat and sugar. Dried egg or milk may also be included, as well as a large number of additives. Follow the instructions: usually liquid ingredients are mixed into dry ingredients.

❖ *All-in-one*

| Advantages of cake mixes | Disadvantages of cake mixes |
|---|---|
| Quick and easy | Expensive for amount in package |
| Give confidence to beginners | Many additives; often over-flavoured |
| Useful in emergencies | High in sugar and salt; low in fibre |

**ACTIVITY**

1. (a) Find out three different types of recipe based on the Madeira mixture.
   (b) What is the function of the raising agent in the mixture?
   (c) What is the function of eggs in the mixture?
   (d) Find out a recipe for icing that you could use on Madeira cake.

2. (a) Find out the cost of one batch of home-made tea scones (see page 62).
   (b) Find out how much the same number of scones would cost to buy.
   (c) How would you adapt this recipe to meet the healthy eating guidelines?
   (d) Name three variations on this recipe.

## Preparing tins

**Flouring:** use for bread and plain scones.

**Greasing:** brush tins with melted fat or oil; used for small cakes, pastry, etc.

**Fatless sponges:** grease tin, then sprinkle with a mixture of caster sugar and flour.

**Base only:** place a circle of greaseproof paper on the base of tin, then grease paper and sides. Use for plain cakes.

**Large cakes:** line whole tin with greaseproof paper. Place tin on paper and outline shape with pencil. Crease (square/oblong) or cut (round tin) on this line. (See diagram.)

❖ *Lining cake tins*

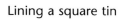

Lining a square tin

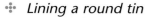

+ *Lining a round tin*

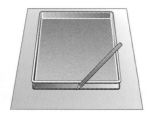

+ *Lining a Swiss roll tin*

## Pastry

Pastry is a mixture of flour and fat bound together with a little water. Richer pastries may contain extra fat, egg, sugar and flavourings, e.g. cheese. All pastry is high in kilocalories.

### Guidelines for making pastry

1. Weigh ingredients accurately.
2. Keep ingredients and utensils as cool as possible to stop fat melting.
3. Introduce as much air as possible.
4. Handle lightly and as little as possible.
5. Knead slightly, then roll lightly. Never stretch pastry.
6. Add water very carefully: too much makes pastry dough sticky; too little makes it dry, crumbly and impossible to roll out.
7. Leave pastry to relax in the fridge before baking to prevent it shrinking in the oven.
8. Start baking in a hot oven, usually 220°C/425°F/Gas 7, to burst the starch cells so that fat is absorbed. The temperature may be reduced later.

*Note: When a recipe states '200g pastry', this refers to the amount of flour in the recipe, e.g. pastry made with 200g flour, 100g fat.*

| Types of pastry: | Used for: |
|---|---|
| Shortcrust pastry | Sweet and savoury tarts, pies, flans |
| Rich shortcrust pastry | Mince pies, sausage rolls |
| Wholemeal shortcrust | Savoury flans, quiches, pies |
| Cheese pastry | Cheese straws, biscuits, savoury tarts |
| Flaky pastry<br>Rough puff pastry<br>Puff pastry | Tarts, sausage rolls, vol-au-vents, mince pies, savoury 'parcels' |
| Choux pastry | Éclairs, profiteroles |
| Filo pastry | Wrapping meat, fish, vegetables, e.g. spring rolls, tartlets |

**REVISION QUESTIONS**

1. Why are cereals a staple food?
2. Name the three parts of the cereal grain. Which is the most nutritious? Why?
3. Describe briefly how cereals are processed.
4. What is meant by fortified foods?
5. Name three cereals and the products made from them.
6. What are the effects of heat on cereals?
7. What is polished rice?
8. Pasta is made from _____ wheat. Name four varieties of pasta.
9. Describe the difference between wholemeal and brown flour, and suggest a use for each.
10. What is gluten? What important property does it have? People with _____ cannot digest gluten.
11. List three guidelines to follow when baking at home.
12. Name four raising agents. Explain how one of them works, and give a use for it.
13. List the basic methods of mixing cakes and buns.
14. Name four types of pastry. Give two uses for each.
15. List six guidelines for pastry-making.
16. List two types of rice available and suggest a dish for each.

Test Yourself
eTest.ie

# Chapter 14 Fruit and Vegetables

Eat four or more servings from the fruit and vegetable group daily.

*Note: Information that applies to **both** fruit and vegetables, such as buying and storing, are placed towards the end of the vegetable section (page 115).*

## Fruit

Fruit is a refreshing, delicious and versatile food. It may be eaten either raw or cooked, and may be used in sweet and savoury dishes, sauces and desserts. It is important in the diet because it is a good source of vitamin C and fibre – yet the Irish eat the least amount of fruit in Europe.

## Food value

**Protein and fat:** Few fruits contain more than a trace of protein or fat (exceptions: avocados, olives).

**Carbohydrates:** Fruit contains carbohydrate in the form of sugar (fructose). Fruit, particularly if the skins are eaten, is a good source of fibre – important for preventing bowel disorders.

**Vitamins:** The main value of fruit in the diet is as a source of vitamin C (especially blackcurrants and oranges). Many red, orange and yellow fruits, such as peaches and apricots, supply vitamin A.

**Minerals:** Most fruit contains calcium and iron; dried fruit is a good source.

**Water:** As fruit has a high percentage of water – often over 90% – it is generally low in kilocalories.

## Average composition of fruit

| Fruit | Protein | Carbohydrate | Fat | Vitamins | Minerals | Water |
|-------|---------|--------------|-----|----------|----------|-------|
| Fresh | Trace | 5–20% | 0% | A, C | Calcium, iron | 80–90% |
| Canned | Trace | 20–30% | 0% | A, C | Calcium, iron | 70–80% |
| Dried | Trace | 50–60% | 0% | A | Calcium, iron | 15–25%* |

## Classification of fruit

| Citrus | Soft fruit/berries | Stone fruit | Hard fruit | Dried fruit | Others |
|--------|--------------------|-------------|------------|-------------|--------|
| Oranges | Strawberries | Plums | Apples | Raisins | Rhubarb |
| Lemons | Raspberries | Apricots | Pears | Sultanas | Bananas |
| Limes | Blackberries | Peaches | | Prunes | Melon |
| Tangerines | Gooseberries | Nectarines | | | Pineapple |
| Grapefruit | Blackcurrants | Cherries | | | |
| Satsumas | Blueberries | Damsons | | | |
| | Cranberries | | | | |

## Uses of fruit in the diet

1. Raw – as a snack or as dessert at the end of a meal.
2. Drinks – orange, grapefruit, apple, blackcurrant juice.
3. For breakfast – as juice; fresh or stewed.
4. As a starter, e.g. melon.
5. In sweet or savoury salads.
6. Hot puddings – stewed, baked, in pies, flans or tarts.
7. Cold sweets – yoghurt, fools, ice cream trifles, mousses and soufflés.
8. Sauces – apple, gooseberry, cranberry.
9. Preserves – jams, jellies, chutneys, etc.
10. Biscuits.
11. Cakes, e.g. using raisins.

*Dried fruit absorbs water when steeped or cooked in water. This increases its water content.

## Effects of cooking on fruit

- Texture changes; fruit softens.
- Cellulose breaks down, making the fruit more digestible.
- Vitamin C content is reduced by up to 25%.
- Minerals dissolve into cooking and canning liquid; use liquid for sauces, etc.
- Micro-organisms such as moulds are destroyed.

## Preparing fruit

1. Prepare fruit just before cooking to avoid loss of vitamin C.
2. Wash well to remove soil and chemicals.
3. Avoid peeling unless necessary; skins are rich in fibre.
4. Remove cores, stones and any bruised parts.
5. Citrus fruits, e.g. oranges, lemons, grapefruit: Scrub in warm water to remove wax and chemicals, if rind is to be grated. Dry and peel, removing white pith.
6. Soft fruits, e.g. raspberries, strawberries, blackcurrants, blueberries: Check for mould; pick out any damaged fruit. If necessary, wash gently in colander; dry gently on kitchen paper.
7. Hard fruits, e.g. apples, pears: Wash, cut in quarters, remove core. If not using immediately, place in a bowl of cold water or toss in lemon juice to prevent browning by oxygen in the air. Peel only if necessary.

**ACTIVITY**

Fruit and vegetables – how much do you eat? We are advised to eat four or more a day. Check your intake with this checklist; tick those you ate yesterday.

| Breakfast: | Half glass fruit juice or one piece of fruit | |
|---|---|---|
| Morning break: | Piece of fruit | |
| Lunch: | Salad, e.g. in roll; vegetable or salad with meal; fruit | |
| Afternoon break: | Piece of fruit | |
| Dinner: | Fruit juice; vegetable or salad with meal; fruit | |
| Supper: | Fruit or raw vegetable snack | |
| Extra snacks: | Fruit or vegetables | |
| | Total: | |

Your score:

0–1: Lots of room for improvement.

2–3: You're on your way.

4 or more: Well done! You are making healthy choices.

# Vegetables

Vegetables add variety, colour and flavour to the diet. They are cheap, nutritious and filling, yet do not add too many kilocalories, as they are low in fat. Many vegetables can be eaten raw – this is healthier and saves fuel.

Current dietary advice is – eat four or more servings of fruit and vegetables a day.

## Classification of vegetables

|  | Roots | Pulses | Greens | Fruits |
|---|---|---|---|---|
|  | *Grow underground* | *Grow in pods* | *Mostly green and leafy* | *Have seeds* |
|  | Carrots | Peas | Cabbage | Tomatoes |
|  | Parsnips | Beans, broad | Spinach | Cucumbers |
|  | Swedes/turnips | Beans, French | Broccoli | Peppers |
|  | Beetroot | Beans, runner | Lettuce | Marrows |
|  | Celeriac | Lentils | Brussels sprouts | Courgettes |
|  | Onions (bulbs) | Dried peas | Cauliflower | Aubergines |
|  | Potatoes (tubers) | Dried beans | Kale | Pumpkins |
| **Average composition** |  |  |  |  |
| Water | 75–95% | 75–95% | 90–95% | 90–95% |
| Protein | 1–2% | 2–7% | 1–2% | 1–2% |
| Carbohydrate | 5–20% | 4–10% | 2% | 2–5% |
| Fibre | Good – eat skins | Very good source | Good source | Good source |
| Vitamins | A, especially carrots | A, a little in most pulses | A, especially lettuce | A, especially tomatoes |
|  | C, especially young veg, e.g. new potatoes | C in fresh, not in dried | C, good source | C, good source |
|  | B, a little | B, a little | B, a little | B, a little |
| Minerals | Calcium | Calcium | Calcium | Calcium |
|  | Iron | Iron | Iron | Iron |

## Food value of vegetables

**Protein:** peas, beans and other pulses are a good source of protein. Most other vegetables contain small amounts, e.g. 0.5–2%.

**Carbohydrate:** Pulses, potatoes and many root vegetables are a good source of carbohydrate in the form of starch. Onions and beetroot contain sugar. All vegetables, particularly if the skin is eaten, are a good source of dietary fibre.

**Fat:** Vegetables rarely contain fat, except for oil-producing plants such as corn (a cereal) and nuts.

**Vitamins:** Vegetables are a good source of vitamins A and C; many, particularly pulses, contain vitamin B.

**Minerals:** Vegetables supply several minerals, particularly calcium and iron.

**Water:** All vegetables contain a high level of water, particularly greens and salad vegetables. For this reason they are not too high in kilocalories, unless cooked or tossed in fat. Dried vegetables lack water, but this is reabsorbed during soaking.

# Fruit and vegetables

## Buying fruit and vegetables

1. Freshness is the most important quality. Fruit and vegetables should be fresh looking, ripe, firm, crisp – not bruised or withered. Fresh produce is heavy for its size because it has not lost water through evaporation.
2. They should have a good, bright colour; a brown, shrivelled orange or a yellow cabbage is obviously stale.
3. Buy young, medium-sized fruit and vegetables; overgrown produce has less flavour.
4. Buy in small quantities; fruit and vegetables do not keep well.
5. Avoid plastic packaging; it encourages mould and often hides blemishes. Remove from packaging as soon as possible.
6. Buy fruit and vegetables when they are in season – at their cheapest and their best.

## Seasonal fruit and vegetables

Most fruit and vegetables grow at a certain time of the year. This is when they are 'in season' – when they are plentiful, cheap and at their best. Strawberries and peas are in season in the summer; celery and sprouts in winter. Lettuce is available all year round as it is grown in hothouses. Eating fresh fruit and vegetables out of season is usually more expensive, as they are often imported.

Processed varieties – frozen, canned, bottled and dried – can be bought all year round.

## Price of fruit and vegetables

This varies, depending on quality, availability, demand and weather. Unusual fruit and vegetables are usually expensive. Organic fruit and vegetables, which are grown without pesticides or other harmful chemicals, are often more expensive.

## Grading/labelling of fruit and vegetables

European Union directives state that produce should be:

- clean, sound and free from soil and chemicals
- graded with produce of similar size
- marked with the country of origin, variety, quality or class and packer or distributor identification (if in its original container).

| | |
|---|---|
| Class extra | Top quality |
| Class I | Good quality |
| Class II | Marketable quality – may have blemishes or defects of shape or colour |
| Class III | Marketable but inferior. |

PRODUCT:APPLE
VARIETY:GALA
ORIGIN:NEW ZEALAND
COUNT:8   CLASS 2
CODE:120435

SPECIALLY PACKED FOR FRUITY FRESH LTD.
BALLYFERGUS IND. EST., DUBLIN 8

## Storing fresh fruit and vegetables

1. Use as soon as possible to retain freshness and flavour.
2. Remove plastic wrappers.
3. Store in a fruit/vegetable rack in a cool, dry, dark, well-ventilated place.
4. Greens, fruit-type vegetables and many fruits (except bananas) keep best in the vegetable drawer of the fridge. Wash greens, spin dry and store in a plastic bag; wash all fresh fruit and vegetables before storing in the fridge.
5. Do not mix washed and unwashed produce. Allow fruit to return to room temperature before eating.

## Processed fruit and vegetables

- **Preserved fruit and vegetables** are available frozen, canned/bottled and dried. Follow the directions on the packet or can regarding storing, thawing, cooking or reheating.
- **Frozen fruit and vegetables:** food value and flavour is just as good as fresh. Texture – some may become softer. Thaw in the fridge or cook from frozen.

- **Canned fruit and vegetables:** appearance and texture change – many become soft. Vitamins reduced; some vitamins and minerals dissolve into the canning liquid – use this when cooking. Canned fruits often have a higher sugar content – look for canned fruit with 'no added sugar'. Cheap to buy and economical on fuel, they need only be reheated.
- **Dried fruit and vegetables.** *Fruit:* colour darkens and sugar increases; vitamin C is much reduced. *Vegetables:* dried pulses are a good source of protein. They usually need to be soaked for several hours before cooking. N.B. Check instructions – they may need to be boiled rapidly for 5 minutes to kill harmful toxins, then simmered until soft. Freeze-dried products have better flavour, texture and food value than traditionally dried foods. Store dried fruit and vegetables in the packet or in an airtight jar in a dry cupboard; use before expiry date.

**CTIVITY** Here are the most popular ways of cooking vegetables. List under these headings the vegetables that may be cooked by each method.

| Baking | Roasting | Grilling | Frying | Stir frying | Steaming | Boiling |
|---|---|---|---|---|---|---|
|  |  |  |  |  |  |  |

## Preparing and boiling vegetables

| Vegetable | Preparation | Cooking | Serving |
|---|---|---|---|
| **Greens** | Remove withered leaves. Separate leaves; wash in cold water. Do not steep. | Cook in a little boiling water until almost soft (5–10 minutes). Test. Drain in colander. | Season and serve at once in a hot vegetable dish. Sprinkle with parsley, coat with sauce or melted butter. |
| **Roots** | Scrub, remove top and tail. Peel only if necessary. Leave whole, slice or dice. | Place in boiling water; simmer for 10–20 minutes, depending on size. Drain; mash. | Serve in hot vegetable dish. Sprinkle with parsley or chives (optional). |
| **Pulses, e.g. peas** | Remove pods, wash in cold water. | Place in boiling water. Simmer until cooked (5–7 minutes). | As above. |
| **Dried pulses** | Soak overnight. Drain and rinse. | Place in cold water; bring to boil. Boil for 5 minutes, reduce heat and simmer until soft. Drain. | As above. |

## Other cooking methods

Although boiling is a traditional way of cooking vegetables in this country, methods that use little liquid are better, because water-soluble vitamins and minerals do not dissolve into the cooking water.

**Steaming** – place vegetables in a covered steamer over boiling water. Steaming takes longer than boiling, but nutrients are retained and there is less chance of overcooking

**Pressure cooking** – uses little water but there is a danger of overcooking.

**Stir frying** – toss a mixture of thinly sliced vegetables in a little hot oil for about 10 minutes. Vegetables remain crisp, nutritious and tasty, but oil adds kilocalories.

**Stewing** – a useful method as the juices are served with the vegetables, e.g. ratatouille

## Microwave cooking

This is a quick, nutritious way to cook vegetables. Because little water is used, fewer nutrients are lost and more colour, flavour and texture are retained.

1. Prepare vegetables as above, then cut into small even-sized pieces.
2. Place in a serving dish with 2–3 tablespoons of water and a small piece of butter, if wished.
3. Cover with a lid, plate or clingfilm, rolling back a corner.
4. Cook on 'high' for 5–8 minutes, depending on size and type of vegetable. Stir halfway through. Remember, the more vegetables there are, the longer the cooking time.
5. Allow 5 minutes' standing time. Season and serve at once.
6. Frozen vegetables are cooked in much the same way but for a shorter time – follow instructions on package.

## Effects of cooking on vegetables

1. Vitamins and minerals dissolve into the cooking liquid.
2. Much vitamin C is destroyed.
3. Cellulose is softened, releasing starch.
4. Heat bursts starch cells, making food more digestible.
5. Starch absorbs water, softening food. Vegetables break up if overcooked.
6. There may be loss of colour, flavour and texture.

## To retain maximum nourishment in fruit and vegetables

1. Use best quality fresh fruit and vegetables.
2. Eat fruit and vegetables raw, if possible.
3. Prepare just before cooking. Use a sharp knife to cut.
4. Avoid soaking – vitamins and minerals dissolve into the water.
5. Cook with skins on, if possible. Otherwise peel thinly.
6. Use the minimum amount of water. Cover cooking pot tightly.
7. Cook for the shortest possible time. Do not overcook. Keep vegetables 'al dente', i.e. with bite.
8. Never use bread soda in water – it destroys vitamin C.
9. Serve at once – avoid keeping food warm for a long time.
10. Use cooking liquid for soups and sauces.

**Did you know?**
Potatoes contain only a small amount of vitamin C, yet because they are eaten frequently, potatoes are one of our most important sources of this vitamin.

**ACTIVITY**

Plan a project on any vegetable, using the design brief. Find out all about the vegetable – varieties, season, how it is grown, how it is cooked, etc.

## Salads

Raw or cooked vegetables and fruit, nuts, meat and fish, cheese, eggs, rice and pasta may be included in salads. As raw fruit and vegetables have a higher food value than when they are cooked, it makes sense to serve raw salads as frequently as possible.

Salads can be served as a main course, as an accompaniment to food and as a starter.

## Salads are useful in the diet

**1** They are a good source of vitamins, minerals and fibre.

**2** They are cool, refreshing and tasty.

**3** They provide contrast of colour and texture to cooked foods.

**4** They are easy to prepare and there is little cooking, which saves fuel.

**5** They can save waste by using up leftovers.

**6** They are useful in emergencies.

**7** Many are low in kilocalories, if a dressing is not used.

## Guidelines for preparing salads

**1** Use really fresh ingredients and prepare shortly before serving.

**2** Use herbs, seasonings, nuts, etc. to add interesting contrasts in flavour and texture.

**3** Wash salad vegetables gently under cold running water, trim, spin in a salad basket, place in a plastic bag and chill in the vegetable drawer of the fridge.

**4** Wash and quarter, slice, dice or grate other vegetables according to kind; small fruit and vegetables may be left whole.

**5** Arrange ingredients in a salad bowl or dish; use attractive vegetables to garnish.

**6** A salad dressing improves flavour, but adds kilocalories. Toss salad in dressing at the last minute, or serve dressing separately.

1. Name three important nutrients in fruit. Name one fruit that is very low in kilocalories.
2. Classify fruit. Give three examples of each.
3. List some uses of fruit in the diet.
4. List the effects of heat on fruit.
5. Name two vegetables rich in (a) protein; (b) starch; (c) vitamin C.
6. What are pulses? Describe how to cook dried kidney beans.
7. List the points you would use to guide you when buying fruit and vegetables.
8. What is meant by vegetables 'in season'?
9. Explain the grading of fruit and vegetables.
10. Describe how to store (a) lettuce; (b) potatoes; (c) bananas; (d) dried beans.
11. Write a note on the food value of two processed fruits.
12. List four ways of cooking vegetables. Name two vegetables that could be cooked using each method. Describe how to cook green vegetables by one of the methods.
13. List six guidelines to follow in order to retain maximum nourishment in vegetables.
14. List four reasons why salads are important in the diet.
15. Explain what is meant by organically grown vegetables.

Food

Test Yourself
eTest.ie

# Chapter
## 15 The Milk, Cheese and Yoghurt Group

This group contains many important nutrients, such as protein, calcium and vitamins A and D. Eat 3 servings daily / 4 for teenagers / 5 in pregnancy.

## Milk

Milk is a very important food. It contains all the nutrients needed by babies for the first 3 months of life. Don't forget that milk is an excellent food for all other groups too, particularly children, adolescents, pregnant women, invalids and elderly people. It is cheap and easy to digest, and, for those who worry about kilocalories, low-fat milk and milk products are available.

Many animals such as goats and sheep provide milk, but cow's milk is the type in common use in this country.

### Food value

Milk is a source of most nutrients:

- protein, for growth
- carbohydrate, which supplies energy
- fat, in an easily digested form, for energy. Skimmed milk has most of the fat removed
- vitamins A, D (a little in the cream) and B
- calcium and phosphorus, important for healthy bones and to prevent osteoporosis
- water (87%).

Milk lacks vitamin C and iron.

## Average composition of milk

| | Protein | Carbohydrate | Fat | Vitamins | Minerals | Water |
|---|---|---|---|---|---|---|
| Fresh | 3.5% | 4.5% | 4% | A, B, D (trace) | Calcium | 87% |
| Skimmed | 3.5% | 5.0% | 0.2% | B | Calcium | 90% |
| Human | 2.25% | 6.5% | 3.5% | A, B, C, D | Calcium | 87% |

## Uses

1. As a drink, on its own or in tea, coffee and milkshakes.
2. With breakfast cereals.
3. In puddings.
4. In sauces, e.g. white sauce.
5. In savoury dishes, e.g. quiches, batters.
6. In baked foods, e.g. bread, scones.
7. As milk products such as yoghurt.

## Types of milk

Milk is classified according to its fat content.

| | |
|---|---|
| **Whole milk** | Standard bottled milk (3.5% fat) |
| **Low-fat milk** | Also called semi-skimmed milk or light milk – contains half the fat of whole milk (1.7% fat). |
| **Skimmed milk** | Most fat is removed (0.2% fat), also vitamins A and D. Protein and calcium remain. |
| **Fortified milk** | Low-fat milk with vitamins A and D and calcium added. |
| **Buttermilk** | Milk remaining after butter-making. Today most buttermilk is made from pasteurised skimmed milk treated with a culture to make it acid. Used for baking. |
| **Flavoured milk** | Flavourings such as chocolate or banana are added. |
| **Organic milk** | Comes from cows that have grazed on pasture that has not been treated with chemical pesticides or fertilisers. The producers must be registered as organic. |

## Grades of milk

Because milk is a liquid food it is likely to be contaminated with bacteria. For this reason it is usually heat-treated to make it safe.

| | |
|---|---|
| **Pasteurised milk** | Most milk is pasteurised before it is treated in other ways. This process kills bacteria without spoiling the taste of the milk. **Milk is heated to 72°C for up to 25 seconds, then cooled quickly.** |
| **Long-life milk** | Ultra heat treated (UHT) milk – heated to 132°C. It keeps for months without refrigeration; it is packed in single portions for catering. |
| **Evaporated milk** | Canned milk. Some water is removed. Used in desserts. |
| **Condensed milk** | Canned milk. Some water removed; sugar added. Used in desserts. |
| **Dried milk** | All water is removed. Useful in emergencies, for picnics, etc. |
| **Homogenised milk** | Milk is treated so that the fat/cream is distributed more evenly. |
| **Soya milk** | This is a vegetable product made from the soya bean; it is used as a milk substitute by vegans. |

❖ *Heat-treated milk*

## Effects of heat on milk

1. Bacteria are destroyed – milk keeps longer.
2. Loss of vitamins B and C.
3. Protein coagulates (sets), forming a skin on the milk.
4. Flavour changes.

## Buying and storing milk and milk products

Milk and milk products are perishable foods. They are easily infected with bacteria, so correct storage is important – in the shop and at home.

1. Check the expiry date before buying or using.
2. Never leave milk in the sun, e.g. on a doorstep – vitamins will be lost.
3. Keep dairy products cool, clean and covered – in their bottle or carton, in a refrigerator away from strong-smelling foods.
4. Use milk in correct order – do not mix milk with different use-by dates or top up jugs, etc.

**ACTIVITY**

Collect samples of six different types of milk, e.g. skimmed, dried, soya.

(a) Taste each and evaluate.

(b) Make a table of their nutritive values.

(c) Find out the kilocalorie content of each and put the information into a bar chart.

(d) Work out the cost of each per 100ml. Which are the dearest and the cheapest?

## Milk products

Milk is a versatile food – it can be made into several products. Cream and butter are high in fats and are not part of the milk/cheese/yoghurt food group; they belong at the top of the food pyramid and should be eaten sparingly.

## Cream

The fat which rises to the top of the milk can be separated in the dairy to make cream. Cream contains fat-soluble vitamins A and D but is high in kilocalories. It is classified mainly according to its fat content.

1. **Standard cream** in Ireland usually contains about 40% fat.
2. **Double cream** is a thick cream which contains 48% fat.
3. **Low-fat** or 'light' cream contains about 30% fat.
4. **UHT cream**, which is treated as for UHT milk (page 124) – 18% fat. Used in catering.
5. **Soured cream** is low-fat cream (18% fat) treated like yoghurt by adding a lactic acid culture to thicken it. It adds a piquant flavour to baked potatoes, dips and goulash, and is useful as a dressing for salads.
6. **Crème fraîche** is similar to soured cream; fat content 30%.
7. **Aerosol cream** has less fat due to its high air content when used.

❖ Crème fraîche

## Butter

**Butter is produced when cream is churned until the fat sticks together.** The remaining milk, called buttermilk, is drained off, and salt is usually added to flavour and preserve the butter.

**Butter** contains 80% fat. Most butter is salted; unsalted butter is used for sweet dishes. Butter may be treated to make it spreadable.

**Low-fat or 'light' butter** contains about half the fat of butter (40% fat).

**Dairy spreads** contain about 50% butter and 50% soya oil, but the same kilocalories as butter. 'Light' spreads have a reduced fat content. Some 'light' spreads are unsuitable for cooking – check before using.

ACTIVITY  Butter is very high in kilocalories – check the food tables (pp. 28–30) and compare the energy value of butter and margarine.

### Yoghurt

Yoghurt is a form of thickened milk. A culture of lactic acid bacteria is added, which thickens it and gives it a pleasant acid taste. It has the same food value as milk; if it is made from skimmed milk it is low in fat. Many yoghurts have added sugar and fruit so they may not be low in kilocalories. Always check the label.

### Types of yoghurt

1. **Natural yoghurt** – unflavoured yoghurt made from whole milk.
2. **Greek yoghurt** – thick, creamy, unflavoured yoghurt.
3. **Fruit yoghurt** – whole-milk yoghurt with added skimmed milk powder, fruit and sugar.
4. **Set yoghurt** – a thicker version of fruit yoghurt.
5. **Low-fat yoghurt** – made from skimmed milk. Diet version contains artificial sweetener.
6. **Drinking yoghurt** has added milk, and is usually flavoured and sweetened.

Yoghurt is useful as an instant snack or dessert. Natural and Greek yoghurt are used for salad dressings and dips and as a low-kilocalorie alternative to cream.

ACTIVITY  **Make your own yoghurt**
1. Bring 500ml milk to the boil. Cool quickly to 42°C.
2. Add 15ml natural yoghurt and stir.
3. Place in a vacuum flask and leave to thicken for 8 hours.

## Cheese

Cheese contains the nutrients of milk in a concentrated form. Cheese is usually made from cow's milk, but it can also be made from goat's or sheep's milk.

Cheese is a very nutritious food. It is good value for money and there is little waste. It needs little or no cooking, although its excellent flavour improves many cooked dishes, such as omelettes and lasagne.

Cheese is thought to have been discovered by accident when an Arab crossing the desert discovered that the milk he had brought for the journey had turned solid. The pouch containing the milk was made from a sheep's stomach, and the enzymes in this had separated the milk into curds (cheese) and whey.

## Food value (hard cheese)

**Protein:** Cheese is one of the best sources of protein in the diet. It is a good substitute for meat or fish.

**Carbohydrate:** As cheese does not contain carbohydrate, it should be eaten with a carbohydrate food.

**Fat:** Cheese contains a high level of saturated fat and cholesterol. For this reason it should be eaten in moderation. Low-fat cheeses are a healthier alternative.

**Vitamins:** A good source of vitamins A and B.

**Minerals:** An excellent source of calcium – important for bones and teeth.

**Water:** Hard cheeses contain more fat and less water; soft cheeses contain up to 77% water.

## Composition of cheese (per 100g)

| | Protein | Carbohydrate | Fat | Vitamins | Minerals | Water | kcal |
|---|---|---|---|---|---|---|---|
| **Hard** | 27% | 0% | 33% | A and B | Calcium: 4% Sodium: 1.7% | 34% | 405 |
| **Cottage** | 15% | 4% | 4% | A and B | Calcium: trace Sodium: 1% | 77% | 114 |

## Uses

Cheese has a wide selection of flavours and uses.

1. In snacks, sandwiches and packed lunches.
2. In salads – grated or sliced.
3. In main meals – quiche, pizza, macaroni cheese.
4. In sauces – e.g. on fish or vegetables.
5. As a cheeseboard at the end of a meal.
6. As a garnish – e.g. grated over soup.
7. In desserts – e.g. cheesecake, tiramisu.
8. In salad dressings – e.g. blue cheese dressing.

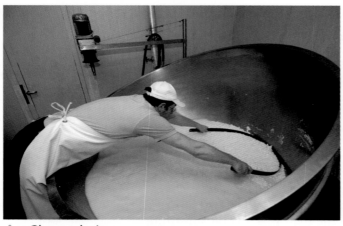

## Manufacture of cheese

Most cheeses are made in much the same way; different varieties can be made by altering the culture, the amount of pressing and the length of maturing.

1. Milk is pasteurised, then a culture (harmless bacteria) is added.
2. The milk is warmed and rennet is added to clot the milk.
3. It separates into curds (solids) and whey (liquid).
4. Curds are chopped, pressed and salted; whey is drained away.
5. The curds are put into moulds and pressed again – lightly for soft cheeses, firmly for hard cheeses.
6. The cheese is left to mature for 3–12 months.

❖ *Cheese being made in a factory*

## Types of cheese

| Hard (full fat) | Semi-soft | Soft | Processed |
| --- | --- | --- | --- |
| (best for cooking) | (mild flavoured) | (creamy) | (blended – mild) |
| Cheddar | Blarney | Camembert | Easi singles |
| Parmesan | Edam | Brie | Cheese spread |
| Gouda | Many farmhouse cheeses | | |
| Pecorino | | | |

## Others

**Blue-veined cheese**, e.g. Danish blue, Stilton, Roquefort, Gorgonzola. Strong-flavoured cheese, injected with needles of harmless mould.

**Unripened**, e.g. cottage, mascarpone, ricotta, feta.

**Cream cheese**, e.g. Philadelphia. Mild flavoured, moist, fresh cheese.

## Buying cheese

Although some cheese keeps well, it is a perishable food and should be bought in small amounts. Check expiry date. Once opened, use up quickly. Prices vary according to type and quality.

## Storing cheese

1. Wrap loosely in greaseproof paper, then overwrap in aluminium foil.
2. Store in the refrigerator, e.g. in the door.
3. Remove from refrigerator one hour before use; flavour is better at room temperature.

## Effects of cooking

Eat raw if possible. Hard cheeses have a better flavour for cooking; grate them to speed up melting.

1. Protein coagulates and shrinks.
2. Fat melts; overcooking makes cheese hard and oily.
3. Cooking at high temperatures makes cheese indigestible.

**ACTIVITY**

1. Investigate six different types of cheese, e.g. hard, soft, blue-veined – not processed.
   Use these headings to compare them: Flavour, Colour, Texture, Appearance, Cost per 100g.
2. Find out the country of origin of the following cheeses:
   Wensleydale, Brie, Port Salut, Stilton, mozzarella, Mileens, Gouda, Gruyère.
3. Find out the best cheese for (a) cooking, (b) pizza, (c) fondue. Explain your answer to (c).

**REVISION QUESTIONS**

1. What are the two most important nutrients in milk? Why are they important for children and teenagers?
2. What nutrients are lacking in milk?
3. Name two savoury dishes that include milk; name two that include cheese.
4. Name five different types of milk. What are the advantages of each?
5. Explain the term 'pasteurised'. Why is milk pasteurised?
6. How should milk be stored?
7. Give two effects of heat on milk.
8. What is done to milk to create (a) UHT milk, and (b) condensed milk?
9. Suggest two ways of encouraging a friend who dislikes the taste of milk to include it in his/her diet.
10. Name two types of (a) cream, (b) butter, (c) yoghurt.
11. What is yoghurt, and how is it made?
12. List four differences between Cheddar and cottage cheese. Which do you consider healthier, and why?
13. Describe briefly how cheese is made.
14. Classify the main types of cheese. Name two of each type.
15. List the effects of cooking on cheese.

# Chapter 16 The Protein Group – Meat, Fish and Eggs

This food group is the main supplier of protein in the diet for most people. It is also a good source of vitamin B, iron and other minerals. As well as meat, fish and eggs, the group includes meat substitutes such as TVP, cheese, and low biological value proteins such as pulse vegetables and nuts. Eat two servings daily; three during pregnancy.

## Meat

Meat is the flesh of animals and birds.

It comes from:

- cattle      beef
- sheep      lamb, mutton
- pigs      pork, ham, bacon
- poultry      chicken, duck, turkey
- game      wild birds and animals, e.g. pheasant.

It also includes offal – the edible internal organs of animals, such as liver and kidney.

# Food value of meat

Meat is an important food. It contains:

- **protein** – lean meat is a good source; meat products such as sausages have much less.
- **fat** – visible (mostly around the edge of the meat) and invisible (hidden within the meat). The amount of fat depends on the type of animal and the cut of meat, e.g. streaky bacon is high in fat; liver and kidney are low in fat.
- **vitamins** – B group; liver and kidney are among the best sources of vitamin A.
- **minerals** – iron, phosphorus and calcium.
- **water** – about 60%, less in fatty meat.

## Average composition of red meat*

| Protein | Carbohydrate | Fat | Vitamins | Minerals | Water |
|---|---|---|---|---|---|
| 15–25% | 0% | 17–30% | B group | Iron, calcium | 50–60% |

# Healthy eating guidelines

It is sometimes recommended that we avoid red meat, as it is high in saturated fat. On the other hand, it supplies a very soluble form of iron, which is particularly important for females. As with most dietary advice, the answer is probably to eat a good mixture: some red meat with all the visible fat removed; some low-fat alternatives, such as chicken and fish; and more vegetable protein – peas, beans and whole cereals.

Because meat contains no carbohydrate, it is often served with starchy foods, such as potatoes, pasta and rice.

# Structure of meat

Meat is made up of bundles of long fibres filled with meat juice. These are held together with tough connective tissue. Between the meat fibres are some fat cells; the amount depends on the age and type of animal.

❖ *The structure of meat*

# Tough or tender?

This depends on:

1. age – older animals have more connective tissue than young animals. This makes their meat tough.
2. activity – meat from active parts such as legs and neck is tough; meat from the back is tender.

Red meat is meat from large animals e.g. beef, lamb and pork.

Tough meat can be made tender:
1. by hanging for a few days – enzymes make the muscle tender
2. by chopping or mincing – this breaks up the fibres
3. by beating with a steak hammer
4. by marinating – this softens the fibres and adds flavour
5. by gentle, moist cooking – this dissolves the connective tissue.

If tough meat is cooked at a high temperature, it will simply get tougher!

## Buying meat

1. Buy from a clean shop which sells good-quality meat.
2. Flesh should be firm, elastic and slightly moist.
3. It should have a good colour and no smell.
4. On prepacked meat, check the expiry date. It may be packed with the better side up – be careful.
5. Choose the correct type of cut for the dish you are making. Expensive cuts (e.g. sirloin) are tender and can be cooked simply and quickly, e.g. by grilling. Cheaper cuts (e.g. shin) are usually tough, with more fat and bone – these take longer to prepare and must be either minced or cooked using a slow method. Both are equally nourishing.

## Storing meat

Health warning! Lots of meat contains bacteria which cause meat to decay. Careless storage in shop or home can lead to food poisoning.

1. Use fresh meat within two days of buying – offal and mince go off particularly quickly. Salted meat such as bacon or corned beef keeps longer.

3. Check date stamp on pre-packed meat. If it is vacuum-packed, leave it in the pack until ready to use.

4. Remove wrapping from fresh meat and place on a plate to avoid drip contamination.

5. Cover loosely with foil or clingfilm, allowing some circulation of air.

6. Meat is normally stored on the bottom shelf of the refrigerator.

7. Place cooked meat on a clean plate. Use within 2 days.

8. Keep cooked meat separate from raw meat to prevent cross-contamination.

## Cross-contamination

- Never store or handle raw meat and cooked meat together.
- Wash hands after handling raw meat.
- Never use the same utensils or chopping surfaces for raw and cooked meat unless they have been thoroughly washed between uses.
- Ideally, a separate chopping board should be kept for raw meat and fish.
- Failure to follow this advice means that food-poisoning bacteria from raw meat could pass to cooked meat. As the already cooked meat will not be cooked, eating it may cause food poisoning. (See diagram on page 71.)

Food hygiene, page 69

## Other safety points

- Do not partly cook meat one day and finish it another day.
- Thaw frozen meat fully before cooking, particularly poultry.
- Never refreeze meat.
- Cook stuffed or rolled meat and poultry thoroughly.

In all these cases, bacteria can survive and cause food poisoning.

## Effects of cooking

1. Surface protein coagulates, sealing the surface.
2. Water evaporates and meat shrinks.
3. Colour changes from red to brown.
4. Fat melts.
5. Flavour improves.
6. Some nutrients, e.g. amino acids and B vitamins, are destroyed, especially if the meat is overcooked.
7. Micro-organisms are destroyed.

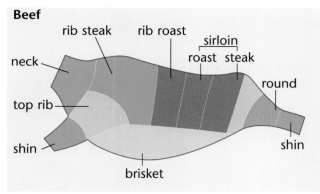

**Beef**

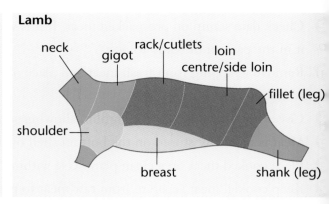

**Lamb**

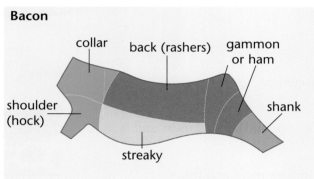

**Bacon**

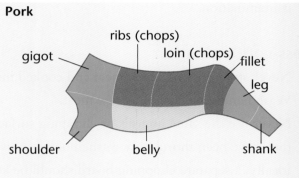

**Pork**

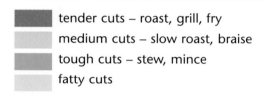

■ tender cuts – roast, grill, fry

■ medium cuts – slow roast, braise

■ tough cuts – stew, mince

■ fatty cuts

❖ *Cuts of meat*

## Preparing meat for cooking

1. Defrost frozen meat in plenty of time, e.g. overnight.
2. Remove meat from refrigerator one hour before cooking. (Why?)
3. Trim away extra fat; remove gristle and bone if wished.
4. Wipe meat with damp kitchen paper.
5. Weigh joints and calculate cooking time.

Meat is cooked:

- to make it tender and digestible
- to improve its flavour and appearance
- to destroy bacteria and make it safe to eat.

## Cooking meat

1. Choose a suitable cooking method for the cut of meat (see opposite page).
2. Start at a high temperature to seal in juices.
   (Exception: salt meat such as bacon.)

| ...ender cuts | Tough cuts |
|---|---|
| ...oasting | Stewing/casserole |
| ...rilling | Braising |
| ...rying | Boiling |
| ...tir-frying | Pressure cooking |

**ACTIVITY**

Accompaniments are foods such as sauces and vegetables that go well with meat.

Find out the accompaniments that go best with the following foods.

| | Sauce or other accompaniment | Carbohydrate |
|---|---|---|
| Roast beef | Horseradish | Yorkshire pudding |
| Roast lamb | | |
| Roast pork | | |
| Roast chicken | | |
| Curry | | |
| Grilled fish | | |

### ...eft-over cooked meat

...areless treatment of leftovers can lead to food poisoning.

1. Use within two days.
2. Place on a clean plate, cool quickly, cover with clingfilm and place in refrigerator.
3. When reusing, prepare as quickly as possible in a cool area. Avoid overhandling.
4. Reheat meat in sauce by bringing quickly to the boil; simmer for long enough to reheat the food thoroughly. Serve at once.
5. Never reheat a second time.

**Add flavour and moisture:** Twice-cooked meat can be insipid; season well and add herbs and well-flavoured vegetables, e.g. onions. Reheat in a sauce to add moisture.

**Add food value:** Improve the food value of reheated foods by serving nutritious accompaniments such as salads and baked potato. Serve a nourishing first or last course.

**ACTIVITY**

1. Suggest four main-course dishes that would use up some of the following left-over foods.
   Cooked chicken
   Hard-boiled eggs
   Roast beef
   Dried-up cheese
   White fish
   Mashed potatoes
   Boiled ham
   Half a packet of white sauce.

2. Name two nourishing accompaniments that you would serve with each of your answers to question 1.

## Offal

Offal is the edible organs from inside the animal, such as liver, kidney and heart.

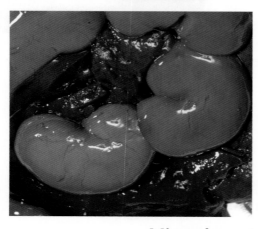

- Offal is very nourishing – it is high in protein, vitamins A and B, and iron.
- Choose offal from young animals; offal from older animals is strong-flavoured.
- It must be eaten on the day it is bought.
- Trim and rinse in warm water before use.
- Offal should be cooked gently for a short time.
- Recipes include baked liver and bacon, liver stir-fry, mixed grill and pâté.

### Minced meat

Tough cuts of meat are minced to make them tender. Some mince is very fatty; it should be cooked and the fat drained away before using. Mince should be used within 24 hours.

A wide variety of dishes can be made from mince, such as hamburgers, chilli con carne and shepherd's pie. Minced beef cooked with tomatoes and onions forms the basis of several dishes:

- spaghetti bolognese
- lasagne
- meatballs
- stuffed vegetables, e.g. peppers, tomatoes, potatoes.

## Processed meat

Meat is available canned and frozen. There is little difference in food value, except for some loss of vitamin B in canned meat, and the fact that nutrients may be lost due to drip loss when thawing frozen meat.

## Meat products

These are usually made from minced meat and meat fat. Many are 'padded out' with cheaper food, e.g. cereals – oatmeal, barley and breadcrumbs. As a result their food value is lower than fresh meat. Many also contain preservatives and other additives. Sausages are enclosed in a thin collagen membrane.

Examples: Fresh sausages, black and white pudding, salami and other smoked sausages, hamburgers, frankfurters, pies and pâté.

## Poultry

Poultry includes turkey, goose and duck, but the most widely eaten is chicken. Chicken is a very healthy, nutritious meat. It contains about the same amounts of protein as other meats, but is low in fat and therefore in kilocalories.

## Buying chicken

Chicken is available whole or in portions. Most chickens weigh between 1.5kg and 3kg.

1. Buy from a clean shop. Chicken should be stored in a refrigerated storage cabinet.
2. Chicken must be absolutely fresh – check expiry date.
3. Skin should be pale, with no bruising or discolouration.
4. There should be no unpleasant smell.
5. Breast should be plump and firm, breast bone pliable.
6. Frozen chicken:
   - check expiry date
   - should be frozen solid
   - there should be no discolouration
   - wrapper should be unbroken.

**Health warning**

Poultry is a frequent cause of food poisoning. Follow the guidelines on cross-contamination (page 71). If you suspect a chicken has 'gone off', do not use it. Be sure to thaw poultry completely and cook fully.

## Storing chicken

1. Remove wrapper and giblets, if any.
2. Cover loosely and place in the refrigerator; it should be on a plate to avoid drip contamination.
3. Use within 3 days.
4. Frozen chicken:
   - there must be no delay between buying and storing in the freezer
   - the freezer should be at –18°C or below
   - if poultry has begun to thaw, use it up. Never refreeze
   - use before expiry date.

## Preparing chicken for roasting

1. If the chicken is frozen, thaw completely.
2. Remove giblets; wash chicken under the cold tap, both inside and out.
3. Dry with kitchen paper.
4. Season inside the chicken with pepper, salt, herbs and a halved onion, if wished.
5. Stuffing: It is considered safer not to stuff poultry, due to the danger that the inside will not reach a high enough temperature to kill bacteria. If stuffing, place stuffing under neck flap rather than inside the carcass and allow extra cooking time.
6. Skewer the wings and leg bones against the body of the bird and weigh (with stuffing, if used) to calculate cooking time (20 minutes per 500g + 20 minutes). Cook at 200°C/400°F/Gas 6.

**ACTIVITY**

1. Find out the traditional accompaniments served with (a) chicken and (b) turkey.
2. Look up four recipes which use up left-over chicken – two hot and two cold. Using the design brief, make one of each and evaluate them.
3. Chicken is considered wasteful because it contains lots of bones. Suggest a way of using these up, and a recipe that would use the result.

LINK-UP

Vegetarian diets, page 39

Food

# Meat substitutes or alternatives

Meat is an expensive, slow and inefficient way to produce protein. It is also high in saturated fat. Nuts, pulse vegetables and dried pulses, particularly soya beans, are useful alternatives.

• *TVP mince*

Meat substitutes have been around a long time: tofu or bean curd has been part of the Chinese diet for centuries. Today meat substitutes are mass-produced from high-protein foods such as soya beans and processed so that they are as close as possible to meat in flavour and texture. They are known as textured vegetable protein (TVP) or soya protein.

## Advantages of TVP

1. Healthier – fat is unsaturated and in small amounts.
2. A good source of calcium. Contains fibre.
3. Long shelf life – refrigeration is not required.
4. A useful food for vegetarians.
5. Cheaper than meat.
6. Can be used to extend meat in pies, hamburgers and stewed dishes, particularly in catering.

✥ *Tofu*

REVISION QUESTIONS

1. Name three important nutrients in meat. Name a disadvantage of red meat in the diet, and explain how it could be reduced.
2. Describe the structure of meat.
3. Name four ways of making tough meat tender.
4. List four guidelines for storing fresh meat.
5. Why should thawed meat not be refrozen?
6. List the effects of cooking on meat.
7. What guidelines should be followed when buying meat?
8. Why have meat substitutes become popular recently?
9. What is offal? Suggest two tasty recipes for using offal.
10. Name four meat products. Compare their food value with fresh meat.
11. What special precautions should be taken when preparing chicken in order to avoid food poisoning?
12. Explain the term TVP. List four advantages of using it.

# Fish

Fish is a particularly healthy and nutritious food and can be cooked quickly in many different ways. Here in Ireland, we eat little fish, despite being an island with an important fishing industry. We eat on average less than 10kg per head per year – the Spanish eat 34kg and the Japanese 70kg!

## Classification and composition of fish (per 100g)

Fish is classified into three groups according to its appearance and nutritional value.

| | Protein | Carbohydrate | Fat | Vitamins | Minerals | Water | kcal |
|---|---|---|---|---|---|---|---|
| **White fish** e.g. cod, plaice, sole | 17–20% | 0% | 0% | B group | Iodine | 70–80% | 100 |
| **Oily fish** e.g. herring, salmon mackerel, trout | 17–20% | 0% | 13% | A, D, B | Iodine | 65% | 200 |
| **Shellfish** e.g. crab, mussels, lobster | 17–20% | 0% | 2.5% | B | Iodine Calcium | 72% | 120 |
| Fish fingers* (fried) | 13.5% | 17% | 12.5% | | Iodine | 55.5% | 223 |

These have been included to show how coating and frying can affect the food value.

## Food value

**Protein** – fish has a similar protein content to meat and is more digestible.

**Fat** – none in white fish; oily fish is a good source of polyunsaturated fat.

**Vitamins** – B in all fish; A and D in oily fish

**Minerals** – fish is a good source of iodine and potassium. Calcium is present in the bones of canned fish.

**Water** – white fish has a higher water content than oily fish.

As fish lacks carbohydrate, it is balanced by serving it with a carbohydrate food, such as potatoes, rice or bread, e.g. tuna sandwiches.

## Buying fish

Some fish is expensive, e.g. wild salmon and lobster; other fish is cheap, e.g. whiting, herring. The cost of medium-priced fish, e.g. cod, haddock, sole, compares well with that of meat.

Cost is not simply a matter of price. Consider the amount of waste (skin, bones, gut) when buying whole fish, and the time spent preparing it. Fish cooks quickly so it saves on fuel.

**1** Buy from a **clean** shop.

**2** Fish must be absolutely **fresh** – it goes stale quickly.

**3** Skin should be **moist** and unbroken and the scales difficult to remove.

**4** Skin **markings should be clear**, not faded, e.g. orange spots on plaice.

**5** Flesh should be **firm**; flesh of white fish should be white, not discoloured.

**6** Sea fish should **smell of the sea**, but not unpleasantly.

**7** Whole fish: gills (breathing flaps) should be red and eyes should bulge.

**8** Many fish are available only when they are 'in season'. Out of season they do not taste as good and are more expensive

**9** Frozen fish:

- should be **frozen solid**
- use **within expiry dat**e
- packet should be **unbroken**
- place in freezer quickly – **never refreeze**.

Fish can be bought:

- whole
- in fillets
- in cutlets/steaks.

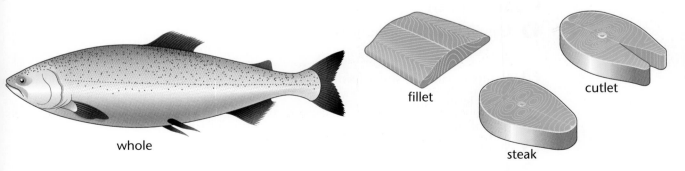

whole · fillet · cutlet · steak

*Cuts of fish*

## Processed fish

The box shows the usual methods of processing fish. It can also be dried, salted or pickled (herrings).

| Frozen | Canned | Smoked |
|---|---|---|
| No change in nutrients | May be canned in oil or brine | Orange/yellow skin, |
| Expensive, but no waste | (a)  oily fish, e.g. salmon, | smoky flavour |
| Plain fillets or cutlets | tuna, sardines | Cod/pollock, haddock, |
| Coated, e.g. fish fingers | (b)  shellfish, e.g. crab, | herrings (kippers), mackerel, |
| Made-up dishes, e.g. in | shrimp, prawns, mussels | salmon, trout. |
| a sauce or stuffed | | |

**ACTIVITY**

Collect labels from the three types of processed fish listed above. Study the nutritive value and compare with that of fresh fish. Compare the cost of 100g of each.

(a)  Which is more expensive – fresh or processed?

(b)  Which has more protein?

(c)  List the additives found in each processed fish.

## Storing fish

1. Remove wrappings and rinse under a cold tap.
2. Store in a dish in the refrigerator. If possible, surround with ice.
3. Cover with lid or clingfilm to prevent from flavouring other foods.
4. Use within 24 hours.
5. **Frozen fish:** Store quickly in a freezer at below –18°C. Use within expiry date. Follow package instructions regarding thawing and cooking. Much fish is cooked from frozen.

## Preparing fish

1. Cut off head; slit underside of fish and remove gut. Flatfish – remove gut under gills.
2. Remove scales in sink (if skin is being left on) by scraping from tail to head with a sharp knife. Rinse.
3. Cut off fins (from tail to head) and tail, using scissors.
4. Wash well, rubbing with salt to remove any black membrane.
5. Rinse and dry with kitchen paper.

## Filleting fish

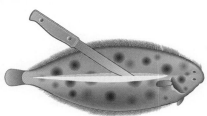

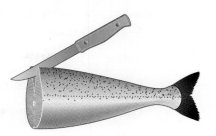

### Flat

Place fish on board, tail facing you.

Use a sharp knife to cut down backbone from head to tail.

Keeping knife close to bone, pare flesh away from bone.

Turn head towards you and repeat with second fillet.

Repeat on underside – four fillets in all.

### Round

Use a sharp knife to cut through flesh along the backbone on the skin side.

Pare away fillet, from head to tail, keeping knife against rib bones.

Turn and repeat with second fillet.

## To skin fish

Place fish on board, skin side down, tail towards you. Shake salt on tail to help get a grip, then, starting at the tail, holding the knife against the skin at a 45° angle, slice away the skin, using to and fro movements and lifting the flesh away from the skin. Trim and rinse.

## Cooking fish

Fish cooks very quickly. It is fully cooked when it loses its translucence and becomes opaque. It breaks up easily, particularly when overcooked.

### Methods of cooking

**Baking:** Bake whole fish, fillets or cutlets. May be stuffed or with a sauce, e.g. salmon.

**Steaming:** In a steamer, or between two plates over boiling water, e.g. plaice.

**Poaching:** In gently 'shivering' liquid (water, milk, wine), e.g. salmon. Never boil.

**Grilling:** A quick cooking method used for fillets, cutlets or small whole fish, e.g. sole.

**Frying:** Coated or uncoated, e.g. in batter; shallow, deep or stir-fried, e.g. cod.

**Stewing:** Firm fish only, e.g. monkfish, in a stew or curry.

**Reheating:** Fish pie, fish cakes.

| Coatings for fried fish | Suitable sauces | Suitable garnishes |
| --- | --- | --- |
| Seasoned flour | Parsley sauce | Cucumber twists |
| Batter | Cheese sauce | Lemon wedges/slices |
| Egg and breadcrumbs | Mustard sauce | Parsley, chopped or sprigs |
| Oatmeal, for herrings | Tomato sauce | Grated cheese |
| Packet crumbs | Tartare sauce | Tomato slices or lilies |

Find out the cost of five types of fish that are currently available in your local shop, and state how you would cook each.

## Effects of cooking on fish

1 Protein coagulates.
2 Fish becomes opaque.
3 Connective tissue dissolves and fish breaks up easily.
4 B vitamins and minerals dissolve into cooking liquid.
5 Micro-organisms are destroyed.

1. Write a note on the food value of fish.
2. Classify fish and name two of each type.
3. List five guidelines for buying fish.
4. Name three ways in which fish is processed; give two examples of each type.
5. How should fish be stored?
6. Describe five steps to follow when preparing fish for cooking.
7. Describe how to skin fish.
8. List the effects of cooking on fish.
9. Name a suitable method for cooking: (a) large whole fish; (b) thin fish fillets; (c) firm chewy fish.
10. Name two reheated fish dishes.
11. Name two sauces and two garnishes that would go well with fish.

Food

# Eggs

Eggs are one of the most useful foods. They are cheap, nutritious and easy to digest. They may be used in many ways.

1. **On their own** – boiled, poached, scrambled.
2. **As a main course** – omelettes, quiches.
3. **Coating** – covering food for frying, e.g. in a batter or with breadcrumbs.
4. **Thickening** – eggs thicken or set mixtures, such as custards and quiches.
5. **Binding** – holding soft or minced food together, e.g. hamburgers, fish cakes.
6. **Holding air** – eggs trap air when whisked, e.g. cold sweets, sponges, meringues.
7. **Glazing** – brushing scones, etc. with beaten egg gives them a good colour and shine.
8. **Emulsions** – egg yolk holds oil and vinegar together, e.g. in mayonnaise.

## Average composition of eggs

| Protein | Carbohydrate | Fat | Vitamins | Minerals | Water |
|---------|--------------|-----|----------|----------|-------|
| 13% | 0% | 12% | A, D, B | 1% (calcium, iron) | 74% |

## Food value

**Water:** most of an egg (74%) is water.

**Protein:** eggs contain a good supply of protein, for growth and repair.

**Fat:** the fat in eggs is in an easily digested form that is good for babies and children. As eggs contain cholesterol, people should not eat too many, particularly if there are other factors that can contribute to heart disease.

**Vitamins:** eggs are a good source of vitamins A, D and B.

**Minerals:** eggs contain iron for blood, calcium for bones, and sulphur.

As they lack carbohydrate, they are usually served with starchy foods, e.g. eggs on toast, omelette and chips. A salad would make up for their lack of vitamin C.

## Buying eggs

EU legislation makes sure that the egg box has the all the information you need in order to buy fresh, best-quality eggs. In Ireland Bord Bia has a stamp on all quality eggs.

Bord Bia
Irish Food Board

A code system of numbers and letters is in place on all quality eggs under the Bord Bí
Scheme. It shows information as follows.

- The number at the beginning tells you how the hen was reared: 1 = organic, 2 = free range, 3 = barn, 4 = caged.
- Two letters in the middle show the country of origin, e.g. the code for Ireland is IE.
- Letter and numbers at the end: the letter represents the county; the number represents the farm which produced the egg.

All of this information is followed by a best before date.

1. Eggs should be fresh, clean and unbroken – a broken egg is easily contaminated.
2. Sizes: Eggs are graded in four sizes – very large, large, medium and small. Use the large size for baking.
3. Class: Quality is indicated by the letter A, B or C – class A eggs are the best quality.

high yolk

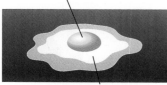

jellied white

*A fresh egg*

stale egg

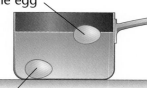

fresh egg

## Checking freshness

Fresh eggs are heavy for their size, with a rough shell. When broken on to a plate the yolk should be high and the white jelly-like – not runny.

As eggs get stale, water evaporates through the tiny pores in the shell. As the water evaporates, the air space at the round end gets bigger and the egg gets lighter. A stale egg will float if placed in a bowl of brine – a fresh egg always sinks to the bottom.

> **Health warning**
> Sometimes eggs get infected with food-poisoning bacteria such as salmonella. Those most at risk are babies and toddlers, pregnant women, invalids and elderly people. These people should not eat undercooked or raw eggs, e.g. in home-made mayonnaise or uncooked desserts. Eggs with broken shells should not be used. Wash hands after handling raw eggs.

## Storing eggs

1. Never wash eggs – this removes their natural protective layer.
2. Store eggs pointed end down – this keeps the air space at the top, so they keep fresh.

**③** Store in a cool place at less than 10°C. The egg compartment of a refrigerator is ideal.

**④** Check expiry date and use in rotation.

**⑤** Keep away from strong-smelling foods – egg shells are porous.

**⑥** If separated, place egg yolks in a cup, cover with water, then clingfilm. Use within 2 days.

Egg whites keep for a week, if stored in the refrigerator in a tightly covered bowl.

**ACTIVITY**

**Effect of heat on eggs**

You will need: thermometer     tablespoon     egg white

          3 small Pyrex bowls    saucepan of water    whole egg + 8 tablespoons milk

1. Place some egg white in a bowl; put the bowl over a saucepan of simmering water. Note the temperature at which (a) egg white starts to coagulate, (b) egg white is fully coagulated.

2. Beat the whole egg. Place one tablespoon of egg in each of two small Pyrex bowls. Add 4 tablespoons of milk to each and stir. Place the first bowl over a saucepan of boiling water and heat quickly, without stirring. Note the result. Place the second over a saucepan of simmering water (bowl must not touch water) and heat gently, stirring all the time. Compare the result with the egg in the first bowl. Explain each result.

## Effects of cooking

**①** Protein coagulates and sets. The white sets first, losing its transparency.

**②** Eggs cooked at too high a temperature or for too long will curdle (the protein shrinks, squeezing out the water).

**③** Overcooked eggs go hard and rubbery and are difficult to digest. A lightly cooked egg is more digestible.

## Cooking eggs

**①** Eggs should be at room temperature before using – remove from refrigerator one hour before cooking. Cold eggs will crack or curdle and will not whisk to a good volume.

**②** Eggs require low cooking temperatures – high temperatures cause curdling.

**③** Allow hot mixtures to cool before adding to egg. Never add egg to a warm mixture, as it is likely to curdle.

LINK-UP

Omelettes, page 202
Batters, page 203

④ When separating eggs, make sure no yolk gets into the white or it won't whisk to full volume. For the same reason, the bowl and beater should be clean and free from grease.

**REVISION QUESTIONS**

1. Name five uses for eggs in cooking.
2. What is the food value of eggs?
3. List the information on an egg box that helps customers when buying eggs.
4. Explain how eggs go stale.
5. Who should not eat raw eggs? Why?
6. List the guidelines to follow when cooking eggs.
7. What are the effects of cooking on eggs?
8. Describe (a) an emulsion, (b) free range eggs.
9. How should eggs be stored?

Test Yourself
eTest.ie

# Chapter 17 Food Preservation and Processing

Most foods have a limited life. Food is preserved to prevent it from spoiling (going bad).

## Why is food processed?

1. Processed food lasts longer and is easier to store.
2. It cuts down on waste.
3. A wide variety of seasonal food is made available all year round.
4. It saves time and energy, as processed foods need little preparation.
5. Commercially, preserved foods are easier and safer to transport and distribute.
6. Home-made preserves usually work out cheaper.

## Preserving or processing?

The term **'preserving'** means **treating foods to make them last longer.** Processed foods include preserved foods and foods that are treated in other ways, e.g. making cheese, milling flour. Much modern food goes through some form of processing to make it easier for us to use, e.g. sliced bread, tinned fish.

For centuries, although they had little understanding of how it worked, people preserved food when it was plentiful for times when it was scarce: meat was salted or smoked, fruit and vegetables dried in the sun and fruit boiled with sugar to make jam. Many of today's methods of processing food are based on traditional practices, although fewer nutrients are lost than in the past due to modern research and technology.

## Food spoilage

Food spoilage is caused by:

1. enzymes  2. micro-organisms  3. oxygen in the air.

Food spoilage, page 68

Conditions required for growth of enzymes and micro-organisms are:

1. food
2. warmth, i.e. temperatures of 30–40°C
3. moisture – present in food and in air
4. time to grow
5. oxygen (in most cases).
6. correct pH; not too acid, not too alkaline.

Food can be preserved by removing one of these conditions, or by using preservatives such as sugar and salt which make it impossible for micro-organisms to grow.

## Methods of preserving

1. Freezing – removing warmth.
2. Drying – removing moisture.
3. Canning/bottling – removing oxygen/air.
4. Using preservatives:
   - salt – salted fish
   - sugar – jam, candied fruit
   - vinegar – pickles, chutney, ketchup
   - smoke – chemicals in smoke preserve food, e.g. smoked fish, ham
   - chemical preservatives, e.g. antioxidants, which are used commercially.
5. Pasteurisation and sterilisation, e.g. of milk.
6. Irradiation – harmless rays are passed through certain foods (approximately 60 different types of food can be irradiated). These kill micro-organisms and insects, inactivate enzymes, and delay ripening or sprouting. Irradiation can destroy some vitamins. Any irradiated food within the EU must carry a label saying it is irradiated, and a symbol called the Radura symbol.

Milk, page 122

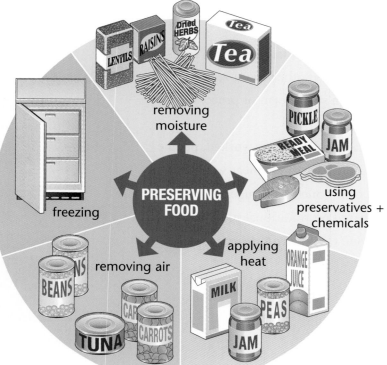

❖ *The Radura symbol*

Food

## Preserving food aims to:

1. prevent enzymes decaying food
2. destroy or inactivate micro-organisms
3. prevent re-entry of micro-organisms/oxygen by sealing food properly
4. maintain the colour, flavour, texture and nutritive value of the food.

## Freezing

Freezing means **reducing the temperature of food to a level at which micro-organisms cannot grow.** They are not killed but are inactivated – they become active again on thawing.

When food is frozen, the water in the food changes to ice. If the food is frozen quickly, i.e. at temperatures below –30°C, small crystals of ice are formed in the food, which do very little damage to the food.

If food is frozen slowly, large ice crystals are formed, which tear the cell walls in the food so that liquid and nutrients are lost when it is thawed.

**Blast freezing** (at –35°C) is carried out commercially – this produces the smallest ice crystals and the best results.

❖ *Large ice crystals*

## Food value of frozen food

Frozen food is almost identical to fresh food in nutritive value. It is often even better than 'fresh' food that has been lying around for a few days. There may be some loss of vitamins B and C – other nutrients remain the same.

The quality of frozen food is excellent when compared with other methods of preserving. Colour and flavour are retained. There is some loss of texture in certain foods, e.g. strawberries, especially if stored too long. Frozen food costs more than fresh food, but there is no waste – it is quick and easy to prepare.

❖ *Small ice crystals*

## Buying frozen food

1. Packaging must be sealed.
2. Food must be frozen solid.
3. Check it is well within expiry date.
4. Check thermometer on shop freezer: it should be –18°C or less.
   Make sure food is stored below the load line of open freezers.
5. The shop should have a high standard of efficiency regarding frozen food storage.

## Storing frozen food

Follow the directions on the packet. Store in a deep freeze for no longer than the recommended time.

## Thawing/cooking

- Follow the directions on the packaging exactly.
- Foods are usually thawed in their container in the refrigerator or in a microwave.
- Many foods are cooked from frozen – thin pieces of meat and fish, such as hamburgers, fish fingers and breaded fillets. Vegetables are usually cooked from frozen.
- Thaw meat, particularly poultry, completely before cooking and make sure to cook fully. Insufficient thawing and undercooking of frozen meat is highly dangerous.
- Once it is thawed, use food quickly. Never refreeze thawed food.

# Home freezing

## Guidelines for freezing

1. Switch freezer to its lowest setting 2–3 hours before freezing. (Why?)
2. Freeze only best-quality fresh food.
3. Freeze in usable quantities.
4. Never freeze more than one tenth of the freezer capacity at one time. Freezing too much food at the same time causes a rise in freezer temperature and large ice crystals in the food (see above).
5. Chill foods before freezing to avoid a rise in freezer temperature.
6. Place food in fast-freeze compartment; allow circulation of air between packets.
7. Open-freeze foods that might stick, such as peas, strawberries and fancy cakes; package when frozen.
8. Defrost freezer regularly – at least twice a year.

## Packaging for the freezer

- Use sealed packaging and containers.
- Allow 'head space' to allow liquids to expand.
- Overwrap sharp objects, such as bones, with aluminium foil.
- Pack food tightly and expel air. Tie with wire ties or clips.
- Label and date foods clearly.
- Use food in rotation and use up within the recommended time.

Good packaging for the freezer includes: polythene freezer bags, especially self-locking bags, plastic boxes, foil trays, waxed cartons and tubs. Recycle old cartons and tubs.

| Foods that freeze well | Foods that do not freeze well |
|---|---|
| Meat, poultry and fish | Cooked potatoes |
| Stews and casseroles | Salad vegetables, e.g. tomatoes |
| Most fruit and vegetables | Green, leafy vegetables |
| Bread and cakes | Bananas, melon |
| Raw or cooked pastry and pastry dishes | Mayonnaise |
| Soups and sauces | Milk, cream, yoghurt |
| Puddings and cold sweets | Whole eggs |

❖ This bag of food has been properly prepared for freezing

### Maximum storage times

| 1 month | Bread, scones |
|---|---|
| 2 months | Reheats |
| 3 months | Minced meats, bacon, stews, stock, raw pastry |
| 4 months | Oily fish, cakes |
| 6 months | Lamb, pork |
| 12 months | Fruit, vegetables, other meats |

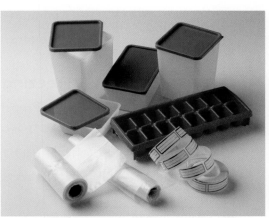

❖ Packaging suitable for using in the freezer

## Freezing meat
1 Trim away bone and extra fat; separate steaks, chops, etc. with waxed paper.
2 Pack in usable portions in freezer bags. Tie.
3 Use the lowest possible temperature (less than –25°C ) to reduce 'drip loss'.
4 Poultry: remove giblets, wash well, dry. Pack in freezer bag. Freeze without stuffing.

## Freezing stews and casseroles
1 Make stew in the usual way, but leave the sauce thin.
2 Shorten cooking time by 20 minutes to allow for reheating.
3 Pack in polythene boxes or oven-to-tableware, allowing head space.
4 Defrost overnight; bring slowly to the boil, stirring regularly, and simmer for at least 10 minutes.

## Freezing vegetables

boiling water

Blanching is used to destroy enzymes which can cause discolouration and damage to vegetables in the freezer.

ice-cold water

1. Prepare vegetables as for cooking. Cut into even-sized pieces, if wished.
2. Blanch by placing vegetables, 500g at a time, into boiling water for the recommended time (see below). Lift out; dip vegetables into iced water at once to cool and finish blanching process.
3. Open-freeze vegetables likely to stick together, such as peas.
4. Place vegetables into freezer bags, remove air, seal and freeze.

### Blanching times

1 minute – peas, mushrooms.
3 minutes – cauliflower, broccoli, celery, French beans, parsnips, turnips.
4 minutes – carrots, sprouts, onions.

❖ *Blanching vegetables*

## Freezing fruit

1. Prepare as for cooking; wash, peel, trim, core, etc.
2. Open-freeze soft fruits where necessary.
3. Pack fruit into polythene bags or tubs.
4. Freeze apples in a syrup or purée.

❖ *Open-freeze strawberries*

## Freezing bread and cakes

1. Bread and cakes may be frozen raw or cooked.
2. Pack into freezer bags and seal.
3. Open-freeze decorated cakes, then pack in rigid boxes. Store upright.
4. Batch baking saves fuel; bake 2 or 4 times the recipe and freeze some.
5. Use bread and scones within 1 month, cakes within 4 months.

❖ *Pack into bags when frozen*

**ACTIVITY** Look up some recipe books and suggest two savoury recipes which could be made in bulk, then used to make several dishes for the freezer. Make a time plan for the assignment and cost the suggested dishes.

# Dehydration (drying)

**Drying** is a method of preserving food by **removing moisture**, **usually by gentle heat**. The food is then sealed in air-proof, moisture-proof containers. Micro-organisms cannot live without water and therefore cannot multiply and spoil the food.

Most dried foods are rehydrated (soaked in water or other liquids) to return their water levels to normal before use. Examples: pulses, pasta, breakfast cereals, fruits.

Freeze drying: in this method the food is first frozen, then dried. Food value and quality are better than in traditionally dried food. Coffee granules are often freeze dried.

## Food value and quality

Processing causes some loss of vitamins A and B and almost total loss of vitamin C, depending on the method. Food may be fortified by replacing or adding extra vitamins.

There is some loss of colour, flavour and texture: this may be reduced by the use of additives.

## Buying and storing dried food

1. Packet must be sealed and undamaged.
2. Check expiry date.
3. Store in packet or airtight jar.
4. Use as directed.

# Canning and bottling

Food is placed in cans/bottles and sterilised at high temperatures to destroy micro-organisms.

## Food value and quality

Some loss of vitamins B and C occurs in the canning/bottling process. Minerals and vitamins also dissolve into the canning liquid, which should be used in cooking. Quality varies according to the food and canning method; loss of texture, and some loss of colour and flavour, is common. Additives may be used to offset this.

### Buying and storing

1. Never buy damaged cans; they should not be bulging, dented, rusted or leaking. (Why?)
2. Check the net weight of food without the canning liquid if you are following a recipe.
3. Check the expiry date: these foods do not last for ever.

### Storing and using

Store in a cool, dry place. Canned/bottled foods are fully cooked and only need reheating.

## Jam making

Jam is made by boiling fruit to kill micro-organisms and enzymes; 65% sugar is added to preserve it.

When jam is cooked, it is poured into sterilised jars and sealed. Successful jam has a good colour and flavour and is well set.

- **Pectin:** In order to a set, jam needs a carbohydrate called pectin, found in ripe fruit.
- **Acid** helps release the pectin from the fruit during boiling.

When a fruit contains only a little pectin, a special pectin-containing sugar, e.g. Sure-set, should be used. Use ripe fruit for jam making.

## Convenience foods

Convenience foods are foods which have **been prepared so that they save time or labour or have been preserved so that they last longer**. They include frozen, dried, bottled and canned foods, cake mixes, instant desserts and ready-prepared meals

### Using convenience foods

1. Do not use convenience foods too often – keep for emergencies as far as possible.
2. Be particular – choose good-quality convenience foods and avoid 'junk foods'.
3. When convenience foods are used, use nutritious vegetables, salads, etc. to increase the food value of the meal.
4. Use for more complicated recipes, e.g. cheese sauce for lasagne, cake mix for apple sponge.
5. Read instructions about storing, thawing and cooking.

Food

## Cook–chill foods

These are foods, usually meals such as lasagne, that have been **prepared, fully cooked and chilled to between 0°C and 3°C** by the manufacturer.

From this time they must be kept below 4°C, e.g. in the refrigerated display units of shops or in the refrigerator at home. When you are shopping cook–chill foods should be treated as frozen, i.e. wrapped well and bought only if you are returning home quickly.

They must be reheated fully according to the directions on the packet, i.e. to a high temperature, or there is a danger that bacteria such as Listeria will survive and cause serious food poisoning in vulnerable people such as babies, pregnant women and the elderly. Food reheated in a microwave must be stirred or moved about to ensure that all the food reaches the required temperature.

## Healthy convenience foods include:

- frozen vegetables and fish
- canned fish, pulses and tomatoes
- pasta, dried fruit and nuts.

| Advantages | Disadvantages |
| --- | --- |
| Save time and labour | Flavour varies, many overseasoned |
| No waste, little cooking | Many additives used |
| Wide variety available | Some nutrients lost in processing |
| Foods available out of season | Often more expensive than fresh food |
| Easy to store | Quality may be inferior, e.g. less meat in pies |
| Useful in emergencies | Portions often small – less than suggested on the packet |
| Handy for unskilled cooks, people with disabilities and elderly people | Many are high in fat, salt and sugar; low in fibre |
| | Many overuse packaging: recycle if possible |

**ACTIVITY** Find out the cost of a three-course meal at a local restaurant. Work out the cost of making the same meal using convenience foods. Then work out the cost of making the meal using fresh foods.

# Food labelling

Labels on food products are a source of important information.

By law, packaged food must show:

- the **name of the food** and **processing method**, e.g. evaporated skimmed milk
- **ingredients** in order of weight – greatest amount first
- **list of additives**, by name or E number
- **net weight** (metric) or quantity
- **date mark** – date by which a food should be used
- **storage instructions**
- **instructions for use**, e.g. cooking time/method
- **place of origin**
- **name and address of manufacturer**.

Nutrition information is optional, unless a claim is made about a nutrient, e.g. low fat.

Nutrition information is useful:

- for those on special diets, e.g. low kilocalorie, low salt
- for those with health conditions such as allergies or coeliac condition.

**Date marking** must be displayed on perishable food. There are two types of date marking:

- **Use by** – on food with a short shelf-life. If foods are eaten after this time they can damage health. They should be stored in a refrigerator.
- **Best before** – the date until which a food can be expected to remain in good condition and be safe. It is usually found on foods, such as flour, with a longer shelf-life.

**Unit pricing:** The price per unit, i.e. per kilogram, must be displayed on food sold loose, e.g. fruit, sausages.

## Food hygiene regulations control:

1. manufacture and quality of food
2. standards of hygiene in food premises, e.g. shops, restaurants.

Environmental health officers enforce these regulations by visiting premises, prosecuting offenders, dealing with complaints, etc.

**ACTIVITY**

1. Study this label and answer the following questions.
   (a) What is the main ingredient in the product?
   (b) How many kcal are in this product?
   (c) Name two additives in the product.
   (d) How should the product be stored?
2. Find out where you would go to complain about bad hygiene in your local shop.

## Nutrition Facts

Serving Size 1 Cup (30g)
Servings Per Container About 8

| Amount Per Serving | |
|---|---|
| **Calories** 110 Calories from Fat 15 | |

| | % Daily Value* |
|---|---|
| **Total Fat** 1.5g | 3% |
| Saturated Fat 0g | 0% |
| *Trans* Fat 0g | |
| **Cholesterol** 0mg | 0% |
| **Sodium** 260mg | 11% |
| **Potassium** 95mg | 3% |
| **Total Carbohydrate** 22g | 7% |
| Dietary Fiber 2g | 10% |
| Soluble Fiber 1g | |
| Insoluble Fiber 1g | |
| Sugars 1g | |
| **Protein** 4g | |

| | | | |
|---|---|---|---|
| Vitamin A 10% | • | Vitamin C 10% | |
| Calcium 6% | • | Iron 45% | |
| Vitamin D 10% | • | Thiamin 25% | |
| Niacin 25% | • | Vitamin B6 25% | |
| Folic Acid 50% | • | Zinc 25% | |

*Percent Daily Values are based on a 2,000 calorie diet. Your daily values may be higher or lower depending on your calorie needs:

| | | Calories: | 2,000 | 2,500 |
|---|---|---|---|---|
| Total Fat | Less than | | 65g | 80g |
| Sat Fat | Less than | | 20g | 25g |
| Cholesterol | Less than | | 300mg | 300mg |
| Sodium | Less than | | 2,400mg | 2,400mg |
| Potassium | | | 3,500mg | 3,500mg |
| Total Carbohydrate | | | 300g | 375g |
| Dietary Fiber | | | 25g | 30g |

Calories per gram:
Fat 9 • Carbohydrate 4 • Protein 4

**INGREDIENTS:** ORGANIC WHOLE GRAIN OATS, ORGANIC RICE FLOUR, ORGANIC SUGAR, SALT, CALCIUM CARBONATE, MIXED TOCOPHEROLS (VITAMIN E) ADDED TO PRESERVE FRESHNESS. **VITAMINS AND MINERALS:** FERRIC ORTHOPHOSPHATE (IRON SOURCE), SODIUM ASCORBATE (VITAMIN C), NIACINAMIDE (NIACIN), VITAMIN A ACETATE, ZINC OXIDE, FOLIC ACID, CHOLECALCIFEROL (VITAMIN D), THIAMIN MONONITRATE (VITAMIN B1), PYRIDOXINE HYDROCHLORIDE (VITAMIN B6).

GOOD MANUFACTURING PRACTICES USED TO SEGREGATE INGREDIENTS IN A FACILITY THAT ALSO PROCESSES PEANUT, TREE NUT (ALMOND), WHEAT AND SOY INGREDIENTS.

# Additives

**Additives are substances put into food during manufacture in order to improve it in some way.** They may be natural, e.g. salt or spices, or artificial.

Additives are used to:

1. preserve food, reducing the risk of food poisoning
2. improve or maintain the colour or flavour of food
3. maintain the condition of food, e.g. its texture
4. restore or improve its food value.

Under EU law, additives must be listed on packages of food, under their name or E number. (Additives considered safe by the EU are given an E number.) The amounts used in food are strictly controlled.

## Types of additive

1. **Colourings** (E100 numbers): These make food look more attractive. Some are available naturally (e.g. beetroot juice) and some are artificial (e.g. E102 – tartrazine – a yellow colour used in soft drinks).

2. **Preservatives** (E200 numbers): These extend the shelf-life of food by preventing the growth of micro-organisms. They can be natural (e.g. salt and vinegar) or artificial (e.g. nitrate – E252).

3. **Flavourings** are added to improve or intensify flavours, e.g. spices. Monosodium glutamate (E621) is a flavour enhancer found in many snack foods – it stimulates the taste buds. Artificial sweeteners make food sweet without kilocalories. They are used in low-calorie drinks and foods. Examples include saccharin (E954) and Acesulfame K (E950).

INGREDIENTS: Skimmed Milk, Whole Milk, Water, Sucrose, Gum Arabic, Flavouring, Emulsifier (Mono and Di Glycerides of Fatty Acids), Vitamin & Mineral Mixture, Stabilisers (Guar Gum, Carrageenan), Colour (Carmine, Beta Carotene).

As with any high fibre diet, it is important to drink at least 6-8 glasses of water, black tea, coffee or low calorie drinks each day.

4 **Antioxidants** (E300 numbers) **prevent the oxygen in air from affecting food. They help prevent fats from going rancid.** They are used in snack foods such as crisps and peanuts. Vitamins C and E are natural antioxidants.

5 **Emulsifiers and stabilisers** (E400 numbers): Emulsifiers help oil and water to mix; stabilisers prevent them from separating. These are used, for example, in mayonnaise and low-fat spreads.

6 **Nutritive additives:** Used to replace nutrients lost in processing or to add food value to a product, e.g. extra vitamin D added to milk.

## Additives – good or bad?

| Positive aspects | Negative aspects |
| --- | --- |
| Preservatives help prevent food poisoning. | Some additives deceive the consumer. |
| They keep food fresh longer, thus reducing waste. | Foods may contain more additives than necessary. |
| They help maintain the quality of preserved food. | Possible side-effects – cancer, hyperactivity, allergies (see below). |
| They give us a wider choice of food. | The 'cocktail effect': the danger that a mixture of 'safe' additives could be dangerous in the long term. |

## Allergies

Some people are highly allergic to certain foods (such as peanuts or milk) and chemicals.

Symptoms include rashes, itchiness, nausea, headaches and vomiting.

To prevent allergic reaction:

1 eat natural foods as far as possible; avoid convenience foods
2 avoid foods known to contain many additives, such as snack foods
3 read food labels carefully.

Children with a severe nut allergy cannot tolerate even a hint of that food or their body will go into shock. Many carry a special pen which can inject a drug into their body should they come into contact with nuts.

# Genetically modified (GM) foods

These are **foods whose chemical structure is altered**. There are a variety of reasons for doing this, but the main aim is to **produce food that is easier and more economical to grow**. GM foods include cereal crops that are grown to be pest-resistant and vegetables that can withstand the cold and be grown all year round. Many people are concerned about the health risks that could possibly result in the future.

**ACTIVITY**

Collect the labels from five packaged foods and list the additives in each. Explain the purpose of each additive. How many do you consider unnecessary?

*Test Yourself* eTest.ie

**REVISION QUESTIONS**

1. Give three reasons for preserving food.
2. What are the causes of food spoilage?
3. Explain the effects of quick and slow freezing on food.
4. Comment on the food value of frozen food.
5. List five guidelines for home freezing of food.
6. How would you freeze vegetables? Name four packaging materials you could use.
7. What is dehydration?
8. Convenience foods have become very popular in the past 15 years. Why do you think this is so?
9. List four advantages and four disadvantages of convenience foods.
10. List five guidelines for using convenience foods in order to ensure a healthy diet.
11. Explain the term 'cook–chill foods'. What are the risks associated with eating these foods?
12. List the information that must be shown on packaged foods.
13. What is the purpose of additives in food?
14. Classify additives and explain the purpose of three types.
15. List three disadvantages of additives.
16. Explain how freezing preserves food.
17. What guidelines should be followed when (a) buying and (b) thawing frozen food? Why should you not refreeze thawed food?
18. Plan a three-course evening meal using both convenience and fresh foods.
19. Name three types of packaging used for convenience foods.

# Chapter 18 Recipes

*Note: Recipes serve 4 unless otherwise stated.*

## Modifying a recipe

Beginners should follow recipes exactly for good results. However, occasionally a cook may wish to 'modify' or change a recipe slightly.

 Be careful: modifying recipes requires experience!

A recipe may be modified or changed in order to:

- reduce or increase a recipe in size
- substitute an ingredient for one which is not available
- introduce variety by adding new ingredients to old familiar recipes
- make it healthier by adapting it to the healthy eating guidelines.

Baking recipes such as cakes can be particularly tricky to change, as their ingredients are carefully proportioned to give an exact result, and changing one core ingredient such as sugar, fat or eggs could cause the recipe to fail.

Substituting or adding extra vegetables to a stew or soup or introducing extra ingredients to pizzas, pastas and other savoury dishes presents no problems.

A healthy way to modify a recipe is to bring it closer to the healthy eating guidelines.

| | |
|---|---|
| **Eat less fat** | Trim all fat from meat; use chicken instead. |
| | Use less meat in recipes; substitute vegetables. |
| | Omit fat – fry meat in a non-stick pan or brown meat under grill. |
| | Halve the fat/oil in scones, stews and sautés. |

| Reduce saturated fats | Use low-fat milk for baking, sauces and puddings.<br>Omit egg yolk from pastry and certain desserts.<br>Use plain low-fat yoghurt instead of cream. |
|---|---|
| Eat less sugar | Omit or reduce sugar in plain breads and scones.<br>Use artificial sweeteners to sweeten stewed fruit.<br>Add raisins, dates, etc. to sweeten breads and desserts.<br>Omit sweet icings and fillings. |
| Eat less salt | Reduce salt or omit it from recipe.<br>Flavour with herbs and spices instead.<br>Use well-flavoured vegetables, e.g. onion, celery, peppers.<br>Avoid using stock cubes and ready-made sauces. |
| Eat more fibre | Substitute brown pasta and rice for white.<br>Add pulses, e.g. kidney beans, to casseroles.<br>Use more wholemeal flour in baking, e.g. in pastry and pizza.<br>Use oatmeal for crumbles or to top savoury dishes, e.g. fish bakes.<br>Avoid peeling fruit and vegetables: unpeeled apples can be stewed, then puréed; potato salad made with unpeeled new potatoes is delicious. |

**Food**

Example

## Traditional spaghetti bolognese

300g spaghetti

1 tbsp olive oil

**Sauce**

1 tbsp cooking oil

300g minced beef

1 medium onion

1 clove garlic, crushed

1 can tomatoes

Pepper and salt

Oregano or mixed herbs

Sprinkle with grated Parmesan

## Healthy modified spaghetti bolognese

300g wholewheat spaghetti

1 tsp olive oil

**Sauce**

1 tsp olive oil (or omit)

200g minced beef (dry-fry, then drain off fat)

1 large onion

1 clove garlic, crushed

1 can tomatoes + 1 finely chopped pepper

Pepper (reduce or omit salt)

Oregano or mixed herbs (increase)

Serve with green salad

**ACTIVITY**

Look up the recipe for quiche Lorraine.

Write down the ingredients on one side of the page. On the other side show how you would modify them to conform with the healthy eating guidelines.

# Breads and scones

## Wholemeal bread

### (High fibre)

**Makes 1 loaf**

150g white flour
$\frac{1}{4}$ tsp salt
$\frac{1}{4}$ tsp bread soda
200g wholemeal flour
25g bran or oatmeal
25g wheatgerm
1 dessertspoon brown sugar
50g butter/margarine
350ml buttermilk

1.  Preheat oven to 200°C/400°F/Gas 6.
2.  Sieve the white flour, salt and bread soda into a mixing bowl. Add the wholemeal flour, bran or oatmeal, wheatgerm and sugar.
3.  Rub in butter. Make a well in the centre of the mixture and add the buttermilk. Mix to a soft wet consistency.
4.  Place in a greased round tin and cut a cross on the top. (A loaf tin may be used, but the bread will take longer to cook.)
5.  Bake in the preheated oven for 40–45 minutes.
6.  Test to see if the bread is done. Tap the base of the loaf: if it makes a hollow sound, it's done.
7.  Turn onto a wire tray to cool, and use within a day or two.

## Brown scones

Mix as above, but add less buttermilk in order to get a drier consistency. Roll out to just over 1cm thick. Cut with a scone cutter, place on a greased baking sheet and bake at 220°C/425°F/Gas 7 for about 15–20 minutes.

## White soda bread

450g plain white flour,
  preferably unbleached
1 level tsp salt
1 level tsp bread soda,
  finely sieved
400ml buttermilk (approx.)

1. Preheat oven to 230°C/450°F/Gas 8.
2. Sieve the flour, salt and bread soda into a large, wide mixing bowl.
3. Make a well in the centre. Pour most of the buttermilk into the flour. Mix in a full circle, drawing in the flour from the sides of the bowl, adding more buttermilk if necessary. The dough should be softish, not too wet and sticky.
4. Mix the dough as quickly and as gently as possible. When the dough all comes together, turn it out onto a well-floured work surface. Wash and dry your hands.
5. Using floured hands, gently roll the ball of dough around for a few seconds, just enough to tidy it up. Then pat it gently into a round shape, about 5cm high.
6. Place the dough on a lightly floured baking sheet. Using a sharp knife, cut a deep cross in the top.

7. Put the dough into your preheated oven for 10 minutes, then turn the heat down to 200°C/400°F for a further 25 minutes, or until cooked. When the bread is cooked it will sound hollow when tapped.

## Banana Nut Bread

150g coarse wholemeal flour
150g/5oz self-raising flour
1 level tsp cinnamon
50g chopped nuts
4 tbsp sunflower oil
3 tbsp honey or golden syrup
2 tbsp hot water
2 eggs (beaten)
3 ripe bananas (mashed)

1. Preheat oven to 170°C/325°F/Gas 3.
2. Place the flours, cinnamon and nuts into a bowl and mix together.
3. In a separate bowl, beat together the oil, honey (or syrup), water and eggs. Stir in the bananas. Pour this mixture into the dry ingredients and stir until smooth.
4. Transfer to a 900g loaf tin and make a cut lengthways down the centre of the dough.
5. Bake for about 1 hour or until risen and firm to the touch.
6. Cool on a wire tray.

Note:
If bread is browning too quickly, cover with a sheet of greaseproof paper.

## Tomato bread

200g white flour
1 tsp salt
3 tsp baking powder
284ml buttermilk (or the
   same amount of whole milk
   with a squeeze of lemon
   juice)
3 eggs
1 tsp tomato purée
2 tbsp olive oil
50g sundried tomatoes in oil
   (about 6–8), coarsely
   chopped
25g Parmesan, grated

1. Heat oven to 180°C/fan 160°C/Gas 4.
2. Mix the flour, salt and baking powder in a large bowl.
3. In a separate bowl, whisk together the buttermilk, eggs, tomato purée and oil. Fold the wet ingredients into the dry, then add the sundried tomatoes and half the Parmesan.
4. Grease a 900g loaf tin and pour in the mixture.
5. Sprinkle the remaining Parmesan on top and bake for 50-60 minutes or until a skewer inserted into the middle comes out clean.
6. Turn out onto a wire rack to cool.

## White Tea Scones

500g plain flour
1 level tsp salt
2 heaped tsps baking powder
100g butter (chilled)
30g caster sugar
200ml milk
1 egg

1. Preheat oven to 200°C/400°F/Gas 6.
2. Sieve the flour, salt and baking powder into a bowl.
3. Cut the butter into pieces and add to flour. Work butter into flour with fingers until it forms a rough sandy texture.
4. Stir in the sugar, add the milk and egg and work the mixture together with a fork.
5. Turn out onto a lightly floured work surface and knead lightly.
6. Roll out on a floured work surface to about 1cm thick and cut into desired shapes.
7. Place on a baking tray and bake for 20-25 minutes or until the base of the scones sounds hollow when tapped.
8. Cool on a baking tray and serve with butter and jam or even cream.

**Variation:** add 25g sultanas with the sugar.

## Cheese scones

225g self-raising flour
$\frac{1}{2}$ tsp salt
1 tsp powdered mustard
$\frac{1}{2}$ tsp cayenne pepper
50g softened, salted butter
50g Cheddar cheese, grated
25g Parmesan, grated
150ml whole milk, plus a
    little to glaze

1. Preheat the oven to 230°C/450°F/Gas 8.
2. Sift the flour, salt, mustard and cayenne into a bowl.
3. Cut the butter into pieces and rub it into the flour mixture with your fingertips until you have a mixture that resembles breadcrumbs.
4. Grate the cheeses and stir them into the flour mixture. Pour all the milk into the bowl with the flour and cheese, and use a knife to bring everything together into a dough.
5. Roll the dough out on a floured surface until it is 1cm thick, and cut into rounds with a cutter.
6. Arrange on a greased baking sheet and brush the top of each scone with milk.
7. Bake for 8-10 minutes, until the scones have risen and are golden.

## Rock buns

$\frac{1}{4}$ tsp mixed spice
200g self-raising flour
25g mixed peel
75g sultanas
25g caster sugar
50g margarine
A little milk
1 egg

1. Preheat oven to 200°C/400°F/Gas 6.
2. Add mixed spice to flour and make dough as for tea scones, adding fruit and sugar before wetting the mixture.
3. Using 2 forks, place small amounts of the mixture on a greased tray, leaving a gap between each one.
4. Bake for 15–20 minutes.

## Gingerbread

200g flour
$\frac{1}{4}$ tsp bread soda
1 tsp ground ginger
75g sultanas or raisins
75g butter/margarine
75g brown sugar
1 tbsp treacle
1 tbsp golden syrup
1 egg
A little sour milk or
    buttermilk

1. Preheat oven to 190°C/375°F/Gas 5.
2. Sieve flour, bread soda and ginger into a mixing bowl. Mix in sultanas or raisins. Melt margarine, sugar, treacle and syrup in a saucepan over a gentle heat; do not boil. Cool slightly.
3. Beat the egg and pour sugar mixture into the centre of the flour, then add the egg and enough milk to make a dropping consistency.
4. Pour into a well-greased 18cm cake tin; a loaf tin may be used but it takes slightly longer.

# Fruit

## Breakfast fruit salad

(Serves 4–6)

1 orange

1 tbsp lemon juice

1 apple

1 pear

1 tbsp honey

1 banana

125ml yoghurt

1. Wash fruit.
2. Peel and segment orange and add to lemon juice in a bowl.
3. Peel and core the apple and pear. Slice and add to the orange segments.
4. Mix the honey into the fruit.
5. Add sliced banana just before serving with the yogurt.

## Fresh fruit crumble

500g fresh fruit, e.g. apples, rhubarb

75g brown sugar

Flavouring, e.g. cinnamon, ginger

150g wholemeal flour or oatmeal

75g butter or margarine

1. Prepare fruit, slice and place in a heatproof dish, layered with half the sugar and half the cinnamon or ginger.
2. Place flour or oatmeal in a bowl and rub in butter or margarine with fingertips. Add remaining sugar and spice.
3. Cover fruit with crumble mixture and bake for 30–35 minutes until the top is crisp.
4. Serve with custard or cream.

## Banana smoothie

(Serves 1)

**Loaded with calcium!**

1 ripe banana

3 tbsp plain yoghurt

200ml milk

$\frac{1}{2}$ tsp brown sugar

Place all ingredients in a blender and blend until smooth. Serve in a chilled glass.

## Berry Smoothie

(Serves 1)

Blend together one teacupful of frozen raspberries and one teacupful of fresh blueberries with 1 tsp honey and 5 or 6 ice cubes until smooth. Serve immediately.

# Soups

## Basic vegetable soup

500g mixed vegetables, e.g. 2 sticks celery, 1 carrot, 1 potato, 1 leek, 1 tbsp peas

**Core ingredients**
1 medium onion
25g butter, margarine or oil
25g flour
1 litre stock or water
Herbs
Pepper and salt
100ml milk or cream (optional)
Parsley to garnish

1. Prepare vegetables: wash, peel if necessary and dice.
2. Melt fat; sauté vegetables on a medium heat for 5 minutes.
3. Add flour; cook on a low heat for one minute, stirring all the time.
4. Gradually stir in the stock; add herbs and seasoning.
5. Bring to the boil, cover and simmer gently for about 30 minutes.
6. Taste and correct seasoning; stir in milk/cream; reheat slightly.
7. Serve in warm soup bowls, garnished with chopped parsley.

## Leek and Potato Soup

1 tbsp vegetable oil
1 onion, sliced
225g potatoes, cubed
2 medium leeks, sliced
1.2 litres vegetable stock
Salt and freshly ground black pepper
150ml double cream or crème fraîche

1. Heat the oil in a large pan and add the onion, potatoes and leeks. Cook for 3–4 minutes until starting to soften.
2. Add the vegetable stock and bring to the boil. Season well and simmer until the vegetables are tender.
3. Whizz with a hand blender or in a blender until smooth. Reheat in a clean pan, stir in the cream or crème fraîche, heat through and serve.

## Carrot and Coriander Soup

1 tbsp vegetable oil
1 onion, sliced
450g carrots, sliced
1 tsp ground coriander
Salt and freshly ground black pepper
1.2 litres vegetable stock
Large bunch fresh coriander, roughly chopped

1. Heat the oil in a large pan and add the onion and carrots. Cook for 3-4 minutes until starting to soften.
2. Stir in the ground coriander and season well. Cook for 1 minute.
3. Add the vegetable stock and bring to the boil. Simmer until the vegetables are tender.
4. Whizz with a hand blender or in a blender until smooth. Reheat in a clean pan, stir in the fresh coriander and serve.

## Mushroom soup

½ onion, roughly chopped
1 large mushroom, roughly
  chopped
1 garlic clove, peeled
30g butter
½ large potato, peeled and
  chopped
150ml water
½ chicken or vegetable stock
  cube
Salt and freshly ground black
  pepper
2 tbsp double cream

1. Place the chopped onion and mushroom into a small food processor with the garlic and blend together.
2. Heat the butter in a saucepan. Add the onion and mushroom mixture and fry for a few minutes. Add the potato, water and stock cube and season with salt and freshly ground black pepper. Cover with a lid and simmer for ten minutes.
3. Add the cream and serve immediately.

## Fish chowder

1 large onion
2 sticks celery
2 medium potatoes
13g butter or margarine
400ml vegetable stock
200g cod, fresh or smoked
Pepper and salt
400ml milk
100g sweetcorn, canned or
  frozen
1 dessertspoon chopped
  parsley
Cream and paprika, to
  garnish

1. Prepare the vegetables. Finely chop the onion and celery and dice the potato.
2. Melt the butter or margarine and sauté the onion and celery for 3 minutes. Add the potato and toss in the fat.
3. Add the stock and bring to the boil. Cover and simmer for 15 minutes.
4. Meanwhile, wash the fish, remove any skin or bones and cut into 2cm dice.
5. Add the fish and seasoning to the vegetables, and simmer for 5 minutes.
6. Add milk, sweetcorn and parsley and simmer for 5 minutes more.
7. Check seasoning; serve in hot soup bowls, with a dash of cream and a little paprika.

# Fish

## Smoked Cod and Salmon Pie

350g smoked cod (or
  smoked haddock)
350g fresh salmon
350ml milk
110g smoked streaky rashers
30g butter
1 large onion
2 sticks celery
30g flour
Pepper

**For the mashed potato:**
10 medium potatoes, peeled
30g butter
110ml milk

1. Preheat oven to 200°C/400°F/Gas 6.
2. Put the cod and salmon in a saucepan and cover with the milk. Simmer for 10 to 15 minutes and then allow the fish to cool in the liquid.
3. Finely chop the rashers and fry in the butter until crisp. Remove with a slotted spoon.
4. Finely chop the onion and celery and sweat them gently in the same frying pan for 10 to 15 minutes until soft.
5. Add the cooked rashers to the pan and stir in the flour.
6. Drain the cooking liquid from the fish and pour the liquid into the pan after you have added the flour. Stir well together and let the mixture come to a gentle simmer for 5 or 6 minutes. It should form a thickish sauce. If it's too thick, add a little more milk. Season with fresh black pepper.
7. Remove all the skin and bones from the fish and break it up into large chunks with your fingers.
8. Take the sauce off the heat and fold the fish into it. Pour the mixture into an ovenproof dish and let it cool while you make the mashed potato.
9. Boil or steam the potatoes and mash well. Heat the butter with the milk and beat this mixture into the potatoes until they look light and creamy. Season with salt and pepper.
10. Spoon the mashed potato gently on top of the fish mixture and then use a fork to ruffle up the top.
11. Bake for 20 minutes until the top is browned and crisp.

## Fish cakes

400g cod fillet
2 large floury potatoes (about
   400g), peeled and
   quartered
25g butter
Freshly grated nutmeg
$\frac{1}{2}$ pack flat-leaf parsley,
   chopped
Finely grated zest of 1 lemon
4 tbsp plain flour
$\frac{1}{2}$ tsp cayenne pepper
Salt and freshly ground black
   pepper
3 tbsp olive oil

**To garnish:** rocket, flat-leaf
   parsley, lemon wedges

1. Poach the cod in enough simmering water to just cover it for 3–4 minutes, until the fish starts to flake and the skin pulls away easily.
2. Drain, discard the skin and pat the fish dry on kitchen paper. Leave to cool.
3. Boil the potatoes for 10–12 minutes, or until just tender. Drain well and mash until smooth. Beat in the butter, nutmeg, parsley and lemon zest, flake the cod into pieces and stir into the mixture. Season to taste, then set aside to cool for 10–15 minutes.
4. Divide the mixture into 8 and shape into ovals about 2.5cm thick. Cover and chill for 30 minutes or until required.
5. Season the flour with cayenne and a pinch of salt. Dip the fish cakes in the flour until lightly but evenly coated.
6. In a frying pan, heat 3 tbsp of the olive oil. Fry the fish cakes (in batches if necessary) for 3-4 minutes on each side or until crisp and golden.
7. Drain on kitchen paper. Arrange on a plate with the lemon wedges, rocket and flat-leaf parsley.

**Note:** You can use other types of fish for this recipe. Smoked haddock and salmon are particularly good alternatives.

## Seafood Pasta Bake

500g pasta of your choice
25g butter
25g plain white flour
$\frac{1}{2}$ pint milk
1 small onion, finely diced
1 sticks celery, finely diced
1 clove garlic, crushed
$\frac{1}{2}$ tsp English mustard
225g mixed seafood, diced
$\frac{1}{2}$ glass white wine
40ml double cream
$\frac{1}{2}$ tin sweetcorn
75g cooked broccoli florets
50g grated cheese mixed
  with 40g breadcrumbs and
  2 tbsp chopped parsley

1. Preheat oven to 210°C/430°F/Gas 6–7.
2. Bring a large pan of salted water to a rapid boil.
   Add the pasta, stirring once or twice and boil till just cooked (al dente). Drain and set aside.
3. Meanwhile, melt the butter in a large saucepan. Stir in the flour and cook on a low heat, stirring, until the flour mix (roux) is smooth and comes away from the side of the pan. Turn up the heat a little, and add the milk, a ladle at a time, stirring constantly until all the milk is absorbed and the mixture is smooth and thickened.
4. Add the onion, celery, garlic and mustard. Cook on a low heat for a few minutes to soften the vegetables.
5. Add the diced fish, wine and cream. Stir everything together, and cook until the fish is just cooked through.
6. Add the sweetcorn and broccoli. If the mix is too firm add a little more milk.
7. Mix into the cooked pasta and pour into an ovenproof dish.
8. Sprinkle with the grated cheese/breadcrumb/parsley mixture and bake on the middle shelf of the oven for 20–30 minutes or until golden on top.

## Baked Salmon with Parmesan and Parsley Crust

(Serves 6)
6 x 150g salmon fillets,
  skinned
Salt and freshly ground black
  pepper
150g cream cheese
Small clove garlic, crushed
Grated rind of $\frac{1}{2}$ lemon
25g fresh white breadcrumbs
25g coarsely grated
  Parmesan
2 tbsp chopped fresh parsley,
  plus extra to garnish
Paprika

1. Preheat the oven to 200°C/400°F/Gas 6.
2. Season both sides of the salmon fillets and place on a greased baking sheet or roasting tin.
3. Mash the cream cheese with the garlic, salt and pepper and lemon rind.
4. Spread the cream cheese mixture on top of the salmon fillets.
5. Mix the breadcrumbs, Parmesan and parsley in a small bowl and season.
6. Sprinkle on top of the cream cheese mixture and dust with paprika.
7. Bake in the oven for about 15 minutes. When the salmon is cooked, it will have changed from translucent to an opaque pink.
8. Serve immediately, garnished with chopped parsley.

## Smoked fish lasagne

**(Serves 8)**

450g smoked fish, e.g. cod, haddock
4 dessertspoons milk
25g butter
25g flour
275ml milk
1 egg yolk
200ml crème fraîche
110g Cheddar, grated
225g 'no cook' lasagne
450g spinach, washed and dried
2 stalks celery, cut into wafer-thin slices
50g pine nuts

1. Preheat the oven to 200°C/400°F/Gas 6.
2. Place the smoked fish on a plate, spoon over the milk and dab with butter. Cover and cook in the microwave or poach gently for 3–4 minutes until the fish is soft enough to flake into pieces. Remove any bones.
3. For the sauce, melt the butter in a pan. Add the flour and cook for 1 minute. Remove from the heat and add the milk, a little at a time, stirring until smooth. Bring the mixture to the boil. Cool slightly and add the egg yolk, crème fraîche and cheese.
4. To assemble, place a layer of lasagne in a rectangular dish. Top with the fish, spinach, celery and half the sauce. Place another layer of lasagne on top and cover with the remainder of the sauce. Scatter the pine nuts over the top and bake in the oven for 25–30 minutes, or until cooked through and golden brown.

## Sauces

### Custards

A custard is a mixture of eggs and milk, cooked gently so that the egg thickens the milk without curdling. Custards are the basis for many hot and cold sweets as well as savoury dishes such as quiches.

**Guidelines:**

1. Use very fresh ingredients.
2. Correct proportions are essential.
3. Use very low temperatures to prevent curdling.
4. Do not overbeat eggs – this causes air holes in baked custards.
5. Heat the milk slightly, then pour the warm milk over the beaten eggs, not the reverse. (Why?)

**Food** 1

## Custard sauce

2 large eggs
2 tsp sugar
400ml milk
2 drops of vanilla essence

1. Put the eggs and sugar in a bowl and beat with a fork.
2. Heat the milk until steam begins to rise – it should not boil.
3. Pour the milk over the beaten eggs, stirring all the time.
4. Strain into a saucepan and stir over a very gentle heat until the custard thickens. Too high a temperature will curdle the custard.
5. Stir in the vanilla and pour into a warm serving jug.

## Puddings based on custard:

- Bread and butter pudding
- Caramel custard
- Queen of puddings
- Crème brûlée
- Fruit fool
- Ice cream

## Bread and butter pudding

75g buttered bread
50g sultanas/raisins
Grated rind of 1 lemon
Ground cinnamon
375ml milk
25g sugar
1 egg
Vanilla essence

1. Preheat the oven to 175°C/350°F/Gas 4.
2. Cut the bread into even pieces and put a layer into the bottom of a greased pie dish.
3. Sprinkle over some of the dried fruit, lemon rind and a little cinnamon.
4. Place another layer of buttered bread on top. Continue in this manner, ending with a layer of bread.
5. Heat milk and dissolve the sugar in it. Beat the egg with a few drops of vanilla.
6. Remove milk from heat and add to beaten egg.
7. Pour the custard mix over bread and leave to soak for 30 minutes.
8. Bake until set.

## Sweet and sour sauce

1 small tin pineapple chunks
125g carrot
1 green pepper
300ml chicken or vegetable
   stock
1 tbsp brown sugar
1 tbsp soy sauce
2 tbsp vinegar
2 tbsp olive oil
1 tbsp cornflour
Salt and pepper

1. Drain the pineapple, keeping the juice.
2. Wash, peel and grate the carrot. Wash, deseed and shred the pepper.
3. Put the pineapple juice and stock into a saucepan and add the carrot and pepper. Bring to the boil and simmer for 5 minutes.
4. Mix the rest of the ingredients together, add to the saucepan, bring to the boil, reduce the heat and simmer for 10 minutes.

**Serve with pork, chicken, fish or vegetables.**

## Barbecue sauce

100g onion, chopped
2 cloves garlic, crushed
2 tbsp wine vinegar
2 tbsp tomato purée
Juice of 1 lemon
Dash Tabasco
400g tin chopped tomatoes
Pinch oregano
Salt and pepper
150ml water

1. Heat the oil in a small saucepan and sauté the onion for 5 minutes.
2. Add the remaining ingredients and simmer for 15 minutes.
3. Liquidise the mixture in a food processor, check seasoning and adjust if necessary.

## Tomato sauce

**Serve with pasta**

1 small onion
1 small carrot
1 small clove garlic
25g butter, margarine or oil
25g flour
Black pepper and salt
400g tomatoes, fresh or
   canned
300ml chicken stock
A little basil or parsley
$\frac{1}{2}$ tsp sugar
1 dessertspoon tomato purée

1. Prepare and dice the onion and carrot; peel and crush the garlic.
2. Heat the fat/oil and sauté vegetables and garlic gently for 5 minutes.
3. Stir in flour and seasoning and cook for 1 minute.
4. Skin and dice the fresh tomatoes or drain if canned; stir into sauce.
5. Add the stock, basil/parsley, sugar and tomato purée.
6. Bring to the boil and simmer for 30–35 minutes. Sieve or blend in processor.
7. Taste, and correct seasoning if necessary.

**Quick tomato sauce:** omit the fat and flour; put all ingredients in processor and blend until smooth. Pour into a saucepan and simmer for 15 minutes until thick.

## White sauce

50g butter or margarine
50g plain flour
500ml milk
Salt and pepper

1. Melt the fat and add the flour.
2. Cook over a low heat for 2–3 minutes.
3. Cool the mix slightly by removing from heat.
4. Gradually add the milk, whisking continuously.
5. Return to the heat, season and continue to stir constantly until thickened.
6. Simmer for a few minutes.

**Variations**
Parsley sauce – add 1 tbsp chopped parsley.
Mustard sauce – add 1 tsp mustard and 1 tbsp vinegar at the end.
Cheese sauce – add 50g grated cheese.

# Cereal recipes

## Cooking rice

There are several methods of cooking rice: here are two. Allow 75–100g per person.

### Method 1

1. Bring a large saucepan of water to the boil.
2. Stir in the rice, bring back to the boil, reduce to a simmer and cook for 12 minutes.
3. Strain through a sieve, rinse and allow to dry slightly in a warm oven, tossing occasionally.

### Method 2

1. Measure 1 cup of rice into a saucepan. Add 2 cups of water.
2. Bring to the boil and cover tightly. Simmer gently for 15 minutes until all the water has gone, stirring twice.
3. Remove from the heat and stir with a fork to let the steam escape.

## Baked rice pudding

**(Serves 4–6)**
75g short grain rice
1 litre milk
25g sugar
Grated nutmeg (optional)
10g butter
1 tbsp caster sugar

1. Place the rice in a sieve and wash thoroughly.
2. Rinse out a saucepan with cold water (to prevent rice sticking).
3. Add the milk and bring to the boil.
4. Add the rice and stir well.
5. Cover and simmer very slowly until a creamy consistency is reached. Note: the surface of the milk should be barely moving.
6. Add the sugar, nutmeg and butter and stir.
7. Pour into a greased pie dish and sprinkle with the caster sugar.
8. Brown in a hot oven.

## Chicken risotto

1 medium–large onion
1 large garlic clove
2–3 streaky rashers
1 green pepper
1 red pepper
75g mushrooms, sliced
2 large uncooked chicken breasts
3 tbsp oil
400g medium or long grain rice
600ml hot stock
Black pepper and salt

1. Peel and roughly chop the onion; peel and crush the garlic; cut the rashers into 5 pieces. Wash, deseed and chop the peppers. Wipe and slice mushrooms.
2. Remove the skin from the chicken breasts and cut into small chunks.
3. Heat 1 tbsp oil in a wok or large saucepan and fry the rashers until beginning to brown. Add the onion and sauté for 1 minute.
4. Add the garlic, peppers and mushrooms and sauté for 1 minute. Remove all the vegetables and set aside.
5. Heat another 2 tbsp of oil in the pan, add the chicken and cook for 3 minutes. Add the rice, stirring the base of pan to prevent it sticking. Sauté for 1 minute until well coated. Season.
6. Return the rashers and vegetables to the pan, pour in the hot stock, stir and bring to the boil.
7. Reduce the heat, cover and simmer gently for about 25 minutes, stirring occasionally.

## Macaroni cheese with mushrooms

450g macaroni
3 tbsp olive oil
225g button mushrooms, sliced
Fresh thyme leaves, to taste
50g plain flour
1 vegetable stock cube
600ml milk
Salt and pepper
1 tsp mustard
175g grated Cheddar
25g pine nuts
25g Parmesan

1. Cook the pasta in plenty of salted boiling water.
2. Meanwhile, heat the oil and cook the mushrooms and thyme. Stir in the flour and remove from the heat. Crumble in the stock cube and stir until blended.
3. Add the milk, a little at a time. Add seasoning, mustard and cheese. Cook until thickened.
4. Drain the pasta, toss in the sauce, scatter with the pine nuts and Parmesan and brown under the grill.

# Vegetables/vegetarian dishes

## Ricotta and basil tart

200g shortcrust pastry (see page 189)
50g basil
25g parsley
125ml extra virgin olive oil
Salt and pepper
2 eggs
1 egg yolk
800g ricotta cheese
100g stoned olives
60g Parmesan, grated

1. Make the pastry, knead, wrap in clingfilm and chill for 20 minutes.
2. Preheat oven to 190°C/375°F/Gas 5.
3. Roll out the pastry dough and use it to line a 10-inch flan case. Bake blind for 12 minutes. Remove the blind filling and cook for 5 minutes more.
4. Reset oven to 180°C/350°F/Gas 4.
5. In a food processor blend the basil, parsley, oil, salt and pepper until smooth.
6. Whisk the eggs and egg yolk in a bowl and fold in the ricotta.
7. Fold in the basil mixture and then the olives. Stir in the Parmesan. Adjust seasoning if necessary.
8. Bake for 30–35 minutes.
9. Serve with a green salad and vinaigrette dressing.

## Vegetable stir-fry

Selection of seasonal, colourful vegetables, e.g. leeks, French beans, mangetout, carrots, red/green/yellow peppers, cauliflower, broccoli, mushrooms, spring onions

1 tbsp oil

1 large onion, chopped

1–2 cloves garlic, crushed

Pinch chilli flakes

2cm fresh ginger, peeled and grated

2–3 tbsp cooking oil

Black pepper

1 tbsp soy sauce

1. Prepare all the vegetables first, according to type. Slice thinly and diagonally if possible. Break vegetables such as cauliflower into florets.
2. Heat the oil to a high temperature in a wok or frying pan. Start by frying the onion, garlic, chilli and ginger. Then add the vegetables that take longest to cook and are cut into thick pieces, such as carrots. Finish with the broccoli (if using) – all frying should be completed within 5 minutes.
3. Season well with pepper and add soy sauce. A commercial Chinese sauce such as oyster, black bean or yellow bean may be stirred in with the soy sauce after frying is completed.
4. Serve with boiled rice.

**Variation:** Meat or fish stir fry
Meat: use only tender cuts of meat, e.g. chicken breast, sirloin steak, pork steak or leg chops of lamb.
Fish: use cod, monkfish, shellfish. Marinating improves flavour and tenderness.
Trim and slice the meat or fish into thin strips. Fry the meat/fish first, then remove while stir-frying the vegetables. Return the meat/fish to the pan and reheat.

## Green risotto

1 medium onion
1 stick celery
2 tbsp olive oil
2 cloves garlic, crushed
300g risotto rice
500ml chicken or vegetable
  stock
100ml dry white wine
  (optional)
2 tbsp frozen peas
Grated rind and juice of half
  a lemon
2 tbsp finely chopped herbs,
  e.g. parsley
Black pepper and salt
6–8 lettuce leaves, washed
2 tbsp grated hard cheese,
  e.g. Parmesan

(Use as an accompaniment or as a vegetarian main course)

1. Peel and chop the onion; scrub and chop the celery.
2. Heat the oil in a large saucepan; sauté the onion, celery and garlic for about 1 minute.
3. Add rice and stir until well coated.
4. Stir in the stock a little at a time, allowing it to be absorbed before adding more. Add the wine and peas and cook until the wine has been absorbed. Stir in lemon rind and juice, herbs and seasoning.
5. Roughly shred the lettuce and stir it in just before serving.
6. Pile into a large dish and sprinkle with cheese.

## Vegetarian lasagne

1 medium onion
200g mushrooms
2 small courgettes
1 tbsp oil
1–2 garlic cloves, crushed
400g tin chopped tomatoes
1 level tsp oregano
1 dessertsp tomato purée
Freshly ground pepper and
  salt
8 sheets of lasagne
50g margarine
50g flour
550ml milk
150g Cheddar cheese, grated

1. Peel and chop the onion. Wipe and slice the mushrooms and courgettes.
2. Heat the oil in a large saucepan. Sauté the onion, then the garlic, until soft but not coloured.
3. Add the mushrooms and courgettes and cook for 5 minutes. Stir in the tomatoes, oregano, tomato purée and seasoning. Cover and cook gently for 10–15 minutes.
4. Preheat the oven to 180°C/350°F/Gas 4.
5. Make a white sauce (see page 177). Stir in most of the cheese.
6. Grease a lasagne dish. Place a layer of vegetable mixture on the base, then sheets of lasagne, then 2–3 tablespoons of the cheese sauce. Repeat until all ingredients are used up, finishing with most of the sauce.
6. Bake for about 30 minutes until the lasagne is soft and the top is golden brown.

**Other suggestions for vegetarian dishes:** Mushroom quiche; asparagus, sweetcorn and red pepper quiche; cheese and tomato quiche; vegetarian pizza.

# Salads

## Salads

(see page 120 for preparing salad vegetables)

### Green salad
1 head of lettuce
A few spring onions
$\frac{1}{4}$ cucumber
Parsley
French dressing

### Summer (mixed) salad
1 head of lettuce
A few spring onions
$\frac{1}{4}$ cucumber
3 tomatoes
3 hard-boiled eggs
French dressing

### Waldorf salad
2 red apples, diced
1 green apple, diced
$\frac{1}{2}$ head celery, chopped
10 walnuts, chopped
Mayonnaise to mix

### Carrot and raisin salad
3–4 carrots, grated
2 tbsp raisins
Small packet peanuts
1 chopped apple or orange
French dressing to mix

### Potato salad
4–6 cooked potatoes, diced
1 onion or 4 spring onions, chopped
Parsley and chives, chopped
3 tbsp mayonnaise

### Pasta and tuna salad
150g cooked pasta shells
1 small can tuna
2 tomatoes, skinned and diced
2 tbsp mayonnaise

### Coleslaw
$\frac{1}{4}$ white cabbage, shredded
1 carrot, grated
2 tbsp mayonnaise

### Red cabbage salad
$\frac{1}{4}$ red cabbage, shredded
25g chopped walnuts
2 tbsp vinaigrette dressing

### Brown rice salad
300g cooked brown rice
1 red pepper, diced
1 green pepper, diced
50g raisins
50g cashews or peanuts
$\frac{1}{2}$ tsp curry paste
French dressing

### Three bean salad
1 small tin red kidney beans, rinsed
1 small tin canellini beans, washed
50g French beans, cooked, chopped
1 tomato, diced
1 red or green pepper, diced
2 spring onions, chopped
Vinaigrette dressing

Prepare and mix ingredients. Season. Mix in the dressing or serve dressing separately.

## French dressing

3 tbsp oil
1 tbsp cider/wine vinegar
Ground black pepper, salt
A little mustard

Shake all ingredients well in a screw-topped jar.

## Vinaigrette dressing

Add $\frac{1}{2}$ tsp each parsley and chives or other fresh herbs to French dressing.

## Blender mayonnaise

1 egg
Ground pepper, salt, mustard
1 tbsp vinegar
125ml oil

Blend all ingredients except the oil in a processor. Slowly dribble in the oil while running the processor on a low speed.

**Food**

# Meat main courses

## Spaghetti bolognese

2 tbsp vegetable oil
450g lean beef mince
1 onion, finely chopped
2 garlic cloves, chopped
1 red pepper, finely chopped
1 green pepper, finely
  chopped
150g button mushrooms,
  sliced
2 tbsp tomato purée
2 bay leaves
100ml red wine
400g can chopped tomatoes
Salt and freshly ground white
  pepper
$\frac{1}{2}$ tsp thyme
1 tsp fresh parsley
$\frac{1}{2}$ tsp dried oregano

**To serve:**
400g spaghetti, cooked
  according to packet
  instructions
Parmesan, finely grated

1. Heat the vegetable oil in a large pan over a medium heat. Add the mince and cook until golden-brown all over.
2. Remove the mince from the pan with a slotted spoon and set aside.
3. Add the onion to the pan and fry for 4–5 minutes, to soften and colour.
4. Add the garlic, red and green peppers and mushrooms and fry for 5–6 minutes, or until softened and lightly coloured.
5. Add the cooked mince, the tomato purée and bay leaves and continue to cook for 8 minutes.
6. Add the wine and tomatoes and bring to the boil. Reduce the heat and simmer for 30–45 minutes.
7. Season to taste with salt and freshly ground white pepper.
8. Add the thyme, parsley and oregano and stir well to combine.
9. To serve, place equal portions of cooked spaghetti into four serving bowls. Spoon equal amounts of bolognese sauce over each portion and sprinkle with finely grated Parmesan.

## Italian shepherd's pie

1. Prepare the bolognese sauce in the recipe above and pour into a greased pie dish.
2. Prepare and boil 4 medium potatoes. Drain and mash with a little butter or milk. Season well with salt and pepper.
3. Spread the potato over the meat mixture and bake at 190°C/375°F/Gas 5 for about 30 minutes.

## Chilli con carne

2 tbsp olive oil
½ onion, finely chopped
1 clove garlic, chopped
300g minced beef
1 red chilli, chopped
½ tsp cumin seeds
Salt and freshly ground black
  pepper
1 tbsp tomato purée
100ml red wine
200ml hot beef stock
½ tsp dried chilli flakes
100g basmati rice, cooked

**To serve:**
1 tbsp Greek-style yoghurt
2 tbsp chopped fresh
  coriander

1. Heat the olive oil in a medium saucepan, add the onion and fry gently for 3–4 minutes, or until softened but not coloured. Add the garlic and fry for 1 minute. Add the beef and fry until browned all over.
2. Add the chilli, cumin seeds, salt and pepper and tomato purée and fry for 1–2 minutes. Add the red wine and simmer for 2–3 minutes.
3. Add the hot beef stock and dried chilli flakes and simmer for 15 minutes, adding a little more stock (or water) if the mixture becomes too dry.
4. To serve, pile the cooked rice onto serving plates and spoon over the chilli con carne. Top with a spoonful of yoghurt and the chopped coriander.

## Cottage pie

1 medium onion, roughly
  chopped
1 medium carrot, peeled and
  roughly chopped
1 clove garlic
½ celery stalk, roughly
  chopped
2 tbsp olive oil
200g button mushrooms,
  thinly sliced
200g minced beef
1 tbsp flour
¼ cup beef stock
1 cup canned tomatoes,
  drained
1 tsp soy sauce or
  Worcestershire sauce
Salt and freshly milled pepper
Mashed potato

1. Put the onion, carrot, garlic and celery into a food processor and pulse to chop finely.
2. Heat the oil in a medium frying pan and stir in the vegetables. Cook for a good 10 minutes, until soft, then add the mushrooms and cook for a further 2 minutes.
3. Add the meat, breaking it up with a wooden spoon. Fry until browned.
4. Sprinkle over the flour and stir well. Then add the stock, tomatoes and soy sauce or Worcestershire sauce. Stir well and simmer for 20 minutes.
5. Season with salt and pepper and cook for another 10 minutes, by which time the meat should be cooked and the mixture not too liquid.
6. Put into a dish, top with potato and bake at 190°C/375°F/Gas 5 for about 30 minutes. To crisp the top, dot with butter and put under a hot grill for a few minutes.

## Chicken and broccoli bake

350g pasta shells or quills
200g broccoli, cut into very small
 florets, stems thinly sliced
2 tbsp olive oil
350g boneless, skinless chicken
 breasts, thinly sliced
175g chestnut mushrooms, quartered
4 tbsp sun-dried tomato paste
80g soft cheese with garlic and herbs
 (e.g. Boursin)
284ml carton single cream

**For the topping:**
Bunch of spring onions, finely
 chopped
85g mature Cheddar, grated
1 garlic clove, finely chopped
50g flaked almonds

1. Preheat the oven to 190°C/275°F/Gas 5. Bring a large pan of salted water to the boil. Throw in the pasta, stir well and return to the boil. Cook for 6 minutes, then add the broccoli and cook for 5–6 minutes more or until the pasta is just cooked. Drain well then return to the pan.
2. Heat the oil in a wide frying pan, add the chicken pieces and fry until lightly browned. Tip in the mushrooms and stir fry for a minute, then stir in the tomato paste, cheese and cream.
3. Gently simmer, stirring, until the cheese has melted to a thick sauce. Season with salt and pepper.
4. Pour the sauce over the pasta, stirring gently until coated, then tip into a shallow ovenproof dish and level the top.
5. Mix the spring onion, Cheddar, garlic and almonds and sprinkle over the pasta.
6. Bake for 20 minutes until golden brown.

## Thai Pork Curry with Jasmine Rice

**(Serves 2)**
200g lean pork (pork steak is good
 for this)
Olive oil for frying
1 aubergine
75ml reduced fat coconut milk
150ml dry white wine
2–3 tbsp Thai curry paste
2 tbsp fish sauce
2 tbsp sugar
5 fresh or dried kaffir lime leaves or
 zest of a lime
Handful fresh basil leaves, shredded

**For the jasmine rice**
Jasmine rice, enough for 2
1 lemon grass stalk, bashed to release
 the flavours
1 garlic clove, halved
1 chilli, halved
Piece of ginger
Dried or fresh lime leaves or lime zest

1. Remove any visible fat from the pork and cut the meat into cubes.
2. In a large non-stick pan or wok heat a drizzle of olive oil and brown the pork. Keep it moving to stop it burning.
3. Dice the aubergine and season with salt. Add it to the pan with the pork and cook for a minute or two.
4. Add the coconut milk. Stir until the pork and aubergine are coated, then add the wine and curry paste and stir in well. Add the fish sauce, sugar and lime leaves (or lime zest) and cook for 8–10 minutes.
6. Add the shredded basil leaves before serving.
7. Cook the rice in boiling water according to packet instructions, along with the lemon grass, garlic, chilli, ginger and lime leaves (or lime zest).
8. Drain well and discard the herbs and spices. Serve alongside the pork.

## Chicken Curry

2 tbsp sunflower oil

4 chicken breast fillets, cut into large dice, about six pieces per fillet

2 large onions, peeled and sliced

3 cloves garlic, crushed

3 tbsp curry powder

1 tbsp Chinese five-spice mix

1l chicken stock (fresh is best, a stock cube is fine) or water

Pinch of sugar and salt

1½ tbsp cornflour (softened with water)

1 bunch fresh coriander leaves, chopped

1. Heat a little sunflower oil in a pan and quickly colour the diced chicken. Remove from the pan and set aside.
2. Add a little more oil to the pan and sweat the sliced onion and garlic until soft, but do not let them colour.
3. Add the curry powder and Chinese five-spice mix and cook for a minute or two, then gradually add the stock.
4. Bring to the boil and skim off any excess fat, if you've used a homemade stock. Season to taste with salt, and add a pinch of sugar.
5. Thicken slightly with cornflour, adding it bit by bit until you have the consistency you like.
6. Now add the chicken to the sauce and simmer for 6–8 minutes. This will ensure the chicken is cooked through but still moist.
7. Finish the sauce with a few tablespoons of the chopped coriander leaves.
8. Serve with boiled rice and naan bread.

## Dublin coddle

450g diced bacon

1l stock

900g pork sausages

4 large potatoes, peeled and halved

2 carrots, thickly sliced

2 large onions, sliced

Salt, pepper

Fresh parsley

1. Place the bacon in a large saucepan with the stock, bring to the boil and allow to boil for 5 minutes.
2. Add the sausages, potatoes, carrots, onions. Return to the boil, season and leave to simmer for 1 hour.
3. Garnish with chopped parsley.

Food

## Colcannon

500g potatoes, cooked
250g cabbage, shredded and
  lightly steamed
2 tbsp cream
Salt and black pepper
1 large or 2 small onions,
  thinly sliced
A little oil

**This is another traditional Irish dish**

1.  Mash the potatoes and mix with the cabbage and cream. Season well with salt and pepper.
2.  Fry the onion in the oil over a moderate heat until it is soft and beginning to brown.
3.  Using a spatula, press half the potato and cabbage mixture in an even layer over the onion and fry for 4-5 minutes until it is well browned and crisp underneath.
4.  Cut the mixture into quarters with a spatula or palette knife and turn them over carefully so that the crisp bit is uppermost. Press the remaining potato and cabbage mixture on to the first layer and after a few more minutes, cut and turn again.
5.  When the bottom is again browned, the potato will have a crisp top, a crisp bottom, and a crisp layer in the middle.

# Pastry

## Shortcrust pastry

200g plain flour
Pinch salt
100g hard margarine or
  butter
About 4 tbsp cold water

1.  Sieve the flour and salt into a mixing bowl.
2.  Cut the margarine or butter into pieces, then rub into the flour with the fingertips until the mixture looks like fine breadcrumbs.
3.  Gradually add water, mixing with a table knife until the pastry holds together but is not moist.
4.  Knead together lightly until smooth, then roll on a lightly floured surface to the required shape.

## Sweet shortcrust pastry

250g plain flour
125g butter or margarine
60g caster sugar
1 egg
2 tsp water or lemon juice

1.  Sieve the flour into bowl.
2.  Cut the fat into pieces and rub into the flour using fingertips until the mixture looks like fine breadcrumbs.
3.  Add the sugar.
4.  Make a well in the centre of the mix and add the egg and water or lemon juice.
5.  Mix well, make into a ball and chill before use.

## Wholemeal pastry

75g wholemeal flour
75g plain flour
Pinch salt
½ tsp baking powder
75g hard margarine or butter
3–4 tbsp cold water

1. Put the wholemeal flour in a mixing bowl; sift in the plain flour, salt and baking powder.
2. Rub in the margarine or butter until the mixture looks like breadcrumbs.
3. Gradually add water and mix with a knife to make a stiff dough.

Use for savoury recipes such as quiche and savoury flans.

## Cheese pastry

50g wholemeal flour
100g plain flour
Pinch salt
Pinch cayenne pepper
¼ tsp mustard (powder or made)
75g hard margarine or butter
75g hard cheese, e.g. Cheddar
Egg yolk (optional)
Cold water

1. Put the wholemeal flour in a mixing bowl; sieve in the plain flour, salt, cayenne pepper and mustard powder.
2. Cut in the margarine or butter and rub together with the fingertips until it looks like breadcrumbs. Mix in the cheese.
3. Mix the egg yolk with made mustard, if using; add to the mixture with 2 tablespoons of water.
4. Mix with a knife to a stiff dough, adding more water if necessary.

Use for savoury recipes such as quiche.

## Sausage rolls

200g shortcrust pastry (see recipe above)
200g sausage meat
Pepper and salt
1 egg, beaten, to glaze

1. Preheat oven to 220°C/425°F/Gas 7.
2. Roll the pastry into an oblong about 30 x 16cm.
3. Divide the sausage meat in two and roll into 2 long 'sausages' the length of the pastry.
4. Divide the pastry lengthways in two and place the sausage meat down the centre of each piece. Dampen the edges of the pastry and roll the pastry around the sausage meat.
5. Press lightly to seal then cut into 5 or 10cm lengths, depending on the size required.
6. Flake edges with a fork, place on a greased tin and chill for 10 minutes in the refrigerator if time allows.
7. Glaze with beaten egg and cut 2 slits on the top of each sausage roll.
8. Bake in the oven for 10 minutes, then reduce the heat to 190°C/375°F/Gas 5 and cook for about 15 minutes more.
9. Remove from the oven and cool on a wire tray. Serve hot or cold.

## Quiche Lorraine

150g cheese pastry (see recipe above)

3 streaky rashers

13g butter or margarine

2 eggs

Pepper and salt

Pinch of nutmeg

175ml milk

100g cheese

1. Preheat oven to 190°C/375°F/Gas 5.
2. Roll out the pastry and use it to line an 18–20cm quiche tin. Chill.
3. Cut the bacon into strips and sauté in the butter or margarine until beginning to brown. Drain.
4. Beat the eggs in a bowl, add seasoning and nutmeg and stir in the milk.
5. Grate the cheese and spread over the base of the flan. Lay the bacon on top.
6. Pour egg mixture over.
7. Bake for about 30–35 minutes until the mixture is set.
8. Remove carefully and serve on a hot dish, garnished with lettuce and tomato.

Variations:

Vegetarian – omit bacon; add 1 sautéed onion, 2 sliced tomatoes, a few broccoli florets.

High fibre – use wholemeal pastry; add 2 sliced tomatoes and peas instead of bacon.

Fish – omit bacon; add 150g fresh/smoked cod pieces and 5–10 prawns instead.

## Chicken pie

1 tbsp butter, plus extra for greasing

300g shortcrust pastry (see recipe above)

$\frac{1}{2}$ onion, sliced

100g mushrooms, sliced

250g cooked chicken, shredded

1 tbsp peas

1 carrot, diced

1 tbsp plain flour

100ml red wine

100ml chicken stock

1 egg, beaten

1. Preheat the oven to 200°C/400°F/Gas 6.
2. Grease a 25cm pie dish with butter.
3. Cut the pastry in half and roll into two circles, one large enough to line the pie dish, the other to top the pie. Use the larger pastry circle to line the dish.
4. Meanwhile, melt 1 tablespoon of butter in a pan over a medium heat. Add the onion and mushrooms and fry for 7-8 minutes, until softened.
5. Add the shredded chicken, peas and carrot. Cook for a further 2–3 minutes.
6. Sprinkle over the flour and cook for two minutes, stirring constantly.
7. Add the wine and stock. Bring to the boil, then reduce the heat and simmer for 25 minutes, until the sauce is thick and glossy. Allow to cool a little.
8. Spoon the filling mixture into the pastry-lined pie dish, leaving a 2.5cm gap from the top.
9. Top with the other pastry circle and press the edges with a fork to seal.
10. Brush the pastry with beaten egg, then bake in the oven for 30 minutes, or until golden brown.
11. To serve, spoon generous slices of the pie onto serving plates, with boiled potatoes and vegetables of your choice alongside.

# Puddings and sweets

## Apple tart

200g shortcrust or sweet shortcrust
    pastry (see page 189)
3 medium cooking apples
Sugar
Cloves or cinnamon
Egg, beaten, or milk, to glaze

1.  Preheat the oven to 220°C/425°F/Gas 7.
2.  Divide pastry in two; roll out each half large enough to fit on an oven-proof plate. Put one half on the plate; fold the second half and put on top of the first half. Place the plate and pastry in the refrigerator to cool.
4.  Peel, core and slice the apples. Remove the top piece of pastry and put the apples on the bottom half of the pastry; sprinkle with sugar and cloves or cinnamon.
5.  Brush the edges of pastry with water, cover with the remaining pastry and press well to seal. Flake and decorate the edges with a fork. Cut 2 slits on top of the pie or prod with a fork: this allows the steam to escape when the tart is being cooked.
6.  Brush with beaten egg and place the plate on a tin (to prevent spills in the oven).
7.  Bake for 10 minutes at preset temperature, then reduce to 190°C/375°F/Gas 5 until cooked (about another 25 minutes more). Serve with whipped cream, ice cream or custard.

## Bakewell tart

**For the pastry:**
300g plain flour, plus extra for
 dusting
125g unsalted butter
30g sugar
1 egg
2 tbsp milk, to bind (if needed)

**For the filling:**
225g butter, softened
225g sugar
225g ground almonds
3 eggs, plus another egg, beaten, to
 glaze
1 lemon, finely grated zest only
50g plain flour
Raspberry jam
Flaked almonds, for sprinkling

1. Make the shortcrust pastry as described on page 189.
2. Turn the dough out onto a floured work surface and roll out until large enough to line a 26cm tart tin. Carefully lift into the tin, then place in the fridge to chill.
3. Preheat the oven to 200°C/400°F/Gas 6.5.
4. For the filling, beat the butter and sugar together in a bowl until pale and fluffy.
5. Mix in the ground almonds, then crack in the eggs one at a time, beating well between each addition – don't worry if the mixture begins to split, just add a little of the flour.
6. Fold in the lemon zest and the flour.
7. Fill the tart case with a sheet of greaseproof paper weighed down with baking beans or rice. Bake in the oven for 15–20 minutes.
8. Remove the pastry case from the oven and turn the temperature down to 180°C/350°F/Gas 8.
9. Spread some of the jam generously across the base of the pastry, leaving a 2.5cm gap around the edge.
10. Spread the filling mixture over the jam and sprinkle over the flaked almonds.
11. Transfer to the oven and bake for 20 minutes, or until set and golden brown. Allow to cool in the tin before serving.

## Country apple cake

200g flour
1 tsp baking powder
$\frac{1}{4}$ tsp ground cinnamon or cloves
75g butter/margarine
2 medium cooking apples
1 egg
50g raisins
100g caster sugar
1–2 tbsp milk (if required)
Brown sugar (to sprinkle)

1. Preheat oven to 190°C/375°F/Gas 5.
2. Sieve the flour, baking powder and spice into a bowl.
3. Rub in the fat until the mixture looks like fine breadcrumbs.
4. Peel, core and finely chop the apples.
5. Beat the egg and add to the mixture with the apples, raisins and sugar. The mixture should be moist but not wet. If the mixture is too dry add a little milk.
6. Empty into a greased sandwich tin and sprinkle brown sugar over the top.
7. Bake for about 40 minutes until golden brown and cooked through.
8. Turn on to a wire tray; serve hot or cold, with butter.

Food

## Madeira mixture (queen cakes)

100g butter or margarine
100g caster sugar
2 eggs, beaten
2 drops of vanilla extract or other
  flavouring
150g flour plus ½ tsp baking powder
  OR 150g self-raising flour

1. Preheat the oven to 200°C/400°F/Gas 6.
2. Cream the fat and sugar together until pale and fluffy.
3. Add the eggs a little at a time, beating well after each addition. Add the vanilla with the final addition.
4. Fold in the flour, in two or three stages, using a tablespoon. Do not beat.
5. Grease patty tins or arrange paper cases in tins. Pile the mixture into each, using a teaspoon.
6. Bake for about 15 minutes. Remove and cool on a wire tray.
7. Decorate by sprinkling with icing sugar, or icing with water icing (see page 197).

**Variations:**
Fairy cakes – add 50g sultanas to the basic mixture.
Chocolate chip cakes – add 50g chocolate chips to the basic mixture.

## Sponge cake

3 eggs
75g caster sugar, plus a little extra for
  dusting
75g flour, plus a little extra for
  dusting
¼ tsp baking powder

**For the filling**
2 tbsp jam
125ml cream, whipped

1. Preheat the oven to 190°C/375°F/Gas 5.
2. Grease two 18cm sandwich tins. Dust with a mixture of caster sugar and flour.
3. Whisk the eggs and sugar together until the mixture is thick and creamy and holds the imprint of the beater. (If using a hand whisk, place the bowl over a saucepan of hot water off the heat – this speeds up thickening. Then whisk until cool.)
4. Sieve the flour and baking powder onto kitchen paper; fold half gently into mixture, using a tablespoon, then fold in the remainder.
5. Divide the mixture between the tins.
6. Bake for about 15–20 minutes. When the sponge is fully cooked, the top should spring back when it is pressed. Turn on to a wire tray to cool.
7. When cool, sandwich together with jam and cream.

## Swiss roll

Ingredients and method as for sponge cake, on page 195.

1. Preheat the oven to 190°C/375°F/Gas 5.
2. Have ready a large Swiss roll tin which has been lined with greaseproof paper (see page 109).
3. At stage 5 of the sponge cake recipe, pour the mixture into the tin, smoothing well into the corners.
4. Bake for about 10 minutes.
5. Have ready a sheet of greaseproof paper on a damp tea towel; sprinkle the paper with caster sugar.
6. Turn out the sponge and carefully peel off the greaseproof paper. Trim off edges to assist rolling and spread cake with warmed jam. Roll up tightly, taking care not to include paper.
7. Leave to cool in the tea towel for 10 minutes, then remove paper and tea towel.

**Cold fillings**, e.g. cream or butter filling: roll without filling but including the greaseproof paper. Allow to cool, then unroll, remove paper and spread with filling of your choice. Roll up again.

## Chocolate cake (all in one)

1 tbsp cocoa powder
1 tbsp boiling water
175g soft margarine
3 eggs
175g caster sugar
175g self-raising flour

1. Line the base of two 18cm sandwich tins with circles of greaseproof paper. Grease.
2. Preheat the oven to 180°C/350°F/Gas 4.
3. Blend the cocoa powder and boiling water and allow to cool.
4. Place all ingredients in a mixing bowl and beat with a wooden spoon for 2 minutes (1 minute with an electric mixer).
5. Divide between the sandwich tins and bake for 25–30 minutes.
6. Turn on to a wire tray to cool. When cool, use chocolate fudge icing (on the opposite page) to sandwich the cake together and to ice the top.

## Icings and fillings

### Glacé or water icing
200g icing sugar
Boiling water
Colouring (as required)
Flavouring (as required)

1. Sieve icing sugar into bowl.
2. Add boiling water teaspoon by teaspoon, beating all the time, until the correct consistency is reached.
3. Beat in colouring and flavouring, as required.

### Butter filling
75g butter or margarine
150g icing sugar, sifted
Flavouring, e.g. vanilla

1. Cream the fat until pale.
2. Gradually beat in the sifted sugar.
3. Add flavouring and beat in 1 tablespoon of warm water to lighten, if wished.

### Orange icing/filling
Add the grated rind of half an orange and a little orange colouring.

### Lemon icing/filling
Add the grated rind of half a lemon and a little yellow colouring.

### Coffee icing/filling
Add 1 tsp coffee granules dissolved in 1 tsp boiling water.

### Chocolate icing/filling
Add 50g melted chocolate or 1 dessertspoon cocoa dissolved in 1 tsp boiling water, then allowed to cool.

### Chocolate fudge icing
50g butter or margarine
50g caster sugar
2 tbsp milk
1 tsp coffee granules
150g icing sugar
1 tbsp cocoa

1. Melt the butter or margarine and caster sugar in a saucepan and stir until the sugar has dissolved.
2. Add the milk and coffee and bring to the boil. Remove from the heat and allow to cool.
3. Sieve the icing sugar and cocoa into a bowl.
4. Add the liquid, beat well and allow to cool before using.

Food

# Home-made biscuits

## Guidelines

- Grease tins well.
- Allow space for biscuits to spread.
- Biscuits don't get crisp until they are cold.
- Cool slightly on the tin, then lift off with a palette knife or egg slice.
- Store in an airtight tin. Never store biscuits with cake or bread – they go soft.

## Chocolate chip cookies

**(Makes 24)**
100g butter
50g caster sugar
110g dark brown sugar
1 egg
$\frac{1}{2}$ tsp vanilla essence
170g plain flour
$\frac{1}{2}$ tsp baking soda
Pinch salt
170g chocolate chips
55g chopped walnuts

1. Preheat the oven to 180°C/350°F/Gas 4. Grease 2 baking sheets.
2. Using an electric mixer, cream the butter and both sugars together until light and fluffy.
3. In a separate bowl, mix the egg and vanilla and then beat into the butter/sugar mix.
4. Sieve in the flour, baking soda and salt and stir well.
5. Add the chocolate chips and nuts and mix.
6. Place heaped teaspoonfuls of the mix on the trays, leaving 5cm spaces gaps between them.
7. Bake for 10–15 minutes.
8. Allow to cool slightly, place on a wire tray and cool thoroughly.

## Lemon biscuits

175g plain flour
1 lemon, grated zest only
110g butter, softened
50g caster sugar

1. Preheat the oven to 180°C/350°F/Gas 4.
2. Put the flour and lemon zest into a mixing bowl and rub in the butter.
3. Add the caster sugar and bring the whole mixture together to form a stiff dough. Do not add any water, however tempting.
4. Roll out the dough to a thickness of about $\frac{1}{2}$ cm and cut into shapes with a cookie cutter.
5. Place carefully on a baking tray and cook in the oven for 6–10 minutes until pale golden.
6. Remove from the oven and allow to cool on a wire rack.

## Raisin and Banana Cookies

85g unsalted butter, softened slightly
80g light brown soft sugar
A few drops of vanilla extract
1 large egg, beaten
1 small ripe banana, peeled and
   mashed
175g self-raising flour, sifted
85g raisins
16 banana chips, to decorate

1. Preheat the oven to 180°C/350°F/Gas 4.
2. In a large bowl combine the butter, sugar and vanilla and beat together with a wooden spoon until light and fluffy. Add the beaten egg and mashed banana and mix together.
3. Stir in the flour and raisins and mix together until all the flour is incorporated.
4. Using a spoon, divide the mixture into 16 equal amounts and place on lightly greased baking trays, leaving about 5cm between them to allow for spreading during cooking.
5. Top each cookie with a banana chip, then bake in the preheated oven for 8–10 minutes or until golden brown.
4. Remove from the oven and leave to cool for 2–3 minutes before removing from the baking trays and transferring to a cooling rack to cool completely.

## Peanut butter and white chocolate blondies

125g plain flour
1 tsp baking powder
100g butter, at room temperature,
    plus extra for greasing
150g crunchy peanut butter
175g soft light brown sugar
1 egg, beaten
1 tsp vanilla extract
75g white chocolate, chopped

1. Preheat the oven to 170°C/325°F/Gas 3. Butter the sides of a 20 x 20cm square cake tin and line the base with greaseproof paper.
2. Sift the flour and baking powder into a small bowl and set aside.
3. In a large bowl, cream the butter and peanut butter together until very soft. Add the sugar, egg and vanilla extract and beat until well combined.
4. Add the flour and baking powder and the chopped chocolate. Mix to form a dough.
5. Place the dough into the prepared tin and bake in the oven for 25–30 minutes, or until golden brown and almost firm in the centre.
6. Remove from the oven and allow to cool in the tin, before removing and cutting into squares.

## Yule log

30g plain flour
30g cocoa powder
$\frac{1}{4}$ tsp salt
3 large eggs, separated
$\frac{1}{4}$ tsp cream of tartar
110g caster sugar
2 drops almond essence
Caster sugar and cocoa powder, for
    dusting

**For the buttercream filling:**
100g butter
150g icing sugar
55g cocoa powder
A splash of brandy or rum

**This is a great alternative to a Christmas fruit cake**

1. Preheat the oven to 180°C/350 Gas 4. Grease a 23cm x 33cm Swiss roll tin and line with baking parchment.
2. To make the sponge: sift the flour, cocoa and salt together and set aside. Sprinkle a large piece of greaseproof paper with caster sugar and set aside.
3. Put the egg whites in a clean bowl and whisk until frothy. Add the cream of tartar and whisk until stiff. Gradually add the sugar until the mixture forms soft peaks.
4. Whisk the egg yolks until pale and thick. Add the almond essence.
5. Using a large metal spoon, stir in the reserved flour and cocoa mixture. Finally, lightly fold in the egg whites until well blended – take care not to beat the air out of the mixture.
6. Spoon the mixture into the Swiss roll tin and level the top. Bake for 15–20 minutes or until sponge-like to the touch.

**Food** **1**

7. Turn the sponge onto the greaseproof paper dusted with caster sugar. Peel away the baking parchment and roll up the sponge with the greaseproof paper inside. Leave to cool.

8. To make the buttercream filling, beat the butter in a mixing bowl until smooth, then gradually beat in the icing sugar and cocoa powder. Add the brandy and mix well.

9. Once the sponge has cooled, unroll it carefully, spread it with half the filling and roll it up again – without the greaseproof paper this time.

10. Spread the rest of the filling over the cake to cover it. Score it with a fork to resemble a log and dust with cocoa powder. Decorate with a sprig of holly.

## Mince pies

1 batch sweet shortcrust pastry
   (see page 189)
450g mincemeat
Icing sugar or caster sugar, for
   dusting

1. Preheat the oven to 200°C/400°F/Gas 6.

2. Roll out the prepared pastry on a lightly floured surface to about 3mm thick. Cut out 18 rounds with a large pastry cutter and roll out again, if necessary, to cut out 18 lids with a smaller cutter. Line patty tins with the larger rounds.

3. Fill the pastry shells to about half their depth with mincemeat, taking care not to overfill. Dampen the edges with a little water and cover with the pastry lids. Seal the edges well.

4. Brush the tops with water and dredge with sugar. Make two small cuts in the top of each pie. Bake for about 15 minutes or until golden brown.

5. Remove the tins from the oven, allow to cool and then dredge with a little more sugar.

# Omelettes

An omelette is a quickly made egg dish suitable for breakfast or a light meal. It consist of lightly beaten egg, seasonings and butter (optional). It may be filled with sweet or savoury fillings and should be served at once. It should be cooked in a non-stick frying pan or a special omelette pan.

## French savoury omelette

2 eggs
1 dessertspoon water
Black pepper and salt
13g butter or margarine
Mixed fresh herbs, chopped

1. Beat the eggs lightly in a bowl, using a fork. Add the water, seasoning, herbs and half the butter.
2. Heat the remaining butter in an omelette pan; when hot pour in the eggs.
3. As the eggs begin to set, use a palette knife or spatula to draw in the mixture from the edges, allowing the uncooked mixture out to the sides.
4. When just set but still moist on top, fold in three and slip on to a warm plate.
5. Serve at once with green salad and sautéed or French fried potatoes.

**Modification: Breakfast omelette**
Add:
1 cooked diced potato
2 rashers bacon, grilled and chopped

**Fillings**
Cheese: sprinkle 2 dessertspoons grated cheese on the omelette halfway through cooking.
Ham: chop 1 slice of ham and sprinkle over the omelette halfway through cooking.
Mushroom: in a separate saucepan, sauté 50g sliced mushrooms in a little fat. Fill the omelette before folding.
Tomato and onion: sauté 1 small, finely chopped onion in a little fat or oil. Add 1 skinned sliced tomato and cook until slightly soft. Use to fill omelette.
Fish: e.g. smoked haddock. Heat flaked haddock in 2 tbsp cream before filling omelette.

# Batters

batter is a mixture of flour, eggs and liquid, e.g. milk. Because it has no raising
agent, it is beaten well to incorporate as much air as possible.

A food processor speeds up batter-making.

## Batters

**Thin batter**
(used for pancakes and
Yorkshire pudding)
100g flour
Pinch of salt
1 egg
250ml milk

**Thick batter**
(used for coating food,
e.g. fruit fritters, fish)
100g flour
Pinch of salt
1 egg
125ml milk

1. Sieve the flour and salt into a bowl.
2. Add the egg and half the milk and whisk until smooth.
3. Gradually add the remaining milk and whisk well to aerate the mixture.

## Pancakes

1. Brush the base of an omelette pan or non-stick frying pan with melted fat or oil.
2. Pour in just enough batter to cover the pan, tilting the to allow the batter to spread evenly.
3. Cook over a medium heat until golden brown. Turn and cook the other side.
4. Keep pancakes warm on a covered plate over a saucepan of boiling water.
5. To serve: sprinkle with caster sugar and lemon juice and roll up. Arrange on a serving dish and decorate with lemon wedges.

**Stuffed pancakes:**
Fill pancakes with one of the following.
Sweet – stewed apples and lemon zest; crushed raspberries and cream; bananas fried in butter and rum.
Crêpes Suzette – pancakes reheated in orange juice and zest, sugar and liqueur or brandy.
Savoury – cream cheese and chives; curried chicken; mushrooms in sauce; smoked haddock in cheese sauce.

# Pizza

## Quick pizza

**For the scone base:**
100g plain flour
100g wholemeal flour
Pinch of salt
1 tsp baking powder
1 tbsp oil
125ml milk or water

**For the topping:**
1 small onion
300g ripe tomatoes or 1 tin chopped
    tomatoes
1 tbsp oil
Black pepper and salt
$\frac{1}{2}$ tsp oregano
100g mozzarella or Cheddar cheese,
    grated or sliced

**Optional extra ingredients:**
50g mushrooms, sliced
2 tbsp sweetcorn
2 slices chopped ham
2 slices pineapple

1. Preheat the oven to 200°C/400°F/Gas 6.
2. To make the tomato topping: peel and chop the onion. Skin and slice the tomatoes, or drain off liquid, if using tinned tomatoes. Heat the oil in a saucepan; sauté the onion and add seasoning, herbs and tomatoes. Simmer gently for about 15 minutes while making the base.
3. Sieve the flours, salt and baking powder into a bowl.
4. Add the oil and enough milk or water to make a dough that is soft but not wet.
5. Roll into a 25cm circle and place on a greased tin.
6. Allow the tomato mixture to cool slightly, then spread over base. Lay the cheese on top, together with any optional ingredients.
7. Bake for about 20–25 minutes. Serve at once with green salad.

**To encourage younger children to eat this, the toppings could be arranged to make pizza faces.**

Consumer
Studies

# Chapter 19 What is a Consumer?

 A consumer is anyone who buys or uses goods and services.

We are all consumers – in our daily lives we use food, clothes, cars, televisions and many other goods. A consumer is not simply a shopper; we consume energy in the form of electricity, gas and oil. We also use services such as those of doctors and mechanics.

In the past people were more self-sufficient; they grew their own food, made their own clothes and built their own houses. Life today is not as simple, so we depend on others to provide us with the goods and services we need. We pay for these with money – either directly, e.g. with cash, or indirectly, through taxes.

 **Reminder:** a resource is something you need to achieve a goal or complete a task.

## Consumer resources

**Money**

**Information**

**Skill** – decision-making

**Time** – to make decisions

## Consumer services

| Direct services | Indirect services (paid for by taxes, etc.) | |
| --- | --- | --- |
| Doctor, dentist | Public lighting | Education |
| Hairdressing | Postal service | Roads |
| Car repairs | Social welfare | Gardaí |
| Dry cleaning | Health services | |

# Decision-making

Decision-making is an important consumer skill. Because such a huge range of goods and services are available, and because few people have an unlimited amount of money, it is necessary to make choices or decisions.

## Decision-making means choosing from several alternatives

A decision is a choice that can be made:

**1** on impulse, i.e. without much thought, or

**2** through a decision-making process.

| The decision-making process | Example |
|---|---|
| 1. **Define the decision.**<br>(What must I decide or choose?) | 1. Whether to buy a new or a second-hand laptop. |
| 2. **Collect information.**<br>(This reduces risk.) | 2. Visit computer shops; look up small ads for second-hand ones. Use the internet. Collect prices of each type. |
| 3. **Consider the alternatives.**<br>(Make a list of these.) | 3. (A) I have enough savings to buy a second-hand one.<br>(B) I would have to borrow money to buy a new one. |
| 4. **Consider the consequences**<br>(of each alternative). | 4. **Pros of Decision B**<br>❧ New laptops last longer.<br>❧ They look better.<br>❧ I could get a part-time job to pay for a new one.<br><br>**Cons of Decision B**<br>❧ I will be in debt.<br>❧ I'll have no money for entertainment, etc.<br>❧ A part-time job means less sport, and my school work might suffer. |
| 5. **Make the decision.** | 5. I will buy a good second-hand laptop now and start saving for a new one. |
| 6. **Act on the decision.** | 6. Buy the computer, using information gathered. |
| 7. **Evaluate, if necessary.** | 7. I've got a computer. It does the work that I want it to. I'm not in debt. I still have money for other things. I've time for sport. My school grades are not affected by a part-time job. |

**ACTIVITY**

Using the example above, write down the decision-making sequence when deciding whether to buy a ticket for a music festival or a pair of jeans.

## Want or need?

One of the first things to consider when choosing a product or service, particularly if money is scarce, is whether or not we really need it.

**A need is something we cannot do without** – our basic needs are food, clothes, warmth and shelter.

**A want is something we would like but do not have to have**, such as a Playstation or a holiday. If we can afford it, it is nice to treat ourselves by satisfying our wants.

Wants and needs are not the same for everyone: for example, we may want a car to save walking, but a doctor may need a car in order to get to patients quickly. Parents usually spend most of their money on needs, such as food, electricity and other bills. Teenagers have most needs met by their parents and are often more concerned with wants, such as phone credit or trendy clothes.

Today it is often difficult to decide what is a need and what is a want – people consider that consumer goods such as washing machines and freezers are needs, yet their grandparents got by without them. A hardworking person might say, 'I need a holiday abroad.' Is this a need or a want?

In most cases it comes down to money – people on low incomes can often satisfy only basic needs, while those on higher incomes can satisfy more of their wants.

 Remember – needs should always have priority over wants.

It is irresponsible to spend money on wants when the bills are not paid and there is no food in the house. Major problems can arise in families because one member of the family is satisfying wants instead of needs, perhaps through an addiction, such as gambling or alcoholism.

## Factors that influence choice

The decisions we make as consumers are influenced by many factors, both internal (personal) and external (outside influences).

1 **Money.** Can I afford it? Lack of money limits choice.

2 **Needs and wants.**

3 **Priorities.** A priority is something that you decide is important to you. Your values will influence your choice – some people would prefer to spend money on music, others on travel. One person might like to spend money on trendy clothes

another to spend it on something more useful, like an evening class. Our choices depend on our priorities.

4. **Family and peer group.** Young children are influenced by their parents' tastes and wishes. Teenagers are more influenced by their peer group – friends and schoolmates.

5. **Trends/fashion.** Young people are often influenced by what is in fashion, e.g. in clothes and music.

6. **Advertising and marketing** have a major influence on the choices we make.

7. **Emotions** sometimes influence our buying habits. Name some emotions that might affect your buying.

**ACTIVITY**

1. Which of the influences listed above are internal and which are external?
2. What was the worst buy you ever made? Describe:
   (a) what you expected
   (b) what you received
   (c) whether you did anything about it. Describe what you did.

**LINK-UP**

Advertising, page 240

## Buying checklist

When you actually come to buy a product it is important to make a wise decision. Take your time and consider the following.

| | |
|---|---|
| Money: | How much can I afford to spend? Is it allowed for in the family budget? |
| Value: | Is it good value for money? Compare prices, products, brands and sizes. |
| Quality: | Is it made from good materials or ingredients? |
| Durability: | Will it last? This applies to goods such as shoes, furniture, technology. |
| Design: | Is it designed to do its job? Does it look good? Is it well finished? |

| | |
|---|---|
| **Purpose:** | Is it effective? Will it do the job it is meant to do? |
| **Safety:** | Is it safe (e.g. electrical items, children's toys)? Consider health, e.g. additives in food, chemicals in cleaning products. |
| **Comfort:** | Clothes, footwear, furniture, e.g. beds, chairs. |
| **Fit, size:** | Clothes, shoes, furniture, bed linen. |
| **Maintenance:** | Is it easy to keep clean and easy to clean? |
| **Brand, model:** | Is it a reliable, well-known brand? Important when buying machines. |
| **Reliable shop:** | Does it have a good reputation? Is it known for quality goods and good value? Does it offer an after-sales service? |
| **Environment:** | Does the product use up limited resources? Does it pollute? Is it biodegradable? Can it be recycled? |

Shopping for clothes, page 348

Buying electrical appliances, page 314

The environment and you, page 329

**ACTIVITY**

Consider the most expensive item of clothing you bought in the past year, and evaluate it under the headings above. You should include at least 10 considerations. Was it a good buy? Have you got good value from it by wearing it often, or is it lying unworn in the back of your wardrobe? Discuss.

**REVISION QUESTIONS**

1. What is a consumer? Name four consumer resources.
2. What is the difference between a need and a want? Give an example of each.
3. What is a priority? Name four typical priorities in family finances.
4. List the main points in a decision-making sequence.
5. List six basic factors to consider when buying a piece of furniture.

Test Yourself eTest.ie

# Chapter 20 Consumer Rights and Responsibilities

Every citizen has rights, such as the right to freedom and the right to vote. We also have consumer rights. These protect us from manufacturers and sellers who might try to take advantage of us. Many consumer rights are protected by law.

Rights come with responsibilities. The first consumer responsibility is to know our rights: no law will protect us from making foolish decisions.

A right is something to which you are entitled.
A responsibility is something for which you are accountable.

| Rights | Responsibilities |
| --- | --- |
| The right to information | To be well informed about prices, products, services and consumer law |
| The right to choice | To make an informed choice and look for value for money |
| The right to quality | To examine products and services carefully before buying |
| The right to safety | To read labels, heed warnings and follow instructions |
| The right to redress if things go wrong | To know your rights and complain when necessary |
| | To choose and use resources wisely and avoid waste |

## 1. The right to honest information

Every consumer has a right to accurate information. It is illegal for manufacturers to give false information about a product, for example to say it is leather when it is not. Food must be labelled accurately so that we know what we are eating. Other useful sources of information are:

* care labels on clothes
* date stamps

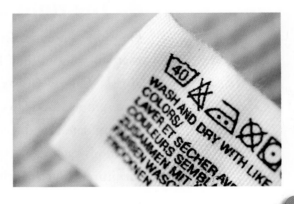

- instructions, e.g. cooking instructions on food, care and use instructions on electrical appliances
- health warnings and hazard labels.

## 2. The right to choice

If there were only one brand of each product we would have no choice. Manufacturers could charge what they liked. Instead we have a wide variety to choose from, and lots of competition between shops and manufacturers, which keeps prices down. When one company is the only producer of a product or service and there is no competition, this is called a **monopoly**, e.g. Iarnród Éireann is the only rail provider in this country.

We can use our right to choose to improve the standard of goods and services. By refusing to accept poor-quality goods and services we can raise standards for everyone. Learn to complain.

**ACTIVITY** Give examples of two situations where you could attempt to improve a service in your locality.

Quality, page 223

## 3. The right to quality

Nobody benefits from shoddy goods. They wear out quickly and have to be replaced. The law says that goods must be of merchantable quality, i.e. they must be of a certain standard and do what they are supposed to do – food must be edible, a washing machine must wash clothes clean. Manufacturers test goods before they leave the factory to make sure that they reach a certain standard; this is known as quality control.

## 4. The right to safety

Consumers are entitled to products and services that will not put their health in danger or their lives at risk. The law insists on certain safety standards; for example, food laws protect us against contaminated food. Laws control safety standards on goods such as electrical items, fire-resistant furniture, children's clothes and toys.

Manufacturers of certain products must carry out safety tests and must provide warning labels and instructions where they are considered necessary for our safety.

## 5. The right to redress

**If you are sold something faulty or a service does not provide what it is supposed to, you have a right to some form of compensation.** Depending on the situation you may be entitled to one of the three Rs: a replacement; a repair; or a refund of your money. Sometimes a credit note is given, which allows the consumer to buy an item or items of the same value at a later date in the same shop. The law sets out your rights clearly. There will be more about complaints later (page 220).

Consumer protection, page 216

**A good consumer:**

- is aware of his or her rights and responsibilities
- gathers information before buying
- shops around to get the best value for money
- examines goods before buying them – checks labels and guarantees
- knows what to do if things go wrong.

**ACTIVITY**

Do you think that it is a right or a responsibility to get value for money? Discuss.

## Consumer information

The consumer has a right to information from the seller and manufacturer but also has a responsibility to look for information before buying. It would be foolish to go into a shop blindfolded. Yet in a way this is what we do when we do not seek information before buying. Gathering as much information as possible in advance gives the consumer time to think about and evaluate the product or service. As a result, he or she is less likely to make mistakes.

Decision-making, page 207

Buying checklist, page 209

## Sources of information

**In advance**

- **Newspapers and magazines**, particularly consumer magazines such as *Consumer Choice* (page 219).
- **The internet.**
- **Telephone directory** and **Golden Pages**.
- **Manufacturers' leaflets, brochures.** These often give detailed specifications, i.e. measurements, etc., of products.
- **Libraries** have reference books and consumer magazines. Librarians can also be helpful.
- **Television and radio** advertisements give information about new products. Some provide useful advice.
- **Word of mouth.** It can be helpful to hear the experiences of other people who have used a product such as a cooker, freezer or car, or who have used a service.

**At the shop or showroom**

- **Examination:** handle and examine products with a critical eye.
- **Sales staff:** well-trained staff have a good knowledge of what they are selling and can be a useful source of information. Some showrooms provide demonstrations of products, e.g. a car showroom would offer a test drive. However, some sales staff can put too much pressure on the consumer, particularly if they are paid on a commission basis. Do not allow yourself to be pressurised into a sale. Take your time before making a decision. If you are well prepared and have a list of questions ready, you are more likely to get a satisfactory result.

## Advice agencies

These can guide the consumer to other sources of information, such as legal aid and local authority departments such as housing or social welfare. Some give expert advice.

### Citizens' Information Centres

These are run by trained volunteers and funded by the Department of Social and Family Affairs. They work out of public and community offices and provide information on services such as:

- social welfare entitlements
- consumer rights
- housing

- employment
- health services
- family law.

## Other agencies

**1** Consumers' Association of Ireland (page 219)
**2** National Consumer Agency (page 219)
**3** Financial Regulator (page 219)
**4** Ombudsman (page 219)

**ACTIVITY**

1. Obtain a copy of *Consumer Choice* and study it. Pick out the article that most appeals to you, and list some reasons why you think it is useful to the consumer.

2. Compile a class report similar to *Consumer Choice* on a product everyone uses regularly, such as toothpaste or copybooks.

**REVISION QUESTIONS**

1. List three consumer responsibilities.
2. List three redress options available after a genuine complaint.
3. List the five consumer rights.
4. What is meant by redress?
5. What are the main sources of information a consumer can use when researching a product?
6. Explain the role of the Consumers' Association of Ireland.
7. What is a monopoly?

*Test Yourself*
**eTest.ie**

# Chapter 21 Consumer Protection

**Consumers are protected by:**

1. the law and the courts
2. government (statutory) agencies, e.g. the National Consumer Agency, the Ombudsman
3. voluntary agencies, e.g. the Consumers' Association of Ireland.

Unfortunately, the law cannot always protect us from ourselves. If we buy on impulse, don't check prices, don't bother to read labels or instructions, we are likely to make many 'bad buys'. Remember the Latin phrase *caveat emptor* – it means 'let the buyer beware'.

## 1. The law and the courts

The strongest form of consumer protection is civil law. Many laws are passed by the state and the EU which protect consumer rights. As new situations arise and new products and services come on stream, such as credit cards and the internet, new laws are made to provide for these.

The courts enforce consumer law: claims up to €2,000 may be dealt with by the small claims procedure, which is administered through the District Court. It is a cheap and fast way for consumers to solve disputes. The most common complaints in recent years have been related to holidays.

Higher claims are dealt with in the Circuit Court and the High Court. Apart from the Small Claims procedure, court procedures should not be taken lightly, as they are expensive and time-consuming.

### The Sale of Goods and Supply of Services Act 1980
**This Act states the basic rights of the consumer.**

1. When you make a purchase or use a service, you are making a contract with the seller which is legally binding. It does not have to be in writing; if you pay for a

product and it is faulty, it is the seller, not the manufacturer, who has a legal obligation to put it right.

2. Goods should be of merchantable quality – in good order and undamaged.

3. Goods should be fit for their purpose – a frying pan should withstand heat; clothes should be wearable.

4. Goods should be 'as described' by the sales person, brochure or packaging, e.g. waterproof, pure silk.

5. They should correspond with a sample, e.g. if you are shown a suite of furniture in a shop and a slightly different one is delivered, it must be replaced with an identical one or you should get your money back.

If goods do not comply with these conditions, the seller has broken the contract. This Act also deals with the following:

★ **Notices in shops.** It is an offence to display notices such as:

> **NO REFUNDS**
>
> **NO EXCHANGES WITHOUT RECEIPT**
>
> **NO EXCHANGE ON GOODS ON SALE**
>
> **CREDIT NOTES ONLY FOR RETURNED GOODS**

★ **Guarantees. A guarantee is an undertaking by a manufacturer that the product you buy will be satisfactory for a certain length of time.** If it is not, it will be replaced or repaired. A guarantee is a bonus and cannot take away your normal legal rights under the Sale of Goods Act. If there is a fault, you can claim under the guarantee or under the Act. As guarantees can vary a lot, the Act states that a guarantee should be written so that it is clear what is offered, how to claim, from whom to claim and any extra charges, e.g. postage.

**The Act tells you your rights when goods are faulty.**

If goods do not conform to the Act, the buyer can reject the goods and get his or her money back. You are not bound to accept a repair or a credit note.

**BUT**

1. You have no rights if the fault was pointed out to you at the time of sale, e.g. a tear in the seam.

2. Faulty goods must be returned 'within a reasonable time'. The sooner you return them, the stronger your case. If you leave it too long, it is assumed you may have used and damaged them.

3. Do not use the product once you discover the fault; do not attempt to repair it or you may lose your rights.

④ You have the same rights if you rent, lease, buy on credit or buy at sales.

⑤ If you simply change your mind after you have bought something, you have no right to a refund or exchange, although many shops will allow this in order to keep your custom.

⑥ If you misuse the goods, e.g. use delicate shoes for mountain climbing, you lose your rights.

## Services

When a service is used, a contract exists between the person who supplies it and the customer who uses it.

**The customer is entitled to expect that:**

➤ the person who supplies the service has the necessary skill to do so, e.g. a mechanic

➤ the service will be provided with proper care and diligence, e.g. a builder, a hairdresser

➤ the materials will be sound and of merchantable quality, e.g. a carpenter.

If any of these are unsatisfactory, the customer may be entitled to compensation.

## The Consumer Protection Act 2007

This Act protects the consumer in several ways.

❶ It prevents false claims about price, characteristics or availability of a product or service.

### Examples of claims

| Goods: | Pure wool | Bone china |
|---|---|---|
| | Leather goods | Waterproof |
| | Mileage 12,000 | Made in Ireland |
| | Weight 100g | 18 carat gold |
| Services: | 24-hour service | |
| | One minute from train/beach | |
| | One hour film developing | |
| | Free delivery | |

- It prevents intimidating sale tactics.
- It prohibits pyramid schemes.
- It prohibits prize draw scams.
- It prevents certain advertising aimed at children.

## Prices

False or misleading claims relating to the present, previous or recommended price are illegal. In sales, when one price is crossed out and another put in, the goods must have been selling at the higher price for a reasonable length of time in the same shop.

## Statutory agencies

### The Ombudsman

Ombudsman is a Scandinavian word meaning 'grievance man'. The Office of the Ombudsman deals with unresolved complaints made about government departments, local authorities, An Post, Eircom and the health boards. The service is free, but should be used only as a last resort.

**Credit Ombudsman:** investigates disputes between banks/building societies and their customers.

**Insurance Ombudsman:** investigates complaints about insurance companies.

### National Consumer Agency

This agency, which was established by the government in 2007, deals with complaints nationally. It also works to inform and educate consumers.

### The Financial Regulator

Established in 2003, the Financial Regulator provides information on financial services to the public and monitors financial institutions.

### Office of the Director of Corporate Enforcement

This organisation makes sure companies stick to the rules.

## Voluntary agencies (non-statutory)

### The Consumers' Association of Ireland

This is an independent, non-profit-making organisation whose aim is to educate and protect Irish consumers. The association publishes a monthly magazine (*Consumer Choice*) and reports to government on the views of consumers.

### 2 Trade organisations

Some manufacturers, retailers and companies operate a code of practice to maintain standards among their members and deal with customer complaints. Examples: CIF (Construction Industry Federation), MIAVI (auctioneers).

## Complaints

You are unlikely to have to complain if you examine the goods carefully when you are buying them.

### If there is a fault:

1. Stop using the product and find your receipt.
2. Make your complaint as soon as possible so that there is less justification for the retailer to say the product was abused.
3. Contact the shop – not the manufacturer. Your contract is with the seller of the goods or service.
4. Know your rights; be polite but firm.

### At the shop:

1. Ask for the customer service manager or the person in charge.
2. Have all relevant information to hand: the receipt, the faulty product, packaging, etc.
3. Be reasonable and calm; speak politely but firmly.
4. Explain exactly what is wrong – make sure your facts are correct.
5. State exactly what you want done about it. Refer to the Sale of Goods Act if necessary – if goods are not of merchantable quality or fit for their purpose you are entitled to have your money refunded.
6. If the shop refuses to co-operate, you may have to put the matter in writing to the head of the company or, as a last resort, threaten legal action. (See below.)

### You have no claim if:

- the fault was pointed out at time of purchase
- you changed your mind, e.g. about size or colour
- you damaged the goods or used them incorrectly.

### A written complaint

1. Write or type neatly a letter to the managing director, giving the following details.
    - Description of what you bought, including brand, make and model number.

- Name of shop, date of purchase, name and number of assistant (if known), and price paid.
- Send photocopy of receipt – never send the original. Do not return goods.

2 Explain the fault and state what action you have already taken, e.g. returning to the shop.

3 State what action you would like the company to take, e.g. a replacement or refund.

4 Wait until you get a satisfactory reply before returning the goods. Keep copies of all correspondence.

5 Allow time for the seller to sort things out. If the reply is unsatisfactory or there is no reply you must decide whether to go further.

## Sample letter

Customer's address

Date

Name and address of company

Dear Sir or Madam

I wish to complain about a Haddington hair straightener, which I purchased in your shop on Tobin Street on 23 June. The model number is H 42112. I enclose a copy of receipt and guarantee. On the third time it was used it overheated, produced sparks and stopped working. As it was correctly wired and was not misused in any way, the fault must lie in the machine itself.

I returned to your shop with the straightener, but since the assistant, Ms Kealy, was unable to help me I am referring the matter to you.

It is clear that the fault lies in the machine, therefore I would like a refund of the cost of the hair straightener, €50.

Yours faithfully

Mary O'Brien

## You may get more advice from:

- The National Consumer Agency
- Citizens' Information Centres.

## Complaints may be made to:

- Environmental Health Officer (matters related to hygiene, e.g. in shops, restaurants)
- The Ombudsman – complaints about public services, e.g. Eircom.

If all else fails:

**1** The Consumers' Association of Ireland offers a Consumer Personal Service – for a fee it will approach the seller where there is a valid complaint. In some cases the case is brought to court.

**2** For a small fee you can bring a small claims procedure for up to €2,000 through the District Court. This deals with complaints about unsatisfactory goods or services quickly, cheaply and informally, without the use of a solicitor.

## Case studies

| Situation | Problem | Questions |
|---|---|---|
| Girl buys blouse to match skirt. | Returns home – it doesn't match. | Can the girl demand that the blouse be changed? What is the shop obliged to do? |
| Man takes 2-month-old DVD player back to the shop because it is faulty. | Trader says as there is a guarantee, he must send it to the manufacturer. | Which rule in Sale of Goods Act is broken? What are the customer's rights? What is the trader obliged to do? |
| Sale in shoe shop. Customer buys half-price shoes. The heel comes off. | Sign says 'no refunds'. Seller says 'no refunds on sale goods – look at the sign'. | Which consumer laws have been broken? What are the customer's rights? What is the seller obliged to do? What else should be done? |

1. Describe how you would go about making a telephone complaint to a supermarket about mistakes in your till receipt.
2. Work out a role play of a mother complaining to the shop manager about a dangerous toy.

1. Explain the following consumer terms:
   - guarantee
   - merchantable quality
   - small claims procedure.
2. List four items of information which should be included in a letter of complaint to a retailer.
3. How does the Consumer Information Act protect the consumer?
4. Explain the function of the Ombudsman.

Test Yourself
eTest.ie

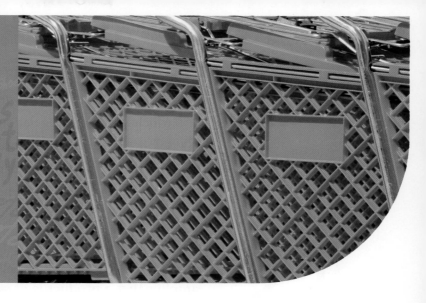

# Chapter 22 Quality

The term 'quality' is used to mean that goods and services are of a high standard.

Before products leave a manufacturer, they should go through a series of tests to make sure they reach a certain standard – this is known as **quality control**.

**A good-quality product will be:**
- suitable for its purpose
- made from good-quality materials
- well designed and finished
- (if food) clean, safe, nutritious, edible, fresh and ripe.

## Quality and standard marks

Quality marks are awarded by various associations to goods and services that reach a high standard of quality.

1. **The Q mark** – awarded to quality Irish businesses and services by the EIQA.
2. **Guaranteed Irish** – awarded to high-quality goods manufactured in Ireland.

❖ *Irish quality mark*  ❖ *Guaranteed Irish*

Standard marks are awarded by the standards authority of many countries for goods that meet their standards of quality, safety, performance, etc. They are withdrawn if standards drop.

❖ *Irish Standards mark*

❖ *European standards mark*

❖ *Kitemark*

**Examples**

❶ **Irish Standards mark** is granted under licence from the NSAI to those products which meet their regulations.

❷ **CE – the European standards mark**, often found on toys.

❸ **Kitemark** – British Standards Institution (BSI). This implies a product is of a high standard of quality and safety.

## Guarantees

A guarantee is another sign of quality. This is **an undertaking by a manufacturer or supplier that a product is of sufficiently high quality to last a certain time**. See also page 217.

## Quality of service

Many consumer complaints are about quality of service. It is a pleasant experience to visit a shop, bank or restaurant where the quality of service is good.

| Good-quality service | Bad-quality service |
| --- | --- |
| Efficient staff | Inefficient staff |
| Friendly, eager to please | Rude, uninterested |
| Co-operative | Unco-operative |
| Punctual | Slow, unpunctual |
| Minimum queuing/waiting | Long queues; customers served out of order |
| Premises well maintained | Dirty, untidy premises |
| Accessible for wheelchairs | No wheelchair access |
| Toilet facilities available and clean | No toilet facilities |

## Packaging

The self-service system of shopping has resulted in a huge rise in the amount of packaged goods.

### The purpose of packaging

❶ It protects products, particularly food, from contamination.

❷ It helps keep foods preserved, e.g. cans, bottles, packets.

❸ It makes products easier to store, distribute and sell.

❹ It carries information and instructions, e.g. on how to use, cook, store the product.

It carries bar codes (see page 237).

Attractive packaging can help to sell products.

| Features of good packaging | Food packaging should also: |
|---|---|
| Strong | Protect food |
| Waterproof | Be well sealed |
| Light | Be non-toxic |
| Easy to open and reseal, if necessary | Be hygienic |
| Biodegradable | |

## Types of packaging

**Paper:** Plain, waxed, cardboard, laminated with a coat of plastic, e.g. Tetrapaks used for milk and juices.

**Glass:** Clean, hygienic, transparent (useful for checking quality of food) but very breakable.

**Metal:** Tin cans, used for fruit, vegetables, meat, fish, juices, pet food. Aluminium cans, used for soft drinks, beer, etc.; foil trays for freezers, takeaways. Aluminium wrap – for overwrapping butter, confectionery, etc.

**Plastic:** Plastic bottles and jars, e.g. fizzy drinks bottles. Polythene bags – widely used for packaging, e.g. food, clothing, hardware. Vacuum packs.

## Packaging disadvantages

It is estimated that one-tenth of each supermarket bill is spent on packaging.

1. This is damaging to the environment as most packaging ends up in landfill; much packaging is not biodegradable.

2. Packaging can deceive the consumer: small amounts in large jars; unrealistic illustrations or descriptions of contents.

3. Products are available only in specific amounts. This may be too much or too little, e.g. rashers.

4. It uses up natural resources e.g. oil used to make plastic.

5. Aerosols are an expensive form of packaging.

## Did you know?

An average milk bottle makes 30 trips. A milk carton makes one, and pollutes the environment.

# The consumer and the environment

One of the main problems of the increase in consumer goods is the effects they are having on our environment.

## How can we help?

| | |
|---|---|
| **Reduce** | the amount of unnecessary things you buy. |
| **Refuse** | overpackaged goods and unnecessary plastic bags. Bring your own bag to the supermarket or use boxes to pack your groceries. |
| **Reuse** | anything at home which can be used again, e.g. bags for shopping, boxes, storage containers, etc. |
| **Recycle** | as much as possible. Homes are now provided with a recycling bin along with their standard bin from their waste provider. This can hold a wide range of packaging materials, e.g. boxes, cartons, tins, etc. |

- Use biodegradable products rather than plastics.
- Use a compost heap for kitchen waste. Local authorities provide them at a reasonable price, as do many hardware shops.
- Bring items to recycling centres. (Usually situated in car parks.)
- Clothing can be given to charity, given to swap shops or recycled.
- Electrical items now come with a product recycling fund charge (PRF). This means that you can return your old item to the store and they will recycle it for you.

**ACTIVITY** Suggest some ways you could persuade your local supermarket to cut down on packaging.

## Labelling

Because so many of today's products are packaged, we rely on labels to tell us what is inside. Information on labels may take the form of symbols, illustrations or written instructions.

**Labels should give the following information.**

- Description of product – what it is made from, weight, size, colour and number of items.

- Instructions for using, storing, caring for and cleaning the product.
- Name and address of manufacturer or producer.
- Various quality symbols and marks.
- Warning about dangers when misused, e.g. bleach.

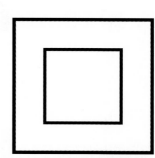

❖ *This label gives nutritional information*

## Types of labelling

1 **Instructions.** These are important in order that we use products correctly and get the most out of them. Failure to follow instructions can lead to damage to the product and injury to the user.

Instructions may be written on the packaging, on a label/swing ticket or in a separate booklet (e.g. kitchen appliances, sound systems and TVs). The instruction booklet should be stored carefully.

2 **Care labels.** Clothing textiles must carry a label stating the fibre from which they are made. Wash care instructions may be given. Care labels are usually stitched onto the garment so that they can be referred to when washing.

3 **Food labelling** (page 158).

4 **Date stamp or expiry date.** The date by which a food, drug, etc. must be used (page 158).

5 **Safety labels**, e.g.:

- double insulated – used on small electrical appliances
- upholstery conforms to standards of flammability; won't be set alight by matches (see page 351)
- children's items such as nightwear, prams, buggies and toys must conform to certain safety regulations and standards. All toys must show the CE symbol to indicate that they are safe when used as intended, by the correct age group.
- cigarette packets must show a government health warning
- dangerous products must carry warning labels, e.g. bleach.

**Safety information also includes:**

- instructions on how to use a product safely
- warning of dangers of using or misusing a product, e.g. poisons, drugs
- wiring instructions must be given with every electrical appliance.

❖ **Double insulated**

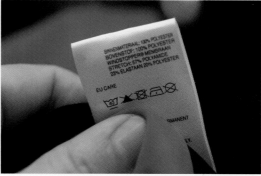

Care labelling
(textiles), page 364

# Logos and symbols

A logo is an easily recognisable symbol or company trademark.

**Examples**

Woolmark: indicating 100% pure new wool.

The Consumers' Association logo combines the initials of the association to form a watchful owl.

The international access symbol indicates areas that are accessible for people with disabilities.

**ACTIVITY**

1. Make a collection of symbols like those shown above and mount the best as a class display.
2. Study packages for symbols and logos not shown in your textbook and find out what they mean.

**REVISION QUESTIONS**

1. List three features of good-quality service.
2. List three purposes of packaging.
3. List the information that should be shown on a ready meal.
4. What are the features of good packaging?
5. List three types of packaging and suggest a use for each.
6. What is a logo? Draw one that you are familiar with.
7. What is the PRF?
8. Suggest six ways in which we could be more environmentally responsible at home.

Test Yourself
eTest.ie

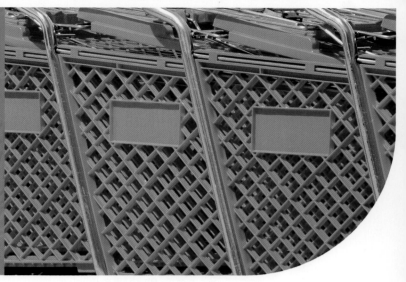

# Chapter 23 Money Management

Money is an important consumer resource. Money management involves planning spending so that we have enough for our needs.

A plan for spending is called a budget. When we plan a budget we must balance income (what we earn) with expenditure (what we spend).

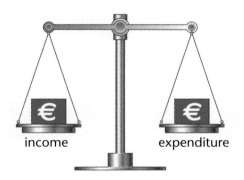

income                expenditure

## The management process

Planning a budget is a good example of management.

**What is my goal?** To balance income with spending.

**Resources:** Time, skill, money.

**Plan:** Work out income and expenditure – on paper.

**Put it into action** – in practice.

**Evaluate:** Did I achieve my goal? If not, how can I increase income or cut back on spending?

### Budgeting skills

**Management:** Learning how to plan, balance and economise, if necessary.

**Information-gathering:** What am I earning? What am I spending? What do I need or want?

**Decision-making:** Making choices between needs or wants. When there are several needs or wants we must decide on priorities.

# Personal budget

A teenager's income might include money from parents and money from part-time work such as babysitting. Most spending will be on yourself – on needs such as fares, lunches and toiletries; and on wants, such as phone credit and clothes. It is important to discuss with parents what your allowance is to cover, in order to prevent arguments. Decide whether you will plan a weekly or a monthly budget.

Transfer this budget to your copy. Try it out for the next week and then evaluate it.

| Income | | Expenses | |
|---|---|---|---|
| | | (Fill in your expenses according to your priorities) Clothes, toiletries, phone credit, CDs or downloads, going out, food, etc. | |
| Allowance | | | |
| Part-time job | | | |
| Other income | | | |
| | | | |
| | | | |
| Total | | Total | |

**Evaluation**

1. Have you balanced your income and expenditure? If not, can you increase income or reduce expenditure?
2. Make a list of things you bought this week that were not absolutely necessary.
3. Have you any money left over for saving? If so, what would you save for? Where will you save it?
4. How could you realistically improve on your budget?
5. Multiply your weekly income by 52 to find your yearly income. Add money you normally get for presents, etc.
6. Compile a list of guidelines to follow in order to make your income stretch as far as possible.

# Budget for a single person

## Income

Not all the money we earn is ours to spend. Some goes to the state to pay for running the country.

## Tax credits

Since 2001, the amount of tax required to be paid by workers is calculated using a system called tax credits. These credits are used to reduce the tax payable on your income. They vary from person to person depending on their income and situation.

## Expenses

When you start at college or work, you will have to allocate more money to needs. You may have bills to pay such as food, fuel, lodgings, fees, books, clothes and perhaps loan repayments. Money for these must be set aside first, then you will know how much you can afford to spend on enjoyment.

# Household budget

Family budgeting is a responsible job. It should be shared between the adults in the family. It must be flexible to allow for changes as circumstances change from year to year, e.g. the arrival of a new baby or loss of a job. Families should be careful not to take on too many commitments, such as buying unnecessary items on credit. This is a frequent source of financial hardship and worry.

**Remember**, needs are more important than wants.

## Family income

This might include:

1 husband's/wife's earnings, less deductions
2 state benefits, e.g. family income supplement, unemployment benefit, child benefit.

## Family expenses

Spending usually falls into three categories:

- regular, daily spending, e.g. food
- regular bills, usually monthly or quarterly, e.g. mortgage or rent, electricity, gas, telephone
- occasional large bills, e.g. car insurance, house insurance, holidays.

A budget takes all these into account, so that money is available for the large bills when they arrive. Basic needs such as food, housing and clothing must be met first. The remainder is divided between other necessities, according to priorities. A budget should cover:

- **food**
- **housing** – rent or mortgage repayments

- **household expenses** – heat, electricity, repairs, telephone, etc.
- **essential clothing**, **shoes**, etc.
- **fares** – travel, car and petrol/diesel
- **medical expenses** – doctor, chemist
- **insurance** – house, contents, life assurance, etc.
- **education**, **sport**
- **personal** – toiletries, extra clothes, books, hobbies
- **non-essential** – entertainment, holidays, pets and other luxuries
- **saving** – (a) for emergencies, (b) for luxuries.

## Credit or saving?

**Credit is a way of borrowing money. It means 'buy now – pay later'.**

It is often used to buy large things such as a house or car. People also use it to buy consumer goods such as a washing machine or TV if they do not have the money to pay for them immediately.

- Credit costs more than paying cash. The credit company or bank charges the borrower interest to cover the cost of borrowing.
- You must be over 18 to get credit.
- Taking on too many credit commitments is dangerous. You may not be able to repay. In this situation the item can be repossessed, i.e. taken back.

### Forms of credit

1. Hire purchase.
2. Loan.
3. Bank overdraft.
4. Credit card.

Things to remember about credit:

- shop around for the cheapest loan and compare interest rates
- be aware of possible penalties for paying off a loan early or making repayments late
- read the credit agreement carefully
- get in touch with the lender if you have any difficulty in meeting repayments, or contact your local MABS centre
- don't take on more debt than you can afford.

## Saving is better

If you want something like an iPod or a holiday, put aside a little from your budget each week until you have enough to pay with cash.

### Advantages

- You don't pay interest – in fact you earn interest on savings.
- The price is lower.
- You have no debt to worry about.

### Where can you save?

1. Bank or building society.
2. An Post
3. Credit Union.

Look for:

- the highest interest
- safety
- ease of withdrawal.

## Advantages of budgeting

1. Spending is kept under control – without a plan there is a danger of overspending on wants and not having enough for needs. With a budget, it is easier to see where overspending occurs and economies can be made.
2. Money is available for large bills, unexpected expenses and seasonal spending.
3. Security and independence – freedom from financial problems and worry.
4. Learning how to budget teaches us responsibility – few people are in a position to buy all the luxuries they want.
5. It gives a good example to children.

**Test Yourself** eTest.ie

**REVISION QUESTIONS**

1. Explain the term 'budget'.
2. Describe three advantages of budgeting.
3. List three deductions you could expect from a weekly income.
4. Name three sources of credit and give two advantages and two disadvantages of each.
5. What should you look for when choosing a place to save?
6. Suggest two savings options available to a teenager.
7. Name four services that are paid for by taxation.

# Chapter 24 Shopping

Shopping has changed greatly in recent times. More choice has developed for the consumer and many buy their products online.

## Types of shop

- **Independent shops** are traditional small shops which are frequently family-run. They are often in small neighbourhoods, and open late and on Sundays. They may offer less choice but provide a personal service. They may deliver, and often offer credit to known customers. Examples include your local newsagent.
- **Specialist shops** concentrate on one particular type of stock, e.g. shoes, jewellery, books, bread.
- A **boutique** is a small shop which usually specialises in more expensive clothes.
- **Supermarkets** are large, self-service shops which offer a wide range of food and other products. Products can be sold more cheaply because supermarkets buy in bulk and staff costs may be lower. They are designed to make you spend as much money as possible. Examples: Dunnes Stores, Tesco.
- **Voluntary chain stores** are groups of independently owned smaller supermarkets. Examples: Londis, Spar, Centra.
- **Department stores** stock a wide selection of goods. They are divided into different departments which usually offer a personal service. They may sell clothing, household linen, furniture, electrical goods, china and kitchen equipment. Examples: Clery's, Arnotts, Brown Thomas.
- **Multiple chain stores** are self-service department stores where one company runs several branches. They have a recognisable

layout and appearance. Examples: Penneys, Marks and Spencer's.

- **Discount stores:** some of these are large outlets specialising in certain products such as electrical goods; others are small shops selling very cheap small items e.g. €2 shops.
- **Other retail outlets:** websites, street markets, vending machines, mail order companies, doorstep selling, party selling.

**ACTIVITY** Find out about and write a paragraph on four of the 'other' types of retail outlet mentioned above.

## Counter service and self-service

In the past, supermarkets were simply large outlets for cheap groceries. They were impersonal and provided little choice of fresh food. Today, competition between them has improved things enormously. There is greater emphasis on friendliness and good service. You are less likely to have to queue for long, or pack your own bags. A wide variety of perishables, such as meat, fish, bread and cheese, are available, both packaged and loose. Hygiene has improved greatly. Large car parks and facilities such as restaurants, crèches and toilet facilities make shopping a more pleasant experience. Many supermarkets now open until late at night, on Sundays or on a 24-hour basis, and offer free delivery or online shopping.

## Self service shopping – advantages

1. Quick and convenient.
2. Usually cheaper, due to bulk buying and low overheads.
3. Own brands particularly cheap.
4. Greater choice of goods – most groceries can be bought in one store.
5. You can take your time to choose.
6. Quick turnover; perishables usually fresher.
7. It's easy to see, examine and compare prices of products.
8. Store cards and credit cards accepted.
9. Trolleys make it easier to shop in bulk.

### Self service – disadvantages

1. Greater temptation to impulse buy, i.e. buy without planning to, or without needing to.
2. Often less personal.
3. Queues at checkouts at peak times.
4. You may have to pack your own groceries.
5. Packaged goods – small amounts may be unavailable.
6. Credit available only with credit card.
7. Car required for out-of-town centres.

### Counter service – advantages

1. Personal service.
2. Easier, especially for elderly people.
3. Usually nearby – handy if you run out of something.
4. May allow credit.
5. Many offer free delivery.

### Counter service – disadvantages

1. May be slow and inefficient.
2. More expensive.
3. Smaller choice of products.
4. Prices not always marked.

## Shopping guidelines

1. Make a list and keep to it – it saves time and reduces impulse-buying
2. Limit shopping trips to once or twice a week; you buy less and save time. Perishables can be frozen.
3. Get to know prices, and shop around for good value.
4. Look for quality and freshness.
5. Check weights, sizes and date stamps.
6. Food shops should be clean and hygienic; assistants clean and well trained, hair tied back or covered; perishable food stored in refrigerated cabinets; tongs or disposable gloves provided for bread, etc.; raw and cooked meat never stored or served together. Smoking is illegal in food shops. Assistants who serve food should never handle money.

## Marketing techniques that encourage you to buy

- 'Special or 'free' offers, 'two for the price of one', etc. – they are only good value if you need them.
- Tempting goods such as cakes at eye level.
- More expensive brands at eye level and cheaper products high up or low down on the shelf.
- Treats at checkouts to encourage impulse buys.
- Soft music and in-store recorded advertisements.
- Essential items such as milk furthest from the entrance.
- The aroma of freshly baked bread as you enter.
- Promotions at ends of aisles where they are difficult to avoid.
- Food sampling.
- Large trolleys, wide aisles.

## At the checkout – bar codes

Computerised registers are used in most large shops. Many of these make use of a **bar code**, which is printed on each product. **This is a series of lines and spaces which can be 'read' by a scanner.**

1. It shows up on an itemised printed receipt so the customer can see exactly what has been bought.
2. It is quicker at the checkout than individual pricing.
3. It helps the retailer as a form of stock control, recording the size and brand of each product bought, so that the shop doesn't run out of a product.
4. Disadvantage: sometimes prices are not displayed on shelves. As goods are not individually priced, it is impossible to know in advance the cost of the product.

# Methods of payment

- **Cash** – quick and easy but may not be suitable for paying large bills. Easy to lose.
- **Cheque and cheque card** – convenient and safe, if kept separately. You will need a bank account; the card guarantees sums up to €130.
- **ATM card**, e.g. Pass, Banklink. Cash can be withdrawn from machines which are sited at banks and many shopping outlets.
- **Debit card**, e.g. Laser – bill is paid by entering a PIN at the cash desk/checkout. The amount is deducted from your account within 1–2 days. Very convenient and flexible (cash back can be drawn in many outlets), but be sure to keep receipts.

🗡 **Credit card**, e.g. Visa, Mastercard – safe and convenient. Customer pays by entering a PIN and has 1 month's credit before it is necessary to pay the bill. Can be tempting to overspend and if the bill is not paid in full a high rate of interest is charged on the balance.

🗡 **Store card** – certain stores, particularly department stores, have their own card. Credit can be run up and paid at the end of the month.

## Online shopping

Many homes regularly use well-known websites to purchase goods or services. Examples include iTunes for music, Tesco for groceries and eBay for almost anything.

Shopping online is convenient because:

🗡 the shopper does not have to leave the house – this makes it ideal for those who find it difficult to get out of the house, e.g. new mothers, convalescents

🗡 discounts may be offered

🗡 the chances of impulse buying other items is reduced

🗡 free delivery is available from some websites

🗡 no salespeople or pressure to buy.

### Disadvantages:

🗡 A computer and internet access is necessary.

🗡 Credit card details are entered so there can be worries about security. Always use a secure site.

🗡 Delivery times vary and can be slow.

🗡 Postage charges can be very expensive on some items.

🗡 Many websites don't deliver to Ireland.

🗡 The item may not be exactly as you thought.

## Shopping terms

🗡 **Receipts. These are an important record of your transaction.** Examine receipts to make sure they are accurate. Keep receipts in case there is a problem with the goods and you want to return them.

🗡 **Unit pricing. This is the price per unit, e.g. per kilogram or litre.** Unpackaged food such as fruit, vegetables, meat and fish must have the price per metric unit displayed on the food or shelf.

🗡 **Bulk buying: buying in large amounts**, usually because there is a special offer, e.g. four for the price of three. A good way of stocking up on tinned goods and other non-perishables if the product is necessary.

- **Loss leaders. This means selling a small range of goods very cheaply, e.g. at cost price**. These are often advertised in newspapers, hand-bills or shop windows in order to encourage customers into the shop, where they are likely to buy other goods too. It is illegal to sell goods below cost.
- **Own brands. Products which are sold under the name of the shop** instead of using a heavily advertised brand name such as Heinz. Costs are kept down by using simple packaging and labelling and little advertising. Examples: Tesco value, St Bernard.
- **Store clubs, travel stamps**, etc. The purpose of these is to reward regular customers by giving them 'free gifts' or travel vouchers.

1. List some of the ways, other than those mentioned in this chapter, in which shopping has changed in the past 10 years.
2. Sales are a great temptation to buy. Make a list of guidelines to follow in order not to overspend at sale time.
3. List your top five websites and explain why you like them.

1. What is a multiple chain store? Name two found in Ireland.
2. What are the disadvantages of (a) individual grocery shops, (b) supermarkets?
3. Explain the term 'bar code'.
4. List five hygiene points to be expected in a food shop.
5. Explain the difference between a credit card and a debit (Laser) card.
6. Explain the term 'unit pricing'. Give two examples.
7. Explain the term 'loss leader'. Give one advantage and one disadvantage of this practice.
8. List four techniques used by supermarkets to encourage consumer spending.
9. Give two advantages and two disadvantages of self-service shopping.
10. List four methods of payment for goods or services.
11. Why can shopping online be useful?
12. What should you look out for when shopping online?

Test Yourself
eTest.ie

# Chapter 25 Advertising and Marketing

Advertising is an important part of modern life. Its main purpose is to sell products.

 An advertisement is a form of mass communication; it gives a message to a large number of people.

## The functions of advertising

1. To inform the consumer and create awareness about new products.
2. To persuade us to buy goods; this increases sales.
3. To promote the brand name and a good image of the manufacturer.
4. To give information about products and services.
5. To introduce a new product.

**ACTIVITY** Describe any two advertisements that you really like and explain why you think they are good.

## Advertising outlets

- Television and radio
- Internet
- Cinema
- DVD
- Newspapers and magazines
- Billboards and bus shelters
- Buses and trains
- Sporting fixtures and sports sponsorship
- Packaging
- Direct mail letters and leaflets
- Labels, logos, carrier bags and clothing.

**ACTIVITY** Choose two types of advertising from the list above and compare their effectiveness.

## Classified advertisements

These are non-commercial advertisements placed in commercial and free newspapers and magazines. They advertise jobs, houses and articles for sale.

## Public information advertisements

These are usually placed in newspapers and public buildings such as health clinics to inform the public about important matters such as health and social welfare issues.

# Advertising techniques

In order to sell products, advertisers use many clever techniques. They portray attractive images such as the friendly pub, sunlit countryside, perfect families. They use glamour, sex and romance, e.g. to sell luxury goods such as perfumes. They use clever language which often has no real meaning e.g. 'whiter than white', 'almost', 'probably' (these are called 'weasel words'). They play on emotions such as envy (keeping up with the neighbours), insecurity (drink this beer and you'll be popular), or fear (take out life assurance now). They use association of ideas, e.g. robins and Christmas; alcohol and excitement. They often employ well-known personalities to promote products.

They emphasise the good points and say nothing about the negative aspects – how many manufacturers tell us that soft drinks can make children hyperactive and rot their teeth?

Most advertising is aimed at a target audience, e.g. toy ads between children's TV programmes, car advertisements during sports programmes, clothes advertisements in teenage magazines.

## ACTIVITY

1. Discuss the advertisements shown above.
2. Some ads are controversial. Describe an advertisement you object to.

# Effective advertising

- captures attention
- keeps one interested enough to continue reading/watching it

- creates desire for the product
- persuades the consumer to buy it.

# What is a good advertisement?

- For the consumer: one that tells us as much as possible about the product – its effectiveness, price, durability, how to use it, etc.
- For the manufacturer: one that will sell the product.

## Advantages of advertising

1. Advertising informs us of new products and services.
2. It creates jobs by employing large numbers of people and by increasing sales of consumer goods.
3. It provides important information on our rights and entitlements, e.g. social welfare.
4. It keeps down the costs of newspapers and other media.
5. It is a source of information, e.g. about sports fixtures and entertainment.
6. It is useful when we want to buy, sell or rent goods, e.g. houses, cars, flats.

## Disadvantages of advertising

1. Advertising increases the cost of many consumer goods.
2. It can be manipulative, affecting the way we think and behave.
3. It persuades people to buy what they may not be able to afford.
4. It often shows unrealistic lifestyles and can make us feel dissatisfied with life.
5. It creates stereotypes – the perfect child; the macho male; the brainless bimbo.
6. It reaches into the home and targets children and young people who may not judge it critically.
7. It can be misleading and often exaggerates. Misleading advertisements are illegal.

# Control of advertising

Advertising is controlled in two ways:

## Legal controls

- The **Consumer Information Act** makes it an offence to make false or misleading claims about goods and services. The advertiser must be able to prove the truth of any claims made, e.g. that a brand of spread lowers cholesterol.
- The **Employment Equality Act** makes it illegal for advertisements to discriminate on grounds of sex or marital status.

## Voluntary controls

The **Advertising Standards Authority for Ireland** promotes high standards of advertising in the Irish media. It demands that advertisements should be legal, decent, honest and truthful.

## Advertising is a powerful medium

In spite of legal and voluntary controls on advertising, clever advertising can still break down our defences and persuade us to buy. The main aim of advertising is to sell. It is up to each consumer to be wise to the tricks of the trade – the persuasive voices, the eye-catching images. The consumer must be vigilant, separating the truths about products from the false claims and fantasies. Pressure and persuasion must be balanced with realism and common sense.

**ACTIVITY**

1. What current TV advertisement appeals to you most, and why? Would it persuade you to buy the product? Why, or why not?

2. Devise a print advertisement and a TV advertisement for a new health food snack.

3. Describe a product you bought because of advertising. Did it live up to your expectations?

4. Which medium (TV, radio, magazine, etc.) do you think best suits an advertisement for: (a) a hairdresser; (b) a headache remedy; (c) a tax payment reminder; (d) a sports fixture? Discuss.

## Marketing

Like advertising, the main aim of marketing is to sell goods. Market research involves gathering information about consumers to find out what they like, e.g. their favourite foods, TV programmes and so on. This is done by conducting house-to-house surveys, phone interviews, questionnaires, etc. The information collected is used to persuade us to buy the product.

## Examples of marketing techniques

* Unsolicited mail, such as leaflets.
* Competitions.
* Sponsorship of large events, e.g. Guinness hurling championship.

- Logos, e.g. McDonald's yellow arches or Audi's four rings.
- Special offers, free samples, free gifts.
- Presentations in shops and shop windows.
- Website marketing.
- Email marketing.
- In-store promotions, such as food tasting.
- High-pressure sales talk.
- Product placement – placing the product in TV programmes, shops and public places.
- Merchandising: spin-offs from popular films, pop tours or sports teams.

**ACTIVITY**

1. Compare the advertisements in a sports magazine and a fashion magazine such as *Image*.
2. Collect six print advertisements and comment on each.
   - What target audience is each aimed at?
   - Are the advertisements effective?
   - Is the brand name catchy?
   - Is it suitable for the product?
   - Does it give any real information about the product?
   - Is the language clever, suitable, manipulative?
   - Are stereotypes or unrealistic lifestyles portrayed?

**REVISION QUESTIONS**

1. Name three functions of advertising.
2. List six advertising outlets near your school.
3. List four disadvantages and three advantages of advertising.
4. Name four different techniques used by the advertiser to sell products.
5. Name a legal and a voluntary control on advertising.
6. Define marketing. Give two examples of marketing.
7. What are the features of effective advertising?

*Test Yourself*
eTest.ie

# Part 3

Social
and
Health
Studies

# Chapter 26 Good Health

Good health is more than an absence of illness. It is a positive feeling of being well and fit. The health of babies and children is the responsibility of their parents. As young people grow towards maturity, they must take responsibility for their own health by developing a healthy lifestyle.

## Steps to good health

Nutrition,
Chapter 2

1. Eat a healthy diet.
2. Take exercise.
3. Get enough rest and relaxation.
4. Take precautions against illness.
5. Develop a positive attitude to life.
6. Maintain good personal hygiene (see Chapter 27).
7. Avoid unhealthy habits (see Chapter 34).

### 1 Healthy diet

Nutrition was discussed in Chapter 2. Make sure that you keep to a balanced diet and follow the healthy eating guidelines.

### 2 Exercise

People in the past led much more active lives than we do today. Work was more physical, whether on the farm, in the factory or in the home – this kept people trim and fit. Today people lead more sedentary lifestyles. They travel mostly by bus and car, and walk less. Teenagers often give up sport when they leave school, spend a lot of time online or watching TV and become overweight and unfit. What is the answer? EXERCISE!

## 3 Social and Health Studies

## Advantages of exercise

- Exercise helps your body to look good and work efficiently.
- It improves muscle tone so the body looks more trim.
- It keeps the body supple (less stiff).
- Your heart, lungs and circulation work more efficiently.
- It helps keep weight down.
- It reduces stress and gives a feeling of well-being.
- It keeps the body youthful, and delays problems of old age such as heart disease and osteoporosis.

**Aerobic exercise** makes your heart and lungs work harder so that you breathe more quickly. This helps prevent high blood pressure and heart disease.

## Posture

Good posture means standing or sitting straight, with your head high, shoulders back and tummy and bottom tucked in. Slouching and bad posture cause back problems and, as the lungs have less room to expand, breathing suffers. Clothes hang better when posture is good.

Good posture and fitness are improved by sport, aerobic exercise and dancing.

## ACTIVITY

1. Name four forms of exercise which would fit into your lifestyle.
2. Name four forms of aerobic exercise.

## 3 Rest and relaxation

Rest and sleep restore energy and relax the mind. Lack of sleep makes us tired and irritable and we find it hard to concentrate. If you have a late night, make up for it the following night by going to bed earlier.

The amount of sleep needed varies from person to person – the average is 8 hours per night.

## Advantages of rest and sleep

- They give us more energy.
- We look and feel better.
- Concentration improves.

**Insomnia** (difficulty sleeping) is usually caused by anxiety and stress. Unfortunately, sleeplessness causes more stress, so the problem gets worse. Physical exercise helps relax the body and helps us sleep. Avoid mental activity such as study for one hour before bedtime. Avoid heavy meals or stimulating drinks such as coffee or tea in the late evening. Avoid sleeping pills; most are habit-forming.

## Leisure

Leisure is the time we have away from work, school or study. Leisure time is important as it helps reduce tension and stress. Leisure time can be used for exercise or for rest and relaxation. It can also be used to enjoy the things we are interested in, e.g. sport, hobbies such as photography, films or music.

 Use your leisure wisely and don't waste it.

Relaxation doesn't mean sitting in front of the TV every night. That makes you overweight, unhealthy and unfit.

Don't say you are bored, and depend on others to keep you occupied. Get up and try something interesting yourself.

Use your leisure time to:

- **get fit**, enjoy sport or other active hobbies
- **keep your brain active**, through reading, puzzles or learning something new, such as a language
- **do something useful**, e.g. clear out stuff that you haven't used in a long time
- **visit places of interest** – museums, historic sights or buildings, art galleries
- **help someone** who needs it.

**ACTIVITY**

1. What type of leisure activity is suitable for someone who works in an office all day? Why? Name three such activities.
2. What forms of leisure would suit someone with a very active job?
3. Name three places in your locality where leisure activities are available.
4. Name three places of interest you could visit in your leisure time.

## 4 Precautions against illness

It is obviously wise to take whatever steps are possible to avoid illness. This is known as **preventative medicine**. The steps to good health we are discussing are the main precautions against illness, but there are others, including the following.

- **Immunisation or vaccination** (see below). The HSE provides free vaccination to babies and children against serious diseases such as TB, diphtheria, whooping cough, measles, mumps, meningitis and polio. Older girls are vaccinated against rubella (German measles). You may also need to be vaccinated against tetanus if you get a deep cut, or against tropical diseases if you are going abroad. Immunisation produces immunity or resistance to disease by stimulating the production of antibodies (blood chemicals which destroy bacteria). Some immunisations require a periodic top-up of antibodies, known as a booster.

- **Health and developmental checks** for children are provided in health centres and primary schools and by public health nurses.

- **Health checks for adults.** It is up to each adult to visit the doctor if they feel unwell. It is also wise for adults to self-examine breasts and testes for lumps, to have occasional cholesterol tests, and for women to have smear tests. As you get older, a complete health screening every 2–3 years is wise.

- **Take steps to avoid cancer.** Don't smoke. If you do, give it up. Only drink alcohol in moderation. Avoid over-exposure to sunlight. Eat plenty of fruit and vegetables. Avoid stress.

## 5 Mental health

Mental health is concerned with the mind and how we think and feel.

**Attitude and self-esteem.** Our attitude is how we think and feel about what goes on around us. People with high self-esteem have a positive attitude to life; they look on the bright side and are usually happy and contented. People with low self-esteem think they are not worth much. They have a negative attitude, concentrate on the bad things in life and are usually critical and gloomy. Our upbringing has a lot to do with whether we have high or low self-esteem.

**ACTIVITY** Write down the opposite to these negative attitudes: mean; proud; hostile; jealous; intolerant; unfair; critical; depressed; spiteful; selfish; insensitive; cruel; dishonest; lying; possessive.

**People who are mentally well:**

- have high self-esteem – they like themselves and feel happy with themselves
- feel comfortable with other people
- can cope with the demands of life
- can cope with their emotions
- live in the present, not in the past or in the future (this avoids guilt or worry).

## Emotions

Three of the most basic emotions are:

- love
- fear
- anger.

Name some other emotions.

### Love

Everyone wants to be loved. Being loved makes us feel secure and happy. The most important person to love is yourself. This is not being selfish. Once we love ourselves we then feel good enough to be able to love others. People who abuse alcohol and take drugs are unhappy people who do not love themselves. They have low self-esteem.

### Fear

Fear is an important emotion which can help keep us safe and away from danger, e.g. when walking through a park late at night.

### Anger

Anger is a perfectly normal emotion. It is often justified. How we deal with our anger shows whether or not we are emotionally mature. Young children have not learned to deal with their anger – they may kick and scream when they do not get their own way. It is unacceptable for adults to behave like that, e.g. by using violence or abusive language. If you are angry, say so and give the reason. Then deal with it as for conflict (see page 276).

## Stress

Stress is a tense feeling that occurs when too many demands are being made on us. A little stress can be useful – it can make us work for exams or hurry to meet deadlines at work. But too much stress can damage the body, causing ulcers, high blood pressure and heart disease.

Things to do to reduce stress:

- reduce your workload
- learn to relax, take time out, etc.
- learn meditation and similar techniques
- get a massage
- take some physical exercise
- get plenty of rest and sleep
- listen to music
- take a bath
- get some fresh air
- discuss problems with a sympathetic person.

 **ACTIVITY**

List some sources of stress in the lives of adolescents. Discuss.

**REVISION QUESTIONS**

1. Describe two situations which may cause a teenager to experience stress. Suggest three ways of dealing with stress.
2. List five steps to good health.
3. List four advantages of exercise.
4. Explain immunisation.
5. List three characteristics of good mental health.
6. Give three reasons why leisure is important.
7. What is aerobic exercise? Give two examples.
8. Explain what is meant by mental health and list some factors that contribute to good mental health.

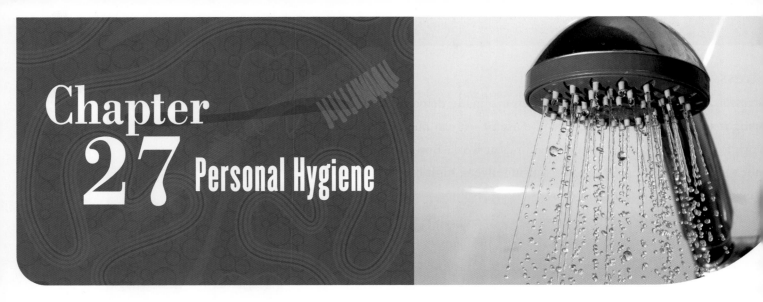

# Chapter 27 Personal Hygiene

## Excretory organs

It is essential for the health of the body that waste matter is removed. Organs that remove waste are called excretory organs. They include:

- the **lungs** – these remove carbon dioxide and water vapour
- the **kidneys** – unwanted substances and water are excreted as urine
- the **large intestine** – removes waste solids remaining after digestion
- the **skin** – removes water and small amounts of other waste, e.g. salt.

## The skin

The skin is the body's largest organ (about two square metres) and is a flexible waterproof layer which covers the whole body. It keeps all our internal parts inside our bodies.

It varies in thickness in different parts of the body; for example, it is thickest on the soles of the feet. It is made up of two layers:

- the **epidermis** on the outside
- the **dermis** on the inside.

The surface of the epidermis is made up of flat, dead cells. These wear away like dust and are constantly being replaced by new cells growing up from beneath. Approximately every month our skin's surface is replaced. You can see this new skin, for example, on a healing burn.

Deep in the epidermis lies the **malpighian layer**. This contains pigment called **melanin**, which determines the colour of the skin and also helps protect the skin from the damaging rays of the sun. The more melanin you have in your skin, the more protected you are and the darker your skin. Therefore those people who live in hotter countries have darker skin. Our climate isn't hot, so Irish people traditionally have fair skin.

❖ *The skin*

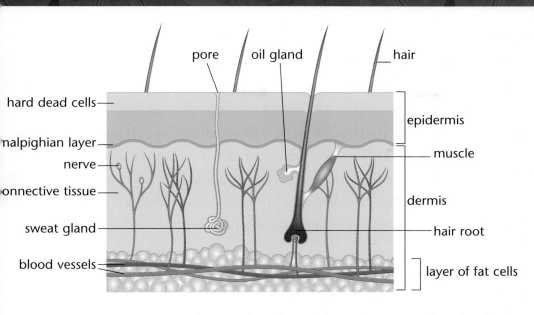

Sunbathing causes more melanin to be released for protection and so the skin darkens, causing a tan.

The dermis is underneath the epidermis, so we can't see it. It contains:

- **blood vessels** – help control body temperature and bring nutrients to the skin
- **nerves** – with which we sense touch and feel heat, cold, pain and pressure
- **sweat glands** – remove waste and excess water from the blood
- **hairs** – grow up from the hair follicles and are found everywhere except the lips, soles of the feet and palms of the hands
- **oil glands** attached to hairs – lubricate the skin and keep the hair in good condition
- **fat cells** beneath the dermis – act as an energy reserve and help us keep warm.

## Functions of the skin

1. **Protects the body** from micro-organisms in the air and from the harmful rays of the sun.
2. **Prevents loss of body fluids** – without skin our body would dry up.
3. **Touch** – the nerve endings near the surface of the skin are sensitive to sensations of heat, cold, pain and touch.
4. **Removes waste** – excess water and salt are removed from the blood and pass out through the pores as sweat.
5. **Temperature control** – by closing or opening surface blood vessels, the skin keeps body heat in when we are cold and releases it when we are warm. Sweating also cools us when we are hot. A layer of fat underneath the skin also insulates.
6. **Vitamin D** is made by the skin from sunlight. This is good for bones and teeth.
7. The skin's fatty layer acts as a **cushion** to protect us from bangs, knocks and tears.

## Skin hygiene

Sweat takes water, salt and other impurities from the blood. The sweat glands release a constant stream of sweat through the pores (about 1 litre a day). This dries on the surface of the skin and, together with the oil from the oil glands and bacteria from the air, forms a sticky layer which needs to be washed off regularly. If not, it would smell, causing body odour (BO). Sometimes the dead cells from the epidermis get trapped with the dried sweat and block the pores, causing blackheads. They may get infected, resulting in pimples. During adolescence hormones cause glands to become more active, increasing the likelihood of BO and skin problems.

## To keep the skin clean

1. **Wash hands frequently**, particularly after using the lavatory and before handling food – dirty hands can lead to skin infections.
2. **Wash the whole body daily**, e.g. in the shower, using warm water and gentle soap or shower gel to remove bacteria, dirt and grease. It is a good idea to use a mild face cleanser for the face twice a day. Remove any make-up before going to sleep.
3. Pay particular attention to **underarms** and the **genital area**. Underarm hair traps perspiration. It is easier to prevent BO if it is removed using a razor or a hair removal cream. Girls should pay particular attention to personal hygiene during menstruation.
4. **Deodorants** help prevent unpleasant smells. **Anti-perspirants** are more efficient because they seal off the underarm area, preventing perspiration.
5. **Shower after strenuous activity**, e.g. games.
6. **Change underclothes and socks** daily and wash outer clothes regularly. Why do you think it is best to wear cotton next to the skin?
7. **Don't squeeze pimples** – this can make the problem worse and push the infected material further into the skin.

## Skin problems

Some people have oil glands that produce little oil. These people have dry skin and hair. They need to use suitable creams and shampoos.

Other people have oil glands that are very active, and they have oily skin and hair. People with oily skin are more prone to blackheads and pimples. They need to be very particular about skin hygiene.

**Acne** is a skin condition that is fairly common during adolescence and normally peaks at the age of 18. It is caused by a number of factors, including too much sebum and hormone changes at puberty. It causes severe spots that are easily infected and can be mild, moderate or severe. In severe cases scarring can occur. Someone who has acne often feels embarrassed when out socially, even though the condition is not their fault. It can be treated with prescription medication (creams, gels or lotions) or through antibiotics.

Follow these guidelines for coping with acne and teenage skin problems.

1. Keep skin absolutely clean. Wash face frequently, using medicated soap. Avoid facecloths. (Why?)
2. Rinse well with cold water.
3. Spots contain bacteria. Never touch, scratch or squeeze them – this spreads the infection.
4. Avoid greasy and junk foods. Eat lots of fibre, fruit and vegetables.
5. Drink lots of water – eight glasses a day.
6. Avoid greasy creams, etc. Use recommended medicated lotions and apply with clean cotton wool.
7. Consult a doctor, if the problem is severe.

## Skin cancer

Too much exposure to the sun causes leathery, wrinkled skin. It also causes certain types of skin cancer. Damage to the ozone layer in recent years has caused an increase in skin cancer. The type of skin you have, the amount of sunbathing you do and the use of sunbeds are also factors.

- Protect children from the sun, as most damage is caused in childhood.
- Cover up if you regularly work out of doors.
- Wear a hat with a protective brim.
- Wear a high protection factor sun screen. Apply total sunblock to children.
- Stay out of the sun during the hottest part of the day, i.e. between 11 a.m. and 3 p.m.
- Wear sunglasses to protect your eyes.

## Hair

A hair begins as a hair papilla or root, deep in the dermis. As it grows outwards it is lubricated by an oil gland attached to the hair shaft. To keep hair in good condition:

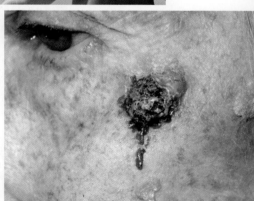

❖ *Skin cancer*

1. Wash at least once a week using suitable shampoo for your type of hair; rinse well to avoid dandruff.
2. Apply conditioner if it is needed, comb through and rinse off.
3. Wrap in a towel to absorb moisture, then comb through. Avoid rough handling.
4. Dry naturally or use a hairdryer to style the hair. Avoid using hairdryers at high settings or too close to the hair.

5  Have hair trimmed regularly.

6  Wash hair, brush and comb regularly.

## Care of hands

1  Wash frequently, using a nailbrush for nails.

2  Dry well, particularly if going out of doors.

3  Use rubber gloves when washing up, doing housework or doing dirty work such as gardening.

4  Keep nails clean and manicured.

5  Use hand cream regularly to prevent chapping.

## Care of feet

1  Wash daily and dry thoroughly, particularly between toes.

2  Have a pedicure regularly; cut toenails straight across to prevent ingrowing.

3  Change socks or tights daily.

4  Wear shoes that are well designed to support the feet. They should be comfortable and give feet room to grow. Some fashion shoes, e.g. high heels, are bad for the feet, causing corns and bunions.

5  Guard against verrucas by wearing protective shoes in swimming pools. (What are verrucas?)

**ACTIVITY**

1. Find out how nails should be manicured, and write in points into your copy.
2. Describe the difference between a corn and a bunion. What do you think is the cause of each?
3. Make a list of guidelines for using swimming pools.

**REVISION QUESTIONS**

1. What is an excretory organ? Name three excretory organs.
2. Describe the function of (a) sweat glands, (b) oil glands.
3. List four other functions of the skin.
4. How does the skin protect us from the sun?
5. List five guidelines for skin hygiene.
6. List four guidelines for healthy skin.
7. List three guidelines for preventing skin cancer.
8. Suggest four guidelines that teenagers should follow to help prevent spots spreading.
9. What is acne and how is it treated?

*Test Yourself*
eTest.ie

# Chapter 28 The Teeth

Our first teeth, which begin growing in the first few months of life, are called **temporary** or **milk teeth** and there are 20 of them. These start falling out around the age of seven and are replaced by **permanent teeth**. By puberty we should have all but the final four, the wisdom teeth, which come within the next few years, usually at 15–25 years of age.

The average adult has 32 teeth, which are grouped according to the job they do.

a) **Incisors** (biting teeth).
b) **Canines** (fang-like teeth for tearing food).
c) **Premolars** – flat-topped grinding teeth.
d) **Molars** – large grinding teeth.

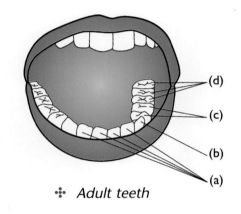

❖ *Adult teeth*

## Structure of a tooth

A tooth consists of two main parts: (a) the **crown** (the part visible in the mouth); (b) the **root**, which is embedded in the gum.

The main part of the tooth is made of **dentine**. The crown is covered with an extremely hard substance called **enamel**, which protects it. In the centre of the tooth is a space called the **pulp cavity**; this contains a nerve and blood vessels which nourish the tooth. The tooth is held in place in the jaw and gum by **cement** and **fibres**.

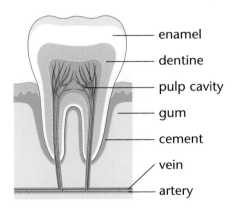

enamel
dentine
pulp cavity
gum
cement
vein
artery

❖ *The structure of a tooth*

## Tooth decay and gum disease

Tooth decay is caused by **plaque**, which forms a sticky film on the teeth between washing. Plaque consists of bacteria and acid formed by the breakdown of food (particularly sugar) in the mouth. Plaque eats away the enamel on the teeth until it reaches the softer dentine, which decays

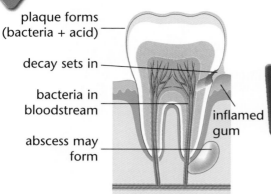

plaque forms (bacteria + acid)

decay sets in

bacteria in bloodstream

abscess may form

inflamed gum

❖ *A cavity forming in a tooth*

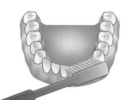

1. Brush from gum to edge of teeth (front)

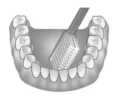

2. Brush back of teeth

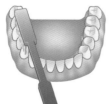

3. Brush grinding surfaces of teeth

very quickly. Toothache occurs when the decay reaches the nerves in the pulp cavity.

 **ACTIVITY**  Failure to look after your teeth leads to bad breath, tooth decay and gum disease.

## Caring for your teeth

1. Eat calcium-rich foods such as milk and cheese and healthy foods such as raw, crunchy vegetables.
2. Avoid plaque-producing foods, e.g. sugary and acid foods. If you do eat these, wash teeth immediately afterwards.
3. Avoid eating between meals.
4. Brush teeth after each meal, or at least every morning after breakfast and last thing at night with a fluoride toothpaste. An electric toothbrush is excellent for older children and adults.
5. Use a good-quality toothbrush and replace it every three months.
6. Clean between teeth with dental floss.
7. Never abuse your teeth, e.g. by using them for opening bottles or by using metal objects to pick your teeth.
8. Use mouthwash where appropriate.
9. Have a check-up at the dentist every six months.
10. Visit a hygienist when necessary for cleaning and polishing.

## Brushing

It is essential to brush your teeth correctly. Do not brush roughly up and down. Hold the brush at the gums and brush from gum to edge of teeth. This is slower but more efficient. Brush the front, the back and the grinding surfaces, and lastly gently massage the gums with a circular motion to stimulate circulation. Rinse mouth well and use a reliable mouthwash if wished. Use dental floss daily before washing.

## Fluoride

This is a mineral found naturally in the water in certain areas and added to drinking water by local authorities. It is known to have a strengthening effect on teeth as it fills minute cracks and cavities in teeth. Fluoride in toothpaste also prevents tooth decay.

**ACTIVITY**

1. Find out the advantages of having healthy teeth.
2. Obtain some disclosure tablets from your dentist. These show up plaque on teeth. Brush teeth well, then chew a tablet and examine them. Have you brushed thoroughly enough?

**REVISION QUESTIONS**

1. Name the four types of teeth in your mouth, giving the function of three.
2. Name the parts of the tooth.
3. List the four most important guidelines for caring for your teeth.
4. What is plaque? How can you avoid it?
5. What is the purpose of fluoride?
6. What are the benefits of using (a) antiseptic mouthwash and (b) dental floss?

Test Yourself eTest.ie

# Chapter 29 The Circulatory System

**The circulatory system consists of the heart, the blood vessels and the blood.** The blood transports oxygen and nutrients and helps collect and remove waste.

**ACTIVITY**

Take your pulse: place your first two fingers on the inside of the wrist below the thumb. Move them until you feel a regular throb – this is the pulse. Count the beats per minute.

## The heart

The heart is a strong muscular organ which acts as a pump for the blood. It lies in the centre of the chest cavity between the lungs. It consists of four chambers – two atria at the top and two ventricles beneath. The walls of the ventricles are much thicker and stronger than those of the atria. The heart contains several valves, which make sure the blood flows in one direction only.

❖ *Structure of the heart, showing blood flow*

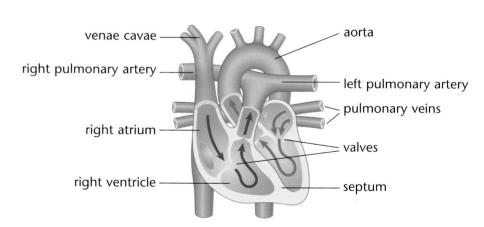

venae cavae

aorta

right pulmonary artery

left pulmonary artery

pulmonary veins

right atrium

valves

right ventricle

septum

# Blood flow through the heart

**1** Impure blood, high in $CO_2$, is collected from all around the body and flows **through the superior and inferior venae cavae** into the **right atrium** of the heart. This contracts, and the blood passes through a valve into –

**2** The **right ventricle**. This contracts and the blood passes through a valve into the **pulmonary artery**, which brings it to the lungs.
**In the lungs carbon dioxide is removed and replaced by oxygen.**

**3** The 'pure', oxygen-rich blood returns to the heart through the four **pulmonary veins**, entering the **left atrium**. This contracts, forcing the blood through a valve into –

**4** The **left ventricle**. This contracts, forcing the blood through a valve into the **aorta**, the largest blood vessel in the body, from where it brings oxygen-rich blood to every part of the body.
It releases its oxygen to the cells and collects carbon dioxide, then returns to the venae cavae where the whole journey begins again.

The **heartbeat** consists of the two atria contracting together, then the two ventricles, followed by a pause. Each heartbeat causes a surge of blood in the arteries which can be felt as a pulse – average 72 beats a minute.

# Blood vessels

Blood vessels are hollow tubes which carry blood all around the body. There are three types of blood vessel:

* **Arteries** – thick-walled, elastic blood vessels which carry pure oxygen-rich blood **away from the heart**.
* **Veins** – thinner, more collapsible blood vessels which carry blood (usually impure) **towards the heart**. Veins have valves which help prevent blood from flowing backwards on its journey back to the heart.
* **Capillaries** – tiny, thin-walled vessels which connect arteries with veins. As they are only one cell thick, materials such as oxygen and nutrients can pass easily in and out through their walls.

# The blood

The average adult has about 5 litres of blood.

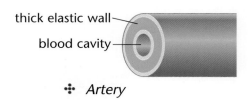

thick elastic wall
blood cavity

❖ *Artery*

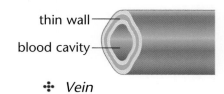

thin wall
blood cavity

❖ *Vein*

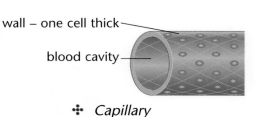

wall – one cell thick
blood cavity

❖ *Capillary*

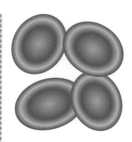

❖ *Red blood cells*

❖ *White blood cells*

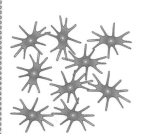

❖ *Platelets*

## Composition of blood

- **Plasma** is a liquid which contains **red cells**, **white cells** and **platelets**.
- Plasma also carries nutrients, carbon dioxide and hormones.
- **Red cells** are like tiny discs. They contain the red pigment **haemoglobin**, which picks up oxygen in the lungs and carries it around the body to every cell. Iron is necessary to make haemoglobin.
- **White cells** are larger than red cells. They attack dangerous substances, such as bacteria, that enter the body, surrounding and destroying them.
- **Platelets** are very small cells whose job is to clot the blood when we get a cut. This hardens to form a scab which protects the wound until it is healed.

## Functions of the blood

1. It transports nutrients, oxygen, carbon dioxide and other waste materials.
2. White cells fight infection.
3. Platelets help blood to clot.
4. It distributes heat through the body.
5. It transports hormones and enzymes.

**REVISION QUESTIONS**

1. Name the four chambers of the heart, and explain the heart's structure.
2. Name three types of blood vessel. Explain the function of each.
3. What is the function of haemoglobin? _____ is necessary for the manufacture of haemoglobin.
4. Name four functions of the blood.
5. Explain the difference between pure and impure blood.

*Test Yourself*
eTest.ie

# Chapter 30 The Respiratory System

Take a deep breath. Air is now passing through a series of passages to your lungs. Together, these are known as the **respiratory tract**.

The purpose of the respiratory system is to take in oxygen from the air, distribute it to all the body cells, then collect the waste gas carbon dioxide and remove it from the body.

## The respiratory tract

1. The **nose** and **mouth**. Air is warmed and filtered as it passes through.

2. The **pharynx** is the wide space at the back of the mouth. At the base of the pharynx is a little 'lid' of muscle, the **epiglottis**, which closes over the windpipe when we swallow so that food doesn't go down the wrong way.

3. The **larynx** or voice box is at the top of the trachea. The vocal cords are stretched across it, and vibrate as air passes through them when we speak or sing.

4. The **trachea** or windpipe is a tube lying in front of the oesophagus or gullet. It is kept open by C-shaped rings of cartilage. It is lined with tiny hairs which trap any dust and bacteria we breathe in and pass them back upwards away from the lungs, which they might irritate.

5. **Bronchi.** The trachea divides into two branches, one bronchus going to each lung. These subdivide and get smaller as the pass further into the lung (**bronchioles**), and end in tiny bundles of **alveoli** or **air cells** (see diagram).

6. The **lungs**
   *Position.* The lungs are like two large purple sponges filling up most of the chest cavity. They rest on a sheet of muscle, the **diaphragm**, with the heart between them. They are protected by the sternum (breast bone) in front, the rib cage, and the backbone behind. *Composition.* Bronchioles, air cells (alveoli), blood vessels, elastic tissue.

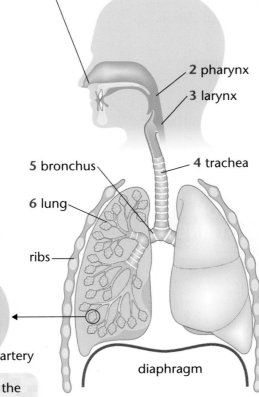

1 nose and mouth
2 pharynx
3 larynx
5 bronchus
4 trachea
6 lung
ribs
diaphragm

❖ *The respiratory system*

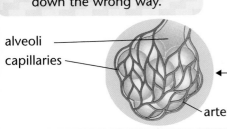

alveoli
capillaries
artery

263

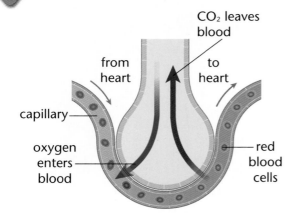

CO₂ leaves blood

from heart

to heart

capillary

oxygen enters blood

red blood cells

❖ *Exchange of gases*

## Exchange of gases

Surrounding the air cells are numerous tiny blood capillaries. When we breathe in, air rich in oxygen passes down the air passages until it reaches the air cells. Here the oxygen passes into the blood vessels and carbon dioxide is removed. Oxygen travels around the body to every cell, where it is used to oxidise (burn) our food to create energy. When food is burned, a waste gas (carbon dioxide – $CO_2$) is produced, which must be removed as it is poisonous. The blood brings the $CO_2$ back to the lungs, from where we breathe it out.

## Functions of the lungs

**1** They take in oxygen.

**2** They remove carbon dioxide.

**3** They release small amounts of water as water vapour.

The carbon dioxide we breathe out is a poisonous gas. It must be removed from rooms and buildings by ventilation.

### Respiratory diseases

- Bronchitis
- Influenza (flu)
- Pneumonia
- Laryngitis

- Tuberculosis
- Emphysema
- Lung cancer

**REVISION QUESTIONS**

1. Name the organs of the respiratory tract.
2. What is the epiglottis?
3. Describe the position of the lungs in the body.
4. Name the gases that are exchanged in the lungs.
5. What is the function of the lungs?
6. What is the function of the larynx?
7. Name two diseases of the respiratory system.

*Test Yourself* eTest.ie

# Chapter 31 The Family

Most people grow up in a family.

A family is a group of people who are related by blood, marriage or adoption. They usually share the same name and home and have close relationships.

## Types of family

There are two main types of family.

**1** The **nuclear family** (from the word 'nucleus', meaning centre or core) is the basic family unit. It usually consists of a father, mother and one or more children, or it may consist of a single parent and children. The single parent may be unmarried, separated, divorced or widowed. The nuclear family is the traditional family in the industrialised world.

**2** The **extended family** is the wider family – the nuclear family plus all the other relations (grandparents, uncles, aunts and cousins). In the past, the extended family often lived together. This is still the case in many cultures today. In Ireland, our extended family may live nearby or they may be spread out over the country. How often do you see your extended family?

## Divorce

Divorce has been legal in Ireland since 1996, which means that there are now new types of family. Divorced parents who remarry will be bringing a stepfather/mother into the home as well as stepbrothers/sisters. This is often called a **blended family**.

In many cases this works out without any difficulty, but in some cases it takes more time to adjust.

The children of divorced parents will have time with both parents and living arrangements decided by themselves or by the courts.

## Functions of the family

A good family provides us with our needs.

1. **Physical needs**
   - food
   - clothing
   - warmth and shelter – somewhere to live, to feel at home
   - protection. Our parents should protect us from danger and look after us when we are ill.

2. **Emotional needs** such as love, support and security. It should be a place where we feel safe. The family is the best setting for bringing children into the world. It provides a secure place to bring up young children and it is where they learn social skills (how to fit into society).

3. **Economic needs.** This means that family members share their possessions and support each other financially. In a farm or business, they may all contribute to the work.

### Rights of a child

- Love and security
- Care and understanding
- Healthy environment
- Freedom from neglect and cruelty
- Freedom from abuse
- Access to education

## Parenthood

Being a parent is a very responsible task. When a man and a woman bring a child into the world, it is the duty of both parents to provide their family with its needs. Single-parent families are most commonly headed by mothers who are left to bring up children on their own. If a parent cannot cope, the state can provide help through the social services.

Becoming a parent doesn't automatically make a person a good parent. Parenting is a skill that has to be learned, like any other. In the past, when young people got married they usually moved in with one set of parents, who taught them parenting skills. Today young parents must learn parenting from research and in the process of caring for their infant.

**ACTIVITY**

1. Describe what you mean by a happy family. Does it mean that all members can do what they like? Discuss.
2. List four ways in which families have changed in the past century.
3. List some skills needed by parents.

## Influences on family life

No two families are alike. Families can be happy or unhappy, rich or poor, employed or unemployed, law-abiding or in trouble with the law. How does a family end up the way it is? There is a huge range of influences on the family, which can help it survive or make things difficult for it.

1. **Social factors** – size of family, background, education, problems such as marriage breakdown or alcoholism.
2. **Economic factors** – whether they are employed and have enough money or have to depend on state support.
3. **Cultural factors** – tradition, rural/urban, social group, influence of religion, influence of media.

Problems such as unemployment, shortage of money or bad health are easier to deal with if the responsibility is shared. Problems in families, such as violence and alcoholism, often pass on from one generation to the next because they are ignored and not dealt with.

## Relationships and roles

Relationships exist between family members and people who are in close contact with one another. In a good relationship we get along and communicate with the other person. Learning how to cope with relationships within the family gives us practice in our relationships with others.

Family relationships include those between:

1. husbands and wives
2. parents and children
3. siblings (brothers and sisters in the same family)
4. grandparents and grandchildren.

## Communication

One of the most important skills in any relationship is the ability to communicate. Communication may be verbal (talking) or non-verbal (ways of showing how you feel without words, e.g. facial expressions, eye contact). When there is no communication, there is no relationship. To communicate well, the message you send must be clear.

- Look the person in the eye.
- Speak clearly.
- Listen attentively.

### Listening

Listening is an important part of communication. If no one listens to you when you talk, there is no communication. Sometimes when the other person is impossible to communicate with, we say, 'It's like talking to the wall.'

Good listening requires effort. A good listener encourages further communication by reacting to show that he or she is listening, e.g. nodding, smiling. A bad listener or a rude person can shut off communication with a word, look or gesture.

1. Describe four ways in which you could show feelings without talking. Do you think each is satisfactory? Split into pairs. Without speaking, communicate four different emotions – let the other person guess what they are.
2. Discuss the habit of 'not speaking' when you are angry with someone. Do you think that this is a good idea? Would the communication be more honest and more clear if you said what you felt instead? List the advantages and disadvantages of both alternatives.

## Roles

A role is the way we are expected to behave because of what we are. In a family, people behave in a certain way according to their position in the family.

### Parents' roles

In the past, mothers and fathers had very separate roles. The father was the 'boss': he was the breadwinner, made the important decisions and was in charge of discipline. He had little to do with the everyday running of the home or the care of children. That was the mother's role.

Today the roles of mother and father are much less clear-cut, and there is greater equality. They are both involved in decision-making and child rearing. The mother may go out to work too and the father is usually more involved in the home life of his family.

## Parents' responsibilities

Parents are expected to behave in a responsible way. They should provide for their family's needs, both physical and emotional, and show a good example to their children.

## Children's roles

Children are expected to behave as children, e.g. to learn, to have fun. They have few responsibilities except to keep to the family 'rules'. These might include doing some household tasks, going to school and doing their homework. Children's roles have also changed. In the past they were expected to be 'seen and not heard'. Today this is not considered to be healthy. They are encouraged to have an opinion. This is good for their self-esteem and self-confidence.

## Adolescents' roles

Adolescence is the period when the role of a child gradually changes to that of an adult. This causes many pressures on adolescents and their parents. There will be more about this later.

## Gender roles

Gender refers to being male or female. **Gender role or sex role is the way one is expected to behave because of one's gender.** We learn this behaviour from those around us – parents, teachers and society. Traditionally, males were expected to behave in one way (i.e. to be strong and brave – 'boys don't cry') and females in another (to be gentle and caring). Like most other roles in today's society, these are changing, and intelligent people can see that the 'traditional' male qualities (such as assertiveness and independence) and what are considered to be feminine qualities (such as sensitivity and caring) are found in both sexes.

A **stereotype** is a **fixed image of how a person or group of people behaves**. To stereotype people is to put them into rigid groups and expect them to behave in a certain way. The traditional gender roles mentioned above are a form of stereotyping.

Functions of the family, page 266

Other examples are:

- all teenagers drink
- all redheads have a bad temper
- all unemployed people are lazy.

Stereotyping is thoughtless and ignorant. It can lead to people being treated badly or discriminated against. It is often a cause of conflict and even war, e.g. the treatment of Jews in Nazi Germany.

## Gender equity

In the past, jobs were usually divided into those performed by males and those performed by females. Up to 1973, women who worked for the civil service had to give up work when they got married. Now people of both genders have an equal choice to do any job, and it is illegal to discriminate against anybody on grounds of gender, marital status or parenthood.

## Employment Equality Act 1998

This law set out areas under which people cannot be discriminated against. These are:

- gender
- marital status
- family status
- sexual orientation
- religious belief
- age
- race
- disability
- membership of the Travelling community.

**ACTIVITY**

1.  Pick one factor from each group of influences on family life (social, economic and cultural factors), and write a paragraph on how it affects family life.

2.  List four jobs that were traditionally performed by males and four traditionally performed by females. Can you think of any good reasons why this was the case?

3.  Can you think of any areas in Irish society where people are still discriminated against, (a) because of their gender, (b) for any other reason? Discuss.

4.  In your house, who does the following tasks: cooking; cleaning; washing; ironing; gardening; DIY; money decisions; decisions regarding children and discipline? Divide the page into two columns and fill in under the headings 'male' and 'female'. Decide whether yours is a traditional or a modern family.

5.  Discuss ways in which you have been treated differently because you are a male or a female – (a) at home, (b) at school, (c) in the community or (d) at work.

**REVISION QUESTIONS**

1.  What is (a) a nuclear family, (b) an extended family?
2.  Name the three main functions of the family.
3.  Name four rights of a child.
4.  Define 'role'.
5.  Define 'relationship'.
6.  What is a stereotype? Give two new examples.
7.  Explain gender equity.
8.  Give two examples each of physical and emotional needs.
9.  Outline some of the changes that have taken place in family life in recent years.

Test Yourself
eTest.ie

# Chapter 32 Adolescence

**Adolescence means the period of time of development between puberty and becoming an adult.**

## Myself as a resource

Everyone wonders occasionally – 'Who am I? What do I want from life? What have I got to offer?'

Each human being has a huge number of resources within himself or herself.

I have energy →

I have knowledge →

I have skills →

← I can give and receive love

← I can co-operate and be helpful

← I can communicate with others

List some examples of the knowledge and skills you have.

 To develop means to progress through a series of changes in a certain sequence.

## Growth and development

From the time we are born, we grow and develop physically, mentally, socially and emotionally. Each type of development is interlinked.

The rate at which children develop is influenced by:

- **heredity** – what has been passed on from parents
- **environment** – healthy surroundings; good family atmosphere (lots of love and encouragement); opportunities for social contact.

# 1 Physical development

Physical development means growth in height and weight, development of physical senses such as sight, and development of motor and manipulative skills such as walking and writing.

Physical development begins at the moment of conception. Cells reproduce to form tissues and organs, and by 28 weeks the baby is fully formed. Young children grow and develop rapidly. They gradually learn to use their muscles and begin to crawl, stand, walk and run.

In adolescence there is a growth spurt and sexual development begins.

# 2 Mental development

Mental or intellectual development is to do with the mind. You are born with a certain level of ability (heredity), and after that your environment (parents, teachers, school) has a large part to play in your mental development. Babies and children are naturally curious – they want to learn. This must be encouraged by those who deal with them or their desire to learn will be lost. Mental development continues throughout life.

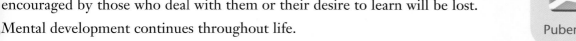

Puberty, page 278

# 3 Emotional development

This involves learning how to handle feelings and emotions. In order to develop emotionally you need to love yourself and feel secure in yourself. This is called self-esteem. When you have good self-esteem you accept yourself and don't put yourself down. You think 'I'm OK'.

A person is more likely to have good self-esteem if they grew up in a secure, loving family and were well treated by others. A person who was physically, mentally or sexually abused or who was bullied at school is unlikely to have much self-esteem. That is not to say that we cannot develop self-esteem later through self-analysis, loving relationships, reading and counselling, if necessary.

A person who is emotionally mature
- feels secure and self-confident
- is accepted by those around them
- is able to cope with their emotions, such as love, fear and anger. For example, they don't fly off the handle at the slightest provocation or go into 'not speaking' moods.

Mental health, page 249

Love, page 250

### Personality

Your personality is a mirror of your emotional development. It determines how you react to life in behaviour and feelings.

Personality and emotional development are shaped by:

**1** **heredity** – what you inherit from your parents, e.g. your mother's fiery temperament or calm, easy-going attitude to life

**2** **environment** – your home life. This may be happy, positive and encouraging or full of problems, quarrelling and negative put-downs. Parents act as role models for their children, so children often turn out just like them.

## 4 Social development

This means **how you learn to get on with (relate to) other people**. It teaches you how to behave in a socially acceptable manner, e.g. have good manners, treat others well. Social development begins within the family, then gradually widens to include friends and the wider community at school and work. During adolescence, the peer group has a great influence on social development.

### Peer group

**Your peer group is the people of your own age with whom you share the same interests**.

The influence of the family lessens as young people become more independent. In the peer group they have a sense of belonging. They feel at ease with people of the same age, who are less critical, who understand them and accept them for what they are.

**Peer pressure**
**This is when peers expect others to behave as they do**, to keep up with the crowd, e.g. to dress a certain way. Vulnerable people feel they won't be liked if they don't conform. Peer pressure can result in bullying.

**ACTIVITY**

Your peer group can have a good or a bad influence on your life and your behaviour. Give three examples of each.

# 5 Moral development

**This means developing an awareness of what is right and wrong.**

Moral development is influenced by parental example, school, community, religion and the media. People are expected to behave in a way which fits in with society and does not hurt anyone or damage their property. This makes life easier for everyone. Moral development begins at home when your parents teach you that you must not do certain things and explain why, e.g. because it might hurt other people. It continues in school, where certain behaviour is unacceptable and there are rules for the good of everyone.

As children, you accepted the moral values that were taught to you. As you approach adulthood you should be deciding on a set of values by which you will live your life.

Adolescents often question the moral standards set by their parents and society, and this can cause upset and conflict.

## Values

**A value is an acceptable moral standard of a person or group.**

This standard is often guided by a set of religious principles, such as the ten commandments. Our values influence our behaviour, for example sexual behaviour. People with strong moral values will treat themselves and others with respect.

## Norms

**A norm is an acceptable way of behaving.**

| Acceptable behaviour | Unacceptable behaviour |
| --- | --- |
| Following rules | Painting graffiti on walls |
| Not using bad language | Littering the neighbourhood |
| Being gentle with children | Using bad language |
| Having good table manners | Vandalism |

Normal behaviour for children is to go to school and to be home at a reasonable hour. Adults have much more freedom to do what they like (within the law). Adolescents fall between the two, and this may create tension between them and their parents. The teenager may want to wear clothes that are different and listen to music that adults do not like. Parents think their teenager is too young for certain things, while the teenagers think they are old enough. This frequently causes conflict and needs to be handled with tact and sensitivity on both sides. Parents may use sanctions to try to control such situations.

## Case studies

Mary wants to go out with friends on Saturday. She is told she may go but she must be home by midnight. She arrives home at 1 a.m., and her parents ground her for the rest of the month.

John receives a weekly allowance on condition that he keeps his room tidy. His room is a mess, and his allowance is stopped for the week.

**ACTIVITY**  Discuss the cases above. Do you think the sanctions are fair? How would you deal with such situations? (See below.)

## Dealing with conflict

Conflict can be dealt with in several ways.

1. Discuss the issue calmly and negotiate at an early stage.
2. Refuse to discuss it.
3. Ignore it and hope that it will go away.
4. Become angry and aggressive, with lots of shouting, etc.

Which is best?

## Adolescence

### The changing role of the adolescent

Adolescence is a time of change. During this period young people have to leave the security of childhood, when they were totally dependent on others, and prepare for life as responsible adults.

They do this by:

- **achieving emotional independence** from parents – a more equal and mature relationship with parents, and other adults, should take the place of emotional dependence
- **learning to behave in a more socially responsible way**, e.g. not taking drugs
- **developing more mature relationships** with peers of both sexes, e.g. having strong friendships with members of the opposite sex without having a crush on them

- **adjusting to sexual changes**, and learning to accept their adult body
- **acquiring a set of values**
- **developing a sense of identity**
- **looking to the future** and deciding on a career
- **concentrating on their education** and passing exams
- **becoming economically/financially independent**, e.g. getting a job.

**ACTIVITY**

1. List some situations in which a teenager might behave in a socially irresponsible way (a) at home, (b) at school, (c) in the community, (d) at work.

2. Lowering of sexual standards is often blamed on the increasing influence of the media and the decreasing influence of family and religion. Discuss.

3. Describe the work of one organisation of your choice which offers support to teenagers.

## Influences on adolescents

Adolescents may be influenced by a wide range of people.

1. **Parents and family.**
2. **Peer group** – influence can be good or bad.
3. The **school** environment.
4. **Adults in the community**, e.g. social workers, youth leaders, employers.
5. The **media** – what they see on TV, online and in magazines. Advertising frequently targets adolescents.

Test Yourself
eTest.ie

**REVISION QUESTIONS**

1. Describe two positive and two negative ways in which adolescents can be influenced by their peers.

2. List any four stages of human development.

3. Outline factors that contribute to (a) positive self-esteem and (b) negative self-esteem.

4. What is meant by: (a) norm; (b) values; (c) morals?

5. What are the main causes of conflict between teenagers and their parents?

6. What are the main changes a teenager has to go through before becoming independent?

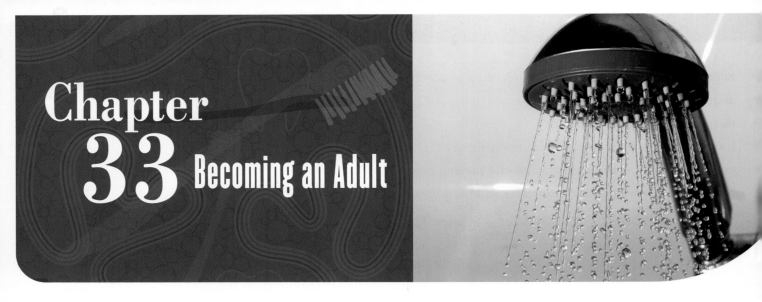

# Chapter 33 Becoming an Adult

Sexual maturity begins at **puberty**, when chemicals called **hormones** activate the sexual organs of boys and girls. These cause changes to take place which prepare the body for producing children. Hormones can also affect the emotions and cause mood swings.

Unlike a young child, whose development is gradual and slow, puberty brings rapid changes which can be difficult to handle. Adolescents may feel awkward at first, but they gradually become used to their new adult body and learn to accept it.

| Changes in girls | Changes in boys |
| --- | --- |
| (usually occur between 12 and 15 years) | (usually occur between 13 and 16 years) |
| Growth spurt (a rapid increase in height) | Growth spurt |
| Pubic hair begins to grow | Pubic and facial hair begin to grow |
| Hair grows under arms | Hair grows under arms |
| The breasts begin to develop | Penis and testes increase in size |
| Hips become more rounded | Larynx (voice box) enlarges and voice becomes deeper |
| Menstruation begins | Erections and ejaculation, which may occur at night as 'wet dreams' |
| Hormone changes may cause outbreaks of pimples, blackheads and acne | Hormone changes may cause outbreaks of pimples, blackheads and acne |

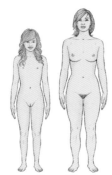

❖ *The main changes in girls during puberty*

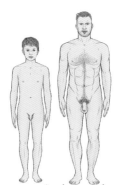

❖ *The main changes in boys during puberty*

# The female organs of reproduction

- Two **ovaries**, situated in the lower part of the abdomen. One egg is produced from one of these each month. The ovaries also produce the female hormones **oestrogen and progesterone**, which control sexual development, menstruation and pregnancy.

- Two **Fallopian tubes**, one leading from each ovary to the uterus. The egg travels to the womb along this tube. Fertilisation happens here.

- The **uterus** or womb – a muscular organ about the size of a pear. This holds a baby during pregnancy.

- The **vagina**, a muscular tube leading out of the body from the cervix or neck of the womb. This holds the penis during intercourse.

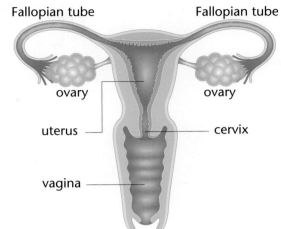

# The menstrual cycle

This is a monthly cycle which occurs in females from puberty until the **menopause**.

The menopause is when periods cease, and usually happens between the ages of 44 and 55. The menstrual cycle varies in length, but averages about 28 days.

- Once a month, an egg is released from one of the ovaries.

- This is called **ovulation**.

- The egg travels along the Fallopian tube, where it may or may not be fertilised.

- It continues into the womb, which has prepared for it by thickening its lining and building up an extra supply of blood.

- If the egg is not fertilised, the thick lining of the womb breaks down and passes from the body with the egg. This is known as menstruation or a period.

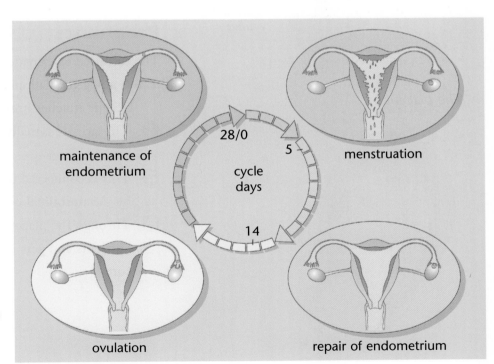

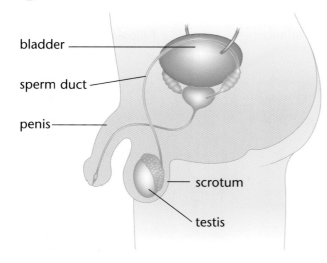

- bladder
- sperm duct
- penis
- scrotum
- testis

## The male organs of reproduction

**1** Two **testes** lie outside the body in a loose pouch of skin called the **scrotum**. The testes produce sperm.

**2** The **penis** lies in front of the testes. This transfers sperm to the female body in a liquid called **semen**.

**3** Two **sperm ducts** bring sperm from the testes to the penis. The testes make the hormone **testosterone**, which controls male sexual development.

## Fertilisation

During sexual intercourse the spongy tissue of the penis fills with blood which makes it erect. It enters the vagina and ejaculates semen, containing sperm, near the cervix. The sperm travel into the womb and then up into the Fallopian tubes. Here, if they meet an egg travelling from the ovary, fertilisation or conception may take place. This occurs when **one sperm penetrates the strong outer wall of the egg and fuses with it**. This is the beginning of a new life.

Fertilisation is most likely to occur within three days of ovulation, but can occur at any time.

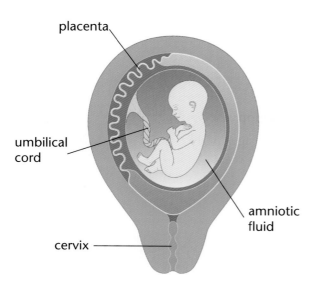

- placenta
- umbilical cord
- cervix
- amniotic fluid

❖ *The placenta*

## Pregnancy

The fertilised egg divides in two, then continues to divide as it travels along the Fallopian tube until it reaches the uterus.

Here it attaches itself to the thick walls of the uterus.

**1** This area eventually develops into the **placenta**, which acts as a filter.

**2** This is connected to the **embryo** (the undeveloped baby) by the **umbilical cord**.

**3** Through the placenta, the embryo receives oxygen and nutrients and gets rid of carbon dioxide via the umbilical cord.

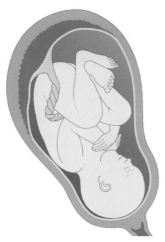

❖ *Position of the baby before birth*

Certain harmful substances can pass from the mother's blood supply into the embryo — these include drugs, viruses (e.g. rubella), alcohol and carbon monoxide (from cigarettes). This is why it is harmful to the baby to take drugs, drink alcohol or smoke during pregnancy.

- Cells begin to group together to make tissues, and eventually organs such as the liver, heart and brain. The developing baby is now called a **foetus**. It is surrounded by a sac containing **amniotic fluid**, which protects it from injury.
- By about six months the foetus has all its organs, but it stays in the uterus growing bigger until it is strong enough to survive alone.
- The duration of pregnancy is about 40 weeks.

## Birth

The baby is usually lying head down when it is ready to be born. The uterus begins **contractions** (labour pains) which gradually increase in strength and frequency. The water sac may break before or after the contractions begin, and the water seeps out. The cervix gradually dilates (widens) and becomes more elastic.

## Delivery

The head usually appears first, and then the rest of the body eases out. The baby begins to breathe on its own and the umbilical cord is clamped and cut. The placenta separates from the uterus and passes out with the cord. This is known as the **afterbirth**.

## Sexual responsibility

A sexual relationship is a fragile thing, involving not just sex but strong emotions and feelings for the other partner. For this reason it should be treated responsibly. Most societies place sexual relationships within the framework of marriage, or at least within a long-term and committed relationship. Casual sex can lead to feelings of being used, unwanted pregnancy, and sexually transmitted diseases such as Aids and chlamydia.

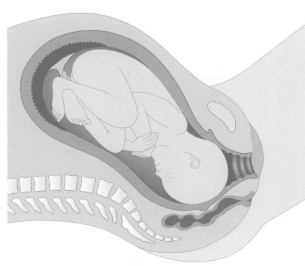

❖ *The position of the baby during birth*

1. The release of an egg from the _____ is called _____.
2. The female sex hormones are _____ and _____.
3. The passage from the ovary to the uterus is called the _____ _____.
4. The time when periods cease in middle age is called the _____.
5. The testes lie in a pouch of skin called the _____.
6. When a sperm fuses with the female egg, it is called _____.
7. The _____ acts as a filter between the blood supply of the mother and the baby.
8. The sac surrounding the foetus is filled with _____ _____.
9. Define menstruation.
10. Outline three physical changes that occur in boys and three physical changes that occur in girls during puberty.
11. Explain (a) embryo and (b) umbilical cord.
12. Outline what happens at each stage of the menstrual cycle.
13. How long does pregnancy last? What are contractions?
14. Name two sexually transmitted diseases.

# Chapter 34 Health Hazards

## Smoking

Even though smoking is known to kill thousands of people each year, many young people still take it up. Nicotine is one of the most addictive substances and, once started, it is extremely difficult to break the habit.

## Why do people start to smoke?

- One or both **parents smoke**.
- **Curiosity** – many teenagers like to try new experiences.
- **Peer pressure** – people feel more comfortable smoking if their friends smoke, or they may be persuaded to join the crowd.
- **Media misinformation** leads some people to think that it can help relieve stress or lose weight.
- They feel **invincible** and don't think of long-term effects.

## Harmful effects of smoking

Carbon monoxide, nicotine and chemicals from smoke form a sticky brown tar which damages delicate lung tissue and blood vessels.

1. **Emphysema** and other respiratory complaints.
2. **Lung cancer** – nine out of ten people who get lung cancer are smokers. Cancer of the mouth, throat, tongue and jaw are more common in smokers.
3. **Heart disease**; smoking causes hardening and narrowing of the arteries. It is a major cause of death from heart disease and stroke. Circulatory diseases may result in amputation of the legs. Smoking causes heart rate and blood pressure to rise, putting a strain on the heart.
4. **Pregnancy dangers.** Research shows that smoking causes distress to the foetus in the womb. Miscarriage and premature births are more common in mothers who

smoke. Babies born to smokers are more likely to be undersized and as a result have a lower survival rate.

**⑤** Passive smoking. Non-smokers who inhale cigarette smoke have increased risk of the above diseases.

### Another disadvantage of smoking

Cost: Work out the yearly cost of 20 cigarettes a day. It would pay for two good holidays abroad or 4–5 complete outfits of clothes.

List five disadvantages of smoking other than those already mentioned.

### Government controls on smoking

**❶** Cigarettes and tobacco products are heavily taxed.
**❷** It is illegal to sell cigarettes to under-18s.
**❸** Cigarette advertising is not permitted on TV or in stores.
**❹** Packets must carry a government health warning.
**❺** Smoking is not permitted in any public place.

Work out a role-play situation in which one friend tries unsuccessfully to persuade another to smoke.

## Alcohol

Alcohol is a legal drug. It is both mood-changing and addictive.

Why do people drink?

- To feel more relaxed and sociable.
- To feel more confident and less shy.
- To cheer themselves up if they are 'down'.
- To fit in – curiosity and peer pressure.
- To mask stress and anxiety.

## Physical effects of alcohol

### In the short term

- It dilates blood vessels – face becomes flushed.
- Loss of control – staggering and slurred speech.
- It depresses the brain – reasoning and common sense go.
- Loss of judgement – people take risks resulting in harm, e.g. road accidents.
- Reduced inhibitions – consuming alcohol changes behaviour. Loss of self-control – aggression, fighting, sexual activity, drinking and driving or illegal drug use.
- Memory loss and/or blackouts – alcohol depresses the brain's control so, as blood alcohol levels increase, periods of time and certain situations and events may not be remembered afterwards.
- Nausea, vomiting – excessive drinking can result in the body attempting to protect itself by getting rid of the alcohol.
- Headaches, hangovers. Hangovers are partially due to the body becoming dehydrated as a result of alcohol consumption.
- Prolonged heavy drinking can cause loss of consciousness and death.

### In the long term

- Addiction to alcohol.
- Permanent damage to the brain – loss of memory, judgement.
- Mental illness, e.g. depression.
- Hardening (cirrhosis) of the liver.
- Heart disease and high blood pressure leading to strokes and early death.
- Cancer of mouth, throat, liver and bladder.
- Foetal alcohol syndrome – mental handicap caused by a woman drinking during pregnancy.

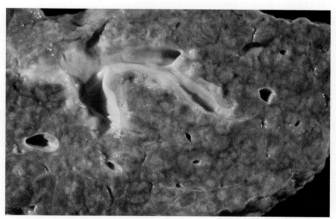

❖ *Cirrhosis of the liver*

## Effects of alcohol abuse

### On family

- Marital conflict – arguments, the silent treatment, growing apart, infidelity, divorce.
- Dysfunctional children – school work suffers.
- Financial problems – loss of job, poor financial decisions, wasting money.
- Violence in the home and community – slapping, hitting, smashing and throwing objects.

## On society

- More road accidents: approximately 40% of road deaths and at least 30% of all road accidents each year are alcohol related.
- Drink-related crime – many criminals have alcohol problems.
- Cost to the state, which pays huge sums of money on treatment for alcoholism and related illness. There are also the costs of traffic crashes and injured people coming into our hospitals. The Strategic Task Force on Alcohol estimated recently that annual costs are in the range of €2.6 billion.
- Absenteeism – absence from work due to drinking binges, or poor performance while at work due to a hangover, etc.

## Alcoholism

**A person is considered to be an alcoholic when drinking affects work and/or family relationships.**

## Drinking guidelines

Alcohol affects different people in different ways. It also depends on the size of the drinker, whether they have been eating, and how quickly and how much they drink. Women should drink less than men because their tissues absorb alcohol more quickly.

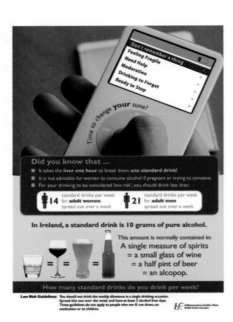

❖ *Each of these is one unit of alcohol*

# What is a unit of alcohol?

*This amount is normally contained in:*
*A single measure of spirits = a small glass of wine*
*= a half pint of beer = an alcopop.*

3 Social and Health Studies

Each of the following contains 1 unit of alcohol:

1 small glass of wine

1 alcopop

½ pint of beer

1 small measure of spirits.

✦ Drink in moderation; never drink more than 14 units per week (women) and 21 units per week (men).

✦ Keep at least two days per week alcohol-free.

✦ Don't drink on an empty stomach.

✦ Sip alcohol slowly – never gulp it down.

✦ Don't mix drinks; stick with the grape (wine, sherry, brandy) or the grain (beer, gin, whiskey).

✦ Regard drunkenness as unacceptable.

✦ Never drive when drinking.

✦ Respect the right of those who do not wish to drink – don't pressurise them. Avoid buying 'rounds'.

Drinking large amounts in one go is called 'binge drinking'. Ireland has a high rate of binge drinkers, with 58% of drinking occasions ending up in binge drinking among men and 30% among women.

## Help for those affected by alcoholism

✦ Alcoholics Anonymous – self-help groups for alcoholics.

✦ Al Anon – help and support for families of alcoholics.

✦ Al Ateen – help and group support for teenage children of alcoholics.

**ACTIVITY**

1. Find out the current legal limit of blood alcohol level for driving. How many drinks would it take a man to reach this?

2. Why has a woman a lower recommended alcohol unit level than a man?

3. Discuss alcohol advertising on TV and at sports fixtures.

# Drugs

**Controlled drugs are those that are provided by prescription.** While many drugs are useful and help prevent or cure illness, the drugs we describe here are addictive unprescribed drugs which are taken for the effect they have on the user. Alcohol and nicotine, which we have already discussed, are also addictive drugs.

Drug abusers are those who:

1. take controlled drugs without a prescription
2. take illegal drugs such as cocaine, ecstasy or heroin
3. inhale solvents, e.g. sniffing glue.

## Reasons why people take addictive drugs

- Curiosity.
- Because friends are doing it.
- Because drugs are so widely available.
- For the 'high' they experience (but don't forget the terrible 'low' when they wear off).
- To hide insecurity and give them confidence.

## Ill-effects of drug abuse

- Health is damaged due to self-neglect and effect of drugs.
- Personality disorders and mental illness. Flashbacks, unwanted recurrences of the drug's effects weeks or months after use.
- Dependence – the user depends on the drug to function and survive.
- The excitement of certain drugs, e.g. cocaine, is followed by a 'crash': a period of anxiety, fatigue, depression, and a strong desire to use more to alleviate the feelings of the crash.
- Addiction – craving for the drug; withdrawal symptoms when it is stopped. Withdrawal symptoms include vomiting, muscle cramps, convulsions, and delirium.
- Users and pushers are breaking the law.
- Aids, hepatitis and other infections from dirty needles.
- Crime – many drug users engage in criminal activity, such as burglary and prostitution, to raise the money to buy drugs.
- Death from overdosing, bad reactions and suicide.

## Addiction

- Dependence can be **physical** – the body craves the drug and suffers unbearably unpleasant symptoms (sweating, cramps, sleeplessness) if it is withdrawn.
- It can be **psychological** – addicts rely on the drug as a means of getting through the day or coping with life. They suffer from anxiety if it is unavailable, and will do anything for the next 'fix'.

## Kicking the habit

1. The first step in giving up any drug – whether nicotine, alcohol or controlled drugs – is to admit you have a problem and to want to give it up. No amount of nagging will get a person to give up.

2. 'Tough love': families and friends must not condone or enable (help) the addict by minimising the problem or helping him or her out of scrapes. Addicts will never see the error of their ways unless they are allowed to experience the consequences of their actions. If they are allowed to hit 'rock bottom', they may come to their senses.

3. Once they have accepted they have a problem and need help, they can be directed to the best place for treatment by professional counsellors, etc. Medical help and hospitalisation may be required for a successful outcome. At this stage you can support them through the rough times.

Help is available from:
- the HSE
- Narcotics Anonymous
- treatment centres.

**REVISION QUESTIONS**

1. Give four reasons why people start to smoke.
2. List four ways in which cigarettes can damage your health.
3. Why should a pregnant woman avoid smoking?
4. What is meant by passive smoking?
5. List three immediate effects and three long-term effects of heavy drinking.
6. Name four ways in which alcoholism can affect the family.
7. Name two sources of help for those affected by alcoholism.
8. List four effects of drug abuse on the body.
9. What is meant by addiction? Describe two types of addiction.
10. What is the best way to help someone who is addicted to a drug or alcohol?
11. List four effects of long-term alcohol abuse on the body.
12. What are controlled drugs?
13. Describe three ways in which the government has attempted to control cigarette smoking.

Test Yourself
eTest.ie

# Part

# 4

# Resource Management and Home Studies

 Management is the skilful use of resources in order to achieve goals.

A good manager plans and uses resources efficiently, without waste.

 **ACTIVITY** Name three types of manager. List the resources they might use and their likely goals.

> Reminder: A resource is something that helps us in our lives to achieve a goal or complete a task.

## Resource management

Resource management means **using resources wisely**:

- budgeting carefully to make the most of our money
- planning in order to save time and energy
- avoiding waste.

When resources are limited, we must work out our priorities. For example, time is scarce for a couple who both have jobs, so it might be worth spending money on a dishwasher.

 **ACTIVITIES**

Activity breakdown (24 hours)

- 4 hours study
- 8 hours sleeping
- 7 hours school
- 3 hours playing sport
- 1 hour watching TV
- 1 hour housework

1. Many people are careless and waste resources. List some ways in which resources are wasted in your home. Make a list of changes you could make to save resources at home.

2. Time is an important resource. Keep a diary of your activities for one week. Work out how many hours a week you spend (a) sleeping, (b) at school, (c) doing homework (d) doing household tasks, (e) watching TV, (f) playing sport. Arrange the results in a bar chart or pie chart.

# Home management

**Home management is the skill of running a home efficiently**: planning tasks and using resources wisely to achieve family goals.

| Planning | Resources used in home management | Family goals might include |
|---|---|---|
| This involves thinking things out in advance and sometimes putting plans down on paper. Examples: a shopping list or a budget. | Human energy and skills<br>Time<br>Money for resources<br>Materials and equipment | A safe, secure, clean home<br>Good health; happiness<br>Good education for children<br>Financial security |

Goals are thought-out aims or objectives. They may be short-term, medium-term or long-term. Most of the family goals above are long-term; producing a meal or cleaning a room are short-term goals. Name some medium-term goals a family might have.

## Home management skills

- Decision-making
- Planning
- Organising
- Evaluating.

LINK-UP

Decision-making, page 207

## Case study

Let's look at two families: the Greens and the Browns. The two families have similar incomes. Mr Green and Mr Brown work at the local factory. Mrs Green and Mrs Brown have part-time jobs.

### The Greens

The Greens sit down to regular meals in a clean, tidy house. Their clothes are well worn, but clean. They bought sturdy second-hand furniture which is wearing well. The children do their homework after school and have certain jobs to complete before they are allowed out to play. Mr or Mrs Green shops at the supermarket once a week and looks out for bargains on special offer. At the end of the week, they usually have a little money over which they put in the credit union. Mr Green's hobby is gardening, which supplies some fresh vegetables. They go to a movie or the pub once or twice a week. Mary made her First Communion last year; her mother made her dress and bought practical accessories in a chain store. Most years they can afford a holiday.

❖ *The Green family*

293

**The Browns**

The Browns live casually. The children are usually left to get their own meals. They tend to live on tinned and packet foods. Billy tried making chips last week and nearly burned the house down. They watch TV when they get home from school and at weekends. Mr Brown got a 'deal' on cheap furniture a couple of years ago, but it is shabby now and some of it is broken. They shop at the local shop, which allows them credit. They usually run out of money well before pay-day, and often borrow from Mrs Brown's sister near by. Mr Brown spends most evenings in the local pub. Mrs Brown usually goes to bingo four nights a week and joins her husband in the pub at weekends. When Betty made her First Communion they borrowed €300 from a moneylender to buy her a very expensive dress and accessories. As they are still paying back the high interest, they can't afford a holiday.

❖ *The Brown family*

**ACTIVITIES**

1. What are the priorities of each family?
2. List the examples of good management in the Green family.
3. List the changes the Browns could make to improve their lifestyle and finances.

## The main tasks involved in running a home

- Budgeting
- Shopping
- Cooking
- Caring for children
- Caring for clothes
- Cleaning and maintaining the home.

These should be shared out fairly and realistically between family members. This means that all members of the family should be involved in running the home according to the amount of free time they have.

In the past, the mother was a full-time homemaker. She usually had a large family and stayed at home to look after them. The household tasks were her responsibility. Today many mothers work outside the home, yet many are still left to do most of the household tasks and childcare. Often daughters, but not sons, are expected to help,

Gender equity, page 270

even though both are studying at school. Is this fair?

Why not look upon the family home as a co-op, where everyone has tasks to do for the good and comfort of the whole family? Parents should give children household tasks from an early age and set a good example by sharing housework themselves.

## Management formula

1. **Identify goal.** What needs to be done? When? Examples: clean kitchen; monthly budget.

2. **What resources are required?** Which do I have? Which must I get? (e.g. cleaning agents, equipment)

3. **Plan.** Make out a work plan (see below).

4. **Action.** Put your plan into action, i.e. do the task.

5. **Evaluate.** Did I have enough resources? Did I use them efficiently? Did I follow good work practices? Could I have done anything better, or faster? Are there any changes I would make the next time I do the job?

# Work plans

Time is an important resource. It is easier to get tasks done if some type of system is followed and the work is done in logical order.

# Planning a weekly cleaning schedule

1. It is a good idea for all the family to have an input when drawing up the weekly schedule.

2. Consider the age, workload and time schedules, e.g. sports commitments, of each family member and allocate jobs accordingly, rotating jobs if the family prefers.

3. List all the jobs that need to be done each day and place them in logical order.

4. Some tasks need to be done daily, some weekly (e.g. ironing) and some occasionally (e.g. cleaning out cupboards). Include a couple of weekly tasks each day, and an 'occasional' task each week, so that they all get done over a certain period.

5. Try out the work plan for a week or two, evaluate it and make any necessary changes.

6. Work in an organised and logical way, e.g. washing followed by ironing.

Making a time plan, page 63

### Sequence for cleaning a room

1. **Tidy**

2. **Dirty work**, e.g. cleaning fires

3. **Dust**

4. **Vacuum**

5. **Wash**, e.g. paintwork

6. **Polish**

**ACTIVITIES**

You plan to give your bedroom a good clean on Saturday morning. Using the management formula, plan the work schedule.

**REVISION QUESTIONS**

1. Explain the following terms: (a) management; (b) resource; (c) evaluate.

2. What are the advantages of good home management?

3. What is a goal?

4. List four family goals.

5. What skills are needed for home management?

6. List the basic steps of the management formula.

7. List the basic sequence for cleaning a room.

8. List two principle resources used in home management.

Test Yourself
eTest.ie

# Chapter 36 Home and Community

## Shelter

Shelter is a basic human need. From the earliest times humans made shelters. Shelter means somewhere to live which protects us from the elements such as the wind and the rain. It keeps us warm in winter and protects us from the sun in summer.

Shelter can be:

1. **A house** – this may be rented or owned. It may be a bungalow, two- or three-storied, terraced, semi-detached or detached.
2. **A flat or apartment** – it may be rented or owned; it may be in a converted house, a small flat complex or a high-rise block. A bedsit is a large room in which one cooks, eats, lives and sleeps.
3. **Sheltered housing** – groups of purpose-built (specially designed) houses or flats where elderly people or people with disabilities can live on their own and share certain facilities. They are usually supervised.
4. **A caravan**, **mobile home or boat** – provides a temporary or permanent mobile dwelling.
5. **An institution** – e.g. a convent, boarding school or nursing home.

**ACTIVITIES**

Discuss the different forms of housing above and choose the one you think most suitable for: (a) a young rural couple saving to buy a house; (b) an elderly woman; (c) a family with school-going children; (d) two third-level students.

## Where to live?

Few people can live exactly where they like. A house may be in a rural area (in the country) or an urban area (in a city).

People usually like to live near other people, in villages, towns and cities. Why do you think this is so?

People like to be near their place of work, so they won't waste time and money travelling.

It makes life easier if we are near schools, shops and public transport.

What other amenities do you think should be near your home?

**Amenities** are facilities usually provided and maintained for leisure. Examples: lakes, playgrounds, parks, sports pitches, swimming pools, leisure centres, museums, art galleries, cinemas and beaches.

## House or home?

Is there a difference between a house and a home? A house is simply a building that provides shelter. A home contains people who are close to one another and provides other needs as well as shelter:

✤ **Physical needs** such as protection; warmth; a place to eat, sleep and store our possessions.

✤ **Emotional needs** – love, care, security and privacy. It provides support and protection for the weaker members of the family (children and older people).

✤ **Social needs** – home is a base from which we live our lives, entertain our friends, go to work and school, and return at night. At home we learn how to live with others so that we fit into the wider community around us.

Think of a homeless person or a refugee. They have none of these things. They have no base.

**ACTIVITIES**

Look up the dictionary definitions of the words 'house' and 'home' and write them down. Now make up your own definition, taking account of the priorities in your home.

# The community

People who live in one locality, such as a village or a suburb, form a community. Our home is part of the community. Each community has a large number of resources.

| Statutory (state or semi-state) services | Voluntary services |
| --- | --- |
| Education (schools) | ISPCC (Childline. Freephone 1 800 666 666) |
| Health (health centres, hospitals) | Samaritans |
| Social welfare (employment offices, FÁS, etc.) | Alone |
| Community centres | Rehab |
| Public libraries | St Vincent de Paul Society |
| Public (local authority) housing | Neighbourhood Watch |
| Gardaí | Salvation Army |
| Public transport | Meals on Wheels |

**ACTIVITIES**

1. Find out about and write down some information about two voluntary organisations that are mentioned above.
2. The class should divide into groups. Members of each group should visit one of the following services. Make a report on the facilities they provide.
   - Health centre
   - Leisure centre
   - Community centre
   - Library
   - Crèche
   - FÁS office

**REVISION QUESTIONS**

1. Name four forms of shelter where people could live.
2. Name the three types of need that are provided in the home.
3. Name four amenities that are necessary near a home.
4. Name two voluntary and two statutory services provided in your nearest town.

Test Yourself
eTest.ie

# Chapter 37 Design in the Home

Design is the arrangement of an object or objects in a form that is functional and pleasing to the eye.

Clothes, homes, cars, furniture and equipment have all been designed by someone. The emphasis in this chapter is on design in relation to the home, i.e. room planning and interior design.

## Features of design

Design using textiles, page 345

1. **Function** – is it suitable for its purpose?
2. **Form** (shape and line)
3. **Colour**
4. **Pattern**
5. **Texture**

### 1 Function

This is the most important feature in design: if an object does not fulfil its function, it is a bad design. An uncomfortable chair, an unsteady table lamp and a room in which one cannot move freely are examples of bad design.

Features related to function:

- comfort
- safety
- ease of use
- ease of maintenance
- durability.

**Durability** is an important feature in designing for the home. Most products, such as furniture and equipment, are expected to be hardwearing and to last a long time.

Some objects in a home do not have a practical function. They are used purely for their aesthetic or decorative value. Can you name some of these?

## 2 Form

**This refers to the shape and line of an object.**

(a) **Shape** is the outline of an object. The four most basic shapes are the square, rectangle, triangle and circle. Many objects in the home are based on these shapes – rooms, furniture, equipment.

❖ *Square*

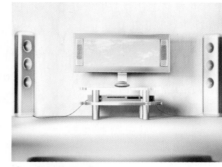

❖ *Rectangle*

(b) **Line** can be:

* **vertical** – vertical lines make the eye look up and down, so things appear narrower or higher

* **horizontal** – horizontal lines make the object appear wider and lower

* **curved** – curves suggest movement. They appear soft and 'feminine'

* **diagonal** – a diagonal line is less common. It can make an object look different and dramatic.

❖ *Triangle*

❖ *Circle*

❖ *Vertical lines*

❖ *A horizontal line*

❖ *Curves*

## 3 Colour

Colour is an important design feature in clothes, fabrics and interiors. It can affect our mood – it can make us feel happy or 'blue'. Colour can be warm or cool; it can harmonise or distract.

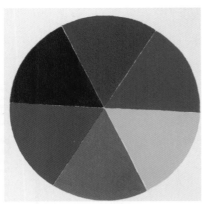

⁂ *The colour wheel*

Look at the **colour wheel**.

- **Primary colours** are red, yellow and blue.
- **Secondary colours** are obtained by mixing two primary colours, e.g. blue and yellow make green. **Tertiary colours** are obtained by mixing a primary and a secondary colour, e.g. blue and green make turquoise.
- **Neutral colours** are black, white and grey.
- **Pastels** are pale colours such as pink, pale green and blue.
- **Warm colours** are red, orange and yellow – they make rooms look cosy.
- **Cool colours** are restful and calming. We feel relaxed in a green room. Name some other cool colours.

### Combining colour

When strong colours are used together, they attract attention. This is useful when we want people to notice a feature, e.g a feature wall in a room.

### Choosing colour

The colours we choose for clothes and rooms express our individuality and personality. There are really no right and wrong colours. It is a matter of personal taste.

## 4 Pattern

**A pattern is a decorative design which is usually repeated over the whole or part of an object**, e.g. a carpet. It can form part of the object (e.g. tartan or gingham fabric) or be printed on to the surface (e.g. printed fabric, wallpaper). Pattern adds interest and contrast to otherwise plain areas. Pattern needs to be used with care – too much can appear fussy, unless cleverly used. Large patterns are usually used for large areas; small patterns may be used on large or small areas.

## 5 Texture

**This describes the feel of an object – whether the surface is hard, soft, rough or smooth.** Like pattern, it adds interest to rooms, clothes and other objects. Rough textures appear warm and cosy, e.g. a carpet in a room. Smooth textures such as marble or tiles usually look and feel cold. They are suitable for bathrooms and kitchens, as they are hygienic and easy to clean.

# Other design principles

The first three principles below help to create harmony in a room.

## Balance

This means that there is **harmony between each part of the design of a room,** e.g. something of a certain height on one side of a room should be balanced by something of similar height on the other. There shouldn't be too much of anything, such as pattern or colour, in one part of the room.

## Proportion

This means that **the dimensions or size of different objects in a room relate to each other** – that nothing is too big or too small. For example, a tiny window in a huge room is not in proportion.

## Rhythm

**Colours or patterns repeated on different objects draw the room together.** The opposite would be to have a huge number of colours and patterns in a room, which would be very unsettling.

## Emphasis

This is where **the eye is drawn to an object**, often because of a contrasting colour or strong shape; e.g. bright yellow cushions on a beige chair, or a piece of modern sculpture. Lighting is often used to give emphasis.

**REVISION QUESTIONS**

1. What is design?
2. Name four important features of design. Give two examples of each.
3. Describe (a) primary colours; (b) pastel colours; (c) texture.
4. Why is important not to use pattern everywhere in a room?
5. What are the main textures one could expect to find in a bedroom and what objects create these textures?
6. How could you emphasise something in a room that you wanted people to notice?

# Chapter
# 38 Room Planning

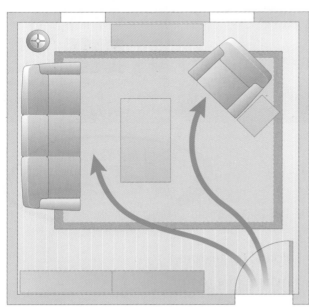

❖ *The flow of traffic through a room*

## Guidelines for room planning

**1** Consider the **function of the room**. What will it be used for? Each room has its own priorities: comfort in living rooms; privacy in bathrooms; safety, hygiene and efficiency in kitchens.

**2** Consider **existing fixtures and fittings** (e.g. position of doors, windows, radiators) when deciding where to place furniture. Use just enough furniture for the needs of the room.

**3** **Storage.** Allow sufficient storage for the needs of the room.

**4** **Traffic flow.** Allow space between furniture for access to the major areas of the room (chairs, windows, doors, fire, TV).

**5** **Heating and lighting** must be decided early, in case plumbing or rewiring is necessary.

**6** Consider **aspect** (the direction the house is facing) when deciding on colour scheme and decor. If a room faces north, use warm colours; if it faces south, cool colours may be used. Pale colours brighten up a dark room.

**7** **Appearance.** Rooms should be comfortable and attractive to look at. Use accessories and soft furnishings (curtains, cushions) to add pattern, texture and style to a room.

# Room design priorities

These vary according to the function of the room.

- Comfort
- Colour
- Storage
- Efficiency
- Safety
- Privacy
- Appearance
- Easy to clean/hygienic.

# Floor plan

When designing or redesigning a room, a floor plan drawn to scale on squared paper saves time and energy. Measure and draw in fixtures and fittings, e.g. doors, fireplace, windows. This allows you to work out what will fit and where it might go before you buy it.

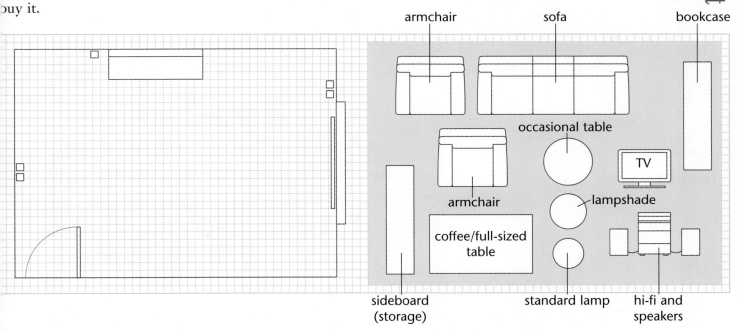

**ACTIVITIES** This is a basic living room floor plan. Trace and cut out the furniture items and arrange them in the most appropriate way, allowing for traffic flow. Redraw the finished plan into your copy.

## Designing a bedroom: options

| | | |
|---|---|---|
| **Colour scheme** | consider aspect and amount of light in room | |
| **Wall finish** | paper or paint, type and colour | |
| **Furniture/storage** | bed | locker |
| | wardrobe | desk |
| | dressing table | chair |
| | fitted units | bookshelves |
| **Floor finish/covering** | carpet | rugs |
| | wood (sanded and sealed) | laminate/click flooring |
| **Soft furnishings** | curtains | duvet cover |
| | blinds | cushions |
| | lampshades | throw |
| **Heating** | central heating radiator | portable convector heater |
| | underfloor heating | |
| **Lighting** | centre light | bedside light |
| | desk light | |
| **Ventilation** | window | |

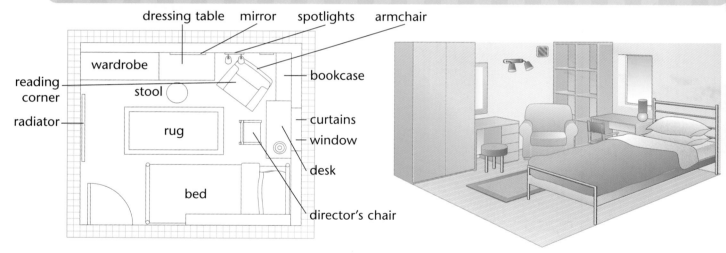

**Bedroom design brief**

1. **Identify the brief**

   Design a study–bedroom for a teenage girl or boy, based on your own bedroom. Measure and draw a plan of your bedroom. Describe the colour scheme and the furnishings you would use (see above).

2. **Analyse the problem. What factors must I consider?**
   - Allow for each activity – sleep, storage, relaxing and study.
   - Consider traffic flow, cost, existing fittings and furniture.

3. **Research/investigation**

Look at some interior design magazines and the internet for ideas. Visit DIY stores. Collect paint charts; price paint and wallpaper. Examine and price fabrics.

4. **Identify possible solutions, and their effects**

(a) Different colour schemes.

(b) Various furniture layouts to make more use of space, e.g. a raised 'platform bed' with wardrobe/storage/desk underneath.

(c) Consider soft furnishings – practical, washable and not too expensive.

5. **Decide on a solution**

6. **Plan assignment**

Measure room and furniture. Draw plan of room on squared paper, and furniture cut-outs to scale. Move these around until you get the best arrangement.

7. **Action**

Assemble project – floor plan, drawings, paint and fabric samples, etc. – in a presentation folder. Write out a description of the room and colour scheme.

8. **Evaluate result**

Did I achieve my goal?

**ACTIVITIES**

1. What are the design priorities in a child's bedroom? Design a bedroom for a three-year-old girl following the design brief example above.

2. Draw a floor plan for a bed-sitter for a college student. There should be places to cook, eat, study, sit to watch TV, and sleep.

## Kitchens

Priorities in kitchen planning are:

- hygiene
- sufficient storage
- efficiency
- good lighting
- safety
- good ventilation.

## Safety in the kitchen
See page 75.

## Ergonomics

**Ergonomics is the study of efficiency in the workplace.** It concerns the arrangement of equipment in the most efficient way so that time and energy are saved.

Ergonomics is very important in kitchen planning, as the position of equipment such as cookers, sinks and storage areas can make a big difference to the efficiency of the kitchen. There should be no unnecessary walking, bending or stretching. In the past, kitchens were very badly designed. Today's kitchens are much more efficient and labour-saving.

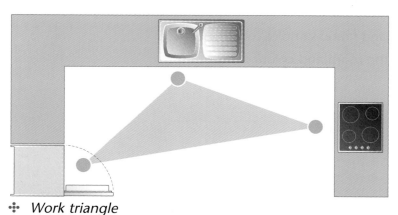

❖ *Work triangle*

## The work triangle

**Most of the walking in a kitchen is done between the cooker, the sink and the refrigerator. If these are placed fairly close to one another so that they form an invisible triangle, much unnecessary walking is cut out, saving time and energy.** This is an example of ergonomics.

Food preparation follows a natural sequence:

STORAGE → PREPARATION → WASHING → COOKING → SERVING

Kitchen equipment should be arranged in that order. It may be placed in a U-shape, in an L-shape or in two parallel lines. Items should be stored near the place where they are most used, e.g. pots, tins and utensils near the cooker and food near the preparation area.

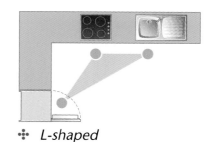
❖ *L-shaped*

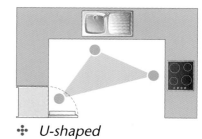
❖ *U-shaped*

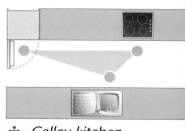
❖ *Galley kitchen*

# Work heights

The average work height is 900mm, so most kitchen floor units and equipment such as cookers are built to this height. Fridges and washing machines may be a little lower so that they can fit under the worktop. Worktops that are too high or low can cause back pain. Wall-hung units save space and are best for food storage. (Why?)

# Kitchen surfaces

These should be hygienic, water-resistant, easy to clean and strong.

- **Walls** – ceramic tiles and washable paint are most practical.
- **Worktops** need to withstand heat and constant use. A continuous worktop made from laminated plastic (Formica) is hygienic and easy to clean, although very hot saucepans, e.g. frying pans, can damage it. Granite is an expensive but hardwearing option. Stain-resistant concrete worktops are now available. Never chop on worktops – use a chopping board.

❖ *Granite worktop*

- **Floor surfaces** should be hardwearing and easy to clean. Tiles are a good choice.

# Ventilation

A great deal of heat and steam are created in a kitchen from cooking and washing. As bacteria thrive under these conditions, it is essential to have a good system of ventilation to remove them. An open window is not sufficient. What is needed is an extractor fan or cooker hood.

❖ *Tiled floor*

Ventilation is necessary to:

- remove steam
- remove stale air
- lower the temperature
- remove bacteria
- remove cooking fumes
- prevent condensation.

❖ *Cooker hood*

**ACTIVITIES**

A well-planned kitchen will have: (a) the sink under a window; (b) lots of electric sockets; (c) good lighting; (d) blinds rather than curtains.

1.  Explain the reason for each of the features listed above.
2.  Design the layout of a kitchen for a small flat following the design brief. Show the position of doors and windows. (Colour schemes, etc. are not required.)
3.  Suggest the best position for an extractor fan in a kitchen, giving reasons for your choice.

**REVISION QUESTIONS**

1.  Explain how to use a floor plan.
2.  List five guidelines to follow when planning any room.
3.  List four points you think are important when planning kitchens.
4.  What is ergonomics? Give an example of its use in a kitchen.
5.  Describe the work sequence used in a food preparation area.
6.  What is the standard work height for kitchen units and equipment?
7.  Name two forms of ventilation suitable for kitchens and state why good ventilation is necessary.
8.  Why is ventilation important in a kitchen?
9.  What is meant by the work triangle when applied to the design of a kitchen?
10. Explain what is meant by (a) aspect and (b) traffic flow.

Test Yourself
eTest.ie

# Chapter 39 Technology in the Home

## Technology

> Technology is the practical application of science.

Advances in technology have played a major part in improving standards of living, reducing labour in the home, and making the home cleaner and more efficient. The last century has brought major developments in home technology.

## Effects of technology in the home

### Materials in the home

In the past, only natural materials such as wood and metals were available to use in the home. Today there is a wide range of new materials.

- Metals are stain- and rust-resistant.
- Non-stick surfaces are applied to saucepans, utensils and ovens.
- Double-glazed windows keep homes warmer.
- PVC or aluminium windows don't need painting.
- Plastic is one of the most versatile materials and is used for a wide range of products such as furniture, utensils, containers, floors, hardwearing paints, wallpapers and floor coverings.
- Solar panels trap heat from the sun and use this energy to heat domestic hot water.

❖ *PVC double-glazed windows*

❖ *Solar panels*

Textiles in the home, page 350

## Textiles

A wide range of man-made fibres is available to suit every purpose. They can be mixed with natural fibres to give them new properties. Special finishes can be applied to make them crease-resistant, waterproof, drip-dry, etc.

## Cleaning

This can be a dirty and tiring job. Technology has made it simpler by producing easy-care products, such as non-iron shirts, and equipment and cleaning agents for almost every household job.

These include:

**Central vacuum systems**, which collect dirt and pass it through a series of pipes under the floor and/or in the walls. The dust is collected in a large container stored in the home and is emptied annually or as required. The hosepipe to carry out the cleaning is plugged into special sockets dotted around the house.

❖ *Central vacuuming system*

**Upright vacuum cleaners with no bags** – a fitted container collects the dust. This is emptied as required.

**Steam cleaners** – useful for cleaning grouted tiles, etc., or any area around the home that needs deep cleaning. A fine jet of steam is forced out under pressure to drive away dirt. Requires no additional cleaning agent.

Some modern **washing machines** have features such as an electronic 24-hour clock which allows you to set the machine to start at the most appropriate time. A digital LCD display shows wash progress information, wash time remaining, cycle and spin speed information, etc.

Intelligent control system sensors within the machine determine the best programme, temperature and duration of the wash, together with the correct spin speed required, so all you do is press 'start'.

Modern washing machines also constantly monitor the load and automatically adjust, using the least amount of water and energy required for each wash, depending on the size of load. Some are available that use solar-heated water with hot water from the domestic supply.

❖ *No-bag vacuum cleaner*

## Lighting

➤ CFLs (compact fluorescent lightbulbs) are much more energy-efficient than conventional bulbs and come in a variety of strengths. Although they are more expensive to buy they will last for many years and use less electricity.

- Glow-in-the-dark light switches allow you to access them easily at night.
- Some security lights can be set to turn on and off automatically to deter burglars.

## Heating

- Underfloor heating – a flexible coiled element is installed under the floor of each room. The temperature is controllable and the floor will be warm underfoot. This system eliminates the need for radiators.
- Wood pellet boilers can be used to provide warm water and/or to heat radiators. As wood is a renewable resource this makes these boilers an environmentally friendly option. The pellets can be bought in bags or in bulk.

## Computers and technology

Computers (either desktop or laptop) are used in the majority of homes. They are generally used as a source of information (e.g. the internet) and to store information (e.g. on the hard drive or memory sticks).

Technology is so advanced that you can install a 'welcome home' button on a remote control that turns on lights inside and outside your home as you pull into your driveway. You could have your favourite music playing when you get through the door!

A 'goodnight' button turns everything off at bedtime. The coffee machine can be turned on from the bedroom by remote control. Outdoor watering and lighting can also be controlled, allowing sprinklers and outside lights to be turned on remotely.

Modern alarm systems are available in a variety of formats.

## Leisure

Technology has revolutionised our leisure time. Twenty years ago no one had heard of a CD or DVD.

Newer and more sophisticated plasma/flat-screen high-definition televisions, DVDs, sound systems and games consoles make leisure time more pleasurable for many. Television can now be used to obtain information, e.g. Teletext and digitally interactive sets. Satellite television is available all over the country, allowing people to access a vast array of new channels. The satellite provider offers different packages to suit different tastes, e.g. sports channels, film channels.

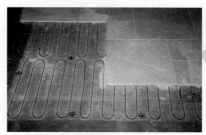

❖ *CFL lightbulbs*

❖ *Underfloor heating*

## Disadvantages of technology

Technology has made life easier, but has certain disadvantages.

❶ Job losses. Many traditional jobs have been replaced by technology.

❷ Machines are expensive.

❸ Servicing and repairs can be costly.

❹ Pollution. Many machines last about 10 years. They are then thrown out and replaced. The rubbish they create is non-biodegradable. A PRF or product recycling fund must be paid on all appliances to allow proper disposal of old ones.

**ACTIVITIES**

1. Transfer this table to your copy and complete, adding six household jobs which can now be done by machine.

| At the beginning of the twentieth century | Today |
| --- | --- |
| Water was collected from tubs | Hot and cold water is plumbed to our taps |
| Clothes were scrubbed in tubs | |

2. Name two metals that are stain- and rust-resistant.

3. Name three easy-care products and three cleaning agents that you consider worthwhile.

4. Some machines are considered necessities, others luxuries. Pick 10 machines used in the home and divide them into those you consider are necessities and those you think are luxuries.

5. Name two cordless appliances.

6. Name two food preparation machines.

## Electrical appliances

### Guidelines for buying electric appliances

Electrical appliances are an important household resource, but they are expensive. In order not to make a mistake when buying, go through the following checklist.

**Cost** Can you afford it? Check cost and running costs. Is the cheapest model the best value?

**Safety** This is a very important priority. Buy from a reliable source. The appliance should carry a safety symbol.

**Efficiency** Will it do the job it is meant to do and that you want it to do? Check details with sales staff. Check energy efficiency label.

**Special features** Appliances come in a range of models, with different programmes, extras, etc. Are you getting the features you require or paying extra for features you don't need?

**Size** Large or small model? Depends on the size of family and your needs. Do you do a lot of baking (mixer)? Have you other drying facilities (tumble drier)?, etc.

**Specifications** (height, width, depth) are given in an accompanying leaflet. They must suit the space in which the equipment will be placed.

**Easy to use?** Instructions should be supplied. Arrange a demonstration if necessary.

**Easy to clean?** Is it easy to take apart, clean and put together again?

**Guarantee** All electrical goods should be fully guaranteed for at least one year.

**Servicing** Make sure servicing and repairs can be done locally, preferably through the shop where the appliance was purchased.

Appliances may be grouped as follows:

**1** **Appliances with a heating element.** Kettles, deep fat fryers, toasters, electric heaters. These have a heating element inside the appliance.

**2** **Appliances with a motor.** The motor moves the working part of the machine (e.g. mixer, blade or fan). These appliances usually make a noise. Examples: food mixers and processors, electric carving knives.

**3** **Large appliances.** Cookers, refrigerators, freezers. Some, such as washing machines and dishwashers, have both an element and a motor.

**ACTIVITIES**

Place the following appliances under the headings **heater** or **motor** in your copybook.

Electric shaver, vacuum cleaner, hair-drier, can-opener, sandwich-maker, steam iron, fan heater.

## Investigating a small appliance: the kettle

### Design principle

An electric kettle has a heating element inside, in direct contact with the water. This makes it quick and economical to boil.

easy pour spout

viewer for checking water level

heat resistant handle

element

thermostatic on/off switch

❖ *Jug kettle*

### Safety first

Keep the flex on the worktop, out of reach of children. Cordless kettles are safer.

❖ *Cordless kettle*

**ACTIVITIES**

1. Kettles are made from many different materials. List as many of these materials as you can.

2. Find out the cost of the following electrical appliances and write them into your copy.
   Family cooker, standard refrigerator, steam iron, dishwasher, washing machine, tumble drier.

3. We cannot always afford all the appliances we want. From the following list of appliances on the left, choose the one that you think best suits each person/group on the right, giving reasons for your choice.

   | | |
   |---|---|
   | Mother with small children | Microwave oven |
   | Large family | Washing machine |
   | Elderly person with arthritis | Tumble drier |
   | Student in a bedsitter | Electric can opener |
   | Couple in a high-rise flat | Dishwasher |

## Cookers

### Design

Most cookers consist of a hob, a grill and an oven. They are made from enamelled steel and insulated to save energy.

❶ The **hob** usually consists of **hotplates** or **burners**.

❷ A **ceramic hob** has heat-resistant glass over the hotplates.

❸ A **halagen hob**, which uses a halogen light, heats up immediately and cools down quickly.

❹ **Dual rings** are economical, as just the inside of the ring can be turned on when using a small saucepan.

❺ **Dual grills** are similar – half the grill is used for small amounts.

   The **grill** is usually:
   - under the hob in a small grill compartment, or
   - in the main oven.

### Common features of standard ovens

- **Electric ovens** are heated by elements at the sides or back, gas ovens by burners at the back.

- A **thermostat** is a device that keeps the oven at the temperature set on the control switch.
- **Metal lining**, which may be non-stick or splash-resistant, and may be removable for cleaning.
- A **glass door** and a **light** for viewing what is cooking.
- Most **gas ovens** are lit by push-button ignition or a pilot light. They should have a 'flame failure device' which stops the flow of gas if the flame goes out.

## Modern features available in some cookers

- **Double oven.** An insulated grill compartment acts as a second oven. They are economical for cooking small amounts.
- **Fan oven.** A fan circulates heat from an element at the back of the oven. The oven heats up faster and the food is cooked more quickly and evenly. Unlike a standard oven, which is hotter at the top, the temperature in a fan oven is the same throughout the oven. This makes it good for 'batch baking'.
- **Split-level cookers.** The hob and oven are 'split' or separated, the oven set into a tall unit and the hob into the worktop. They are most commonly found in fitted kitchens.
- **Autotimer** or **automatic oven**. This oven has a device which can turn the oven on at a preset time, cook the food and switch it off when the cooking is finished. It is useful if the family is at work.
- A **timer** is a simpler device. It can be set for a certain length of time, e.g. 12 minutes, and it rings when the time is up.
- **Pre-programmed options.** You choose a food, enter the weight and the cooker determines all the details and sets itself.
- **Defrost:** Circulates air inside the oven without heat, defrosting freezer food or cooling cakes and pies.
- **Pyroclean:** Self-cleaning when the temperature is turned up.
- **Cool touch doors:** Doors and external side panels are designed to keep to safe temperatures of 60°C or below.
- **Steam setting:** Cooks food very gently without making it tough or dry.
- **Rotisserie:** Has a metal skewer onto which you can thread meat. The skewer revolves, cooking the meat and keeping it tender.

❖ *Gas cooker*

❖ *Split-level cooker*

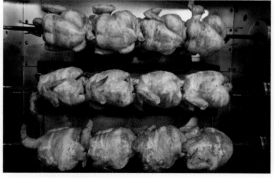

❖ *Rotisserie*

## Cooker care

1. Never drag pans over the hob, as they will scratch it.
2. Wipe up spills immediately.
3. Wash grill pan after each use. If grill pan is lined with foil, only the rack needs washing. The foil can be thrown out after use.
4. Harsh abrasives such as metal pot scrubs and oven cleaners can damage the hob surface. Use cream cleaners as far as possible, and ceramic cleaner for ceramic hobs.
5. Wipe out oven after each use, and clean properly at regular intervals.

## Cleaning a cooker

1. Preparation: collect resources; protect hands and clothes; turn off electric current/pilot light.
2. If very soiled, apply oven cleaner a few hours before cleaning.
3. Remove loose fittings and soak them. Wash in hot soapy water, rinse and dry.
4. Wash out oven, rinse and dry.
5. Wash outside of cooker from top down, rinse and dry. Polish chrome with a soft cloth.

Buying electrical appliances, page 314

## Choosing a cooker

1. Choice of fuel is electricity, gas, oil or solid fuel (e.g. an Aga). Natural gas is piped only to some cities. Electricity is cleanest.
2. Gas ovens and electric fan ovens heat most quickly.
3. Decide whether you want a split-level (expensive) or slot-in cooker (level with worktop).
4. Decide what type of hob and grill you prefer.
5. Double ovens, autotimers and ceramic hobs cost extra.

# Microwave ovens

See page 87.

# Refrigerators

A refrigerator works by taking heat from inside the refrigerator so that the temperature is lowered to between 2°C and 5°C. The cold slows down growth of bacteria so that food keeps fresh longer.

Modern refrigerators are well insulated for energy efficiency, are thermostatically controlled, and have moulded interiors, plastic-coated shelves, salad drawers and a door fitted with a magnetic seal. Larger American-style fridges with water and ice dispensers have become popular. New features include multimedia touch screens with digital and music technology so that you can watch television or listen to your favourite music while you are in the kitchen.

## Advantages of a refrigerator

* It protects food from dust, flies and other sources of bacteria.
* Food keeps fresh longer.
* It cuts down on waste.
* Fewer shopping trips are needed.
* It is useful for chilling foods and making cold sweets.

❖ *American-style fridge*

## Using a refrigerator

1. Place away from heat sources such as cookers, as these would force the motor to run constantly, and waste electricity.
2. Keep the fridge door closed for the same reason.
3. All foods should be clean and cool before storing. Hot foods raise the temperature of the fridge, causing other foods to go off.
4. Cover all foods to prevent them from drying out and to prevent fats absorbing flavours from other food, e.g. fish.
5. Store each type of food in the most suitable position.
6. Allow space for circulation of air between foods.
7. Check foods regularly for expiry dates, and use up left-overs within 1–2 days.
8. Clean and defrost the fridge regularly.

## Defrosting and cleaning

(*Note:* Automatic refrigerators defrost by regularly switching themselves off and on, so they do not need defrosting.)

1. Defrost regularly to avoid a build-up of ice, which would make the fridge inefficient.
2. If there is a freezer section, remove frozen foods, cover them with plastic and an insulating material such as a blanket.
3. To defrost, push defrost button or switch off fridge, depending on type.
4. Remove food during defrosting.
5. Remove shelves and other loose parts and wash, rinse and dry separately.

**6** Wash out inside the fridge with a solution of bread soda (2 tablespoons bread soda to 1 litre warm water).

**7** Rinse and dry; replace parts. Wash outside from the top down. Rinse, dry and polish. Replace food.

**REVISION QUESTIONS**

1. What do we mean by technology in relation to the home?
2. List three changes that technology has brought about in the last hundred years.
3. List three examples of improvements that technology has made to materials in the home.
4. Explain what is meant by a cordless appliance.
5. How does a central vacuum system work?
6. Give two advantages of having a computer.
7. What are some of the modern features of today's washing machines?
8. Give four disadvantages of technology.
9. List five guidelines for buying an electrical appliance.
10. Explain (a) ceramic hob, (b) dual grill, (c) thermostat, (d) split level.
11. What is (a) a fan oven, (b) a rotisserie?
12. List the advantages of a refrigerator.
13. Explain how to defrost a refrigerator.
14. Explain what guidelines should be followed when (a) using and (b) cleaning a refrigerator.
15. What is automatic defrost?
16. Name two household electrical appliances with a motor and two with a heating element.

# Chapter 40 Services to the Home

The main services to the home are:

- gas
- electricity
- water.

## Gas

### Sources

**Natural gas** is found under the seabed and was first piped ashore in 1976. It is piped to many large towns and cities through large underground pipes called mains. From these a service pipe enters a home. Here a valve can turn the flow on or off, and a digital meter records the consumption of gas in cubic metres.

Gas is used to power boilers, cookers, underfloor heating and gas fires. Natural gas is currently available in 19 counties, with over 630,000 customers now connected to the gas network in Ireland.

**Liquid petroleum gas (LPG)** is available to households that do not have a natural gas supply. It is delivered to storage tanks, e.g. for central heating, or sold in cylinders as 'bottled gas'.

❖ *Gas boiler*

| Advantages of gas | Disadvantages of gas |
|---|---|
| Clean and efficient: has low carbon emissions | Highly flammable |
| Piped directly to businesses and homes (in cities and some towns) – no carrying, etc. | While it is non-toxic, it can suffocate in enclosed spaces |
| Is always available – never has to be stored, ordered or carried | Carbon monoxide (a colourless and poisonous gas) can be produced by any appliance that burns a fossil fuel such as gas, coal or oil |
| Versatile | Requires a ventilator in each room |
| No soot or ashes to clean out | Network availability; not everyone has access to piped natural gas |
| Flame is easily controlled for cooking | Bottled gas is inconvenient and heavy to carry; it's easy to run out |
| Not interrupted by power cuts | |

## Using gas

1. By law only a Registered Gas Installer (RGI) is permitted to carry out work in domestic natural gas installations.
2. Follow instructions (for central heating system, cylinders, appliances, etc.).
3. Rooms with gas appliances must be well ventilated. (Gas uses up oxygen and produces carbon monoxide, a toxic gas. A two-way ventilator called a balanced flue removes gas and admits oxygen.) Make sure ventilators don't get blocked.
4. Keep appliances and central heating systems clean and serviced.
5. Only buy appliances with a safety mark.

## Gas leaks

- Ensure gas appliances haven't been left on and unlit.
- Don't smoke or use a naked flame.
- Don't uplug or switch anything electrical on or off.
- Open the windows and doors to let the gas disperse.
- If your appliances are off but the smell persists, turn off the gas at the meter.
- Call the natural gas 24-hour emergency service on 1850 205050.
- If you smell gas on the street, don't assume someone else has reported it – call 1850 205050.

## Electricity

Electricity is not a fuel but a clean and efficient form of energy. It can be used for heating, for lighting, to drive the motors of machines, to transmit sound and to make electronic systems work.

## Sources

* Electricity power station

Electricity is generated at **power stations** around the country from coal, gas, oil, peat and water. It leaves the power stations and passes across the country in huge high-powered cables. It enters each home through a **fuse box** or **consumer unit**.

The fuse box/consumer unit contains a **main fuse/switch**, which must be turned off when any repairs are being carried out. Cables pass from the consumer unit bringing power to each room in the house.

An **electric meter** records the amount of electricity we use in units.

A second meter can be installed in homes to enable them to use cheaper off-peak **Nightsaver** electricity (between 11 p.m. and 8 a.m.).

❖ *Fuse box*

Flexes of appliances have at least two wires: a **live wire** (coloured brown), bringing electricity to the appliance; a **neutral wire** (coloured blue) taking the return current. An appliance with only two wires must be double insulated and carry the double insulation symbol. Most appliances have a third wire, the **earth wire** (green and yellow stripes), which brings the current safely to the earth if a fault occurs.

## Possible faults

- Overloading a circuit by using too many appliances at one time or overloading an adaptor.
- Short circuit – a live wire touching a neutral wire in wiring or appliance, or an incorrectly wired plug.
- Overheating of appliance, e.g. due to faulty thermostat.

A **fuse** is a safety device. It is a deliberate weak link in the wiring system. It melts when a fault occurs. This disconnects the electricity and so prevents a fire. Fuses are found in three-pin plugs and in fuse boxes. Modern systems use circuit breakers instead of fuses; they are simply switched on again when the fault is corrected.

## Replacing the fuse in a plug

1. Disconnect appliance and check for faults.
2. Unscrew plug cover and check plug for loose wires.
3. Correct the fault, e.g. the plug wiring, before replacing the fuse, or the fault will recur.
4. Remove old fuse from clips and replace with a fuse of the same strength. (Lights, 6 or 10 amp; appliances, 16 amp.)
5. Replace plug cover.

## Wiring a plug

1. Unscrew the large central screw. Remove cover.
2. Loosen flex-grip screws and remove fuse.
3. Loosen screws of the three terminals: E (earth), L (live) and N (neutral).

❹  Trim away about 3cm of the outer covering of flex and push flex through flex-grip, allowing sufficient length on the three coloured wires to position them in their terminals. Tighten cord grip.

❺  Trim away 5mm of insulation from ends of wires, twist tops and carefully insert each into its terminal. There should be no loose wires. Tighten screws.

❻  Give a final check that each wire is in the correct terminal: Brown to Live; Blue to Neutral; Green/Yellow to Earth. Replace fuse, screw down cover and test.

❖ *Wiring a plug*

loosen flex-grip, remove fuse

insert wires into correct terminals

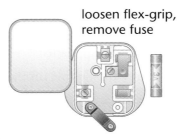

replace fuse, screw down cover

1.  Make a list of all the electrical appliances you have in your home.

2.  What is meant by a unit of electricity? Find out the cost of one unit.

3.  Find out more about Nightsaver electricity. Write five points explaining it.

# Lighting

Good lighting is necessary:

❶  to provide enough light for our activities
❷  to prevent eye strain
❸  to prevent accidents
❹  for good hygiene
❺  to create atmosphere in rooms.

| Natural light | Artificial light |
| --- | --- |
| Daylight enters buildings through windows, doors, skylights, glazed panels. | Electricity is the main source: filament, fluorescent, compact fluorescent lamps (CFLs). |

**Filament lamp:** a glass bulb which lasts about 1,000 hours. Available with bayonet and screw-in tops. Available in clear, pearl, coloured or part mirrored (spotlight) glass. Sold by number of watts, which determines strength of light: 40W and 60W are used for table lamps, etc.; 100W for lighting rooms.

**Fluorescent lamps:** glass tubes 30cm–2.5m long. Expensive to buy, they give out more light and last three times as long as filament lamps.

**Compact fluorescent lamps (CFLs)** are energy-saving bulbs. They are expensive but use 80% less electricity and last about eight times longer than filament lamps.

## Replacing a bulb

Switch off the light. Allow used bulb to cool, then remove. Check wattage and discard carefully. Fit new bulb of correct wattage, turning carefully until it is secure. Test.

❖ *Filament lamp*

❖ *Fluorescent lamp*

# Water

Water is one of our most important resources. It is the responsibility of our local authorities to make sure we have a supply of good, clean drinking water.

## Source

The water in our taps begins as rain. It falls to earth, collects underground and leaves the earth as springs, which flow into rivers and lakes. It is collected in lakes and reservoirs and treated by local authorities.

❖ *CFL lamp*

1. It is filtered to get rid of grit and other impurities.
2. Lime may be added to remove chemicals that cause hardness.
3. Chlorine is added to kill bacteria.
4. Aluminium may be added to make it clear and sparkling.
5. Fluoride may be added to strengthen teeth.

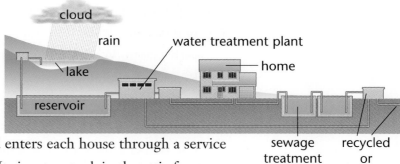

Water is brought to our home through mains, and enters each house through a service pipe where there is a main valve to turn it on/off. It rises to a tank in the attic from where it flows to taps (with the exception of the kitchen sink, which gets direct water), lavatory, boilers and the immersion heating cylinder, where it may be heated.

## Water heating

1. Back boiler, behind fire grate.
2. Instant heater or shower.

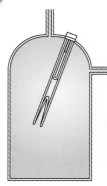

❸ Immersion heater (electric element fitted into cylinder in hot press).

❹ A central heating system may also heat water.

❖ *Immersion heater*

## The kitchen sink

### Position

Sinks are usually placed under a window, not just for the pleasant outlook but also:

- to provide good light so you can see what you are doing
- for ventilation – an open window lets out steam
- to make plumbing easier, as pipes can go through the outside wall.

❖ *Double sink*

### Sink design

Sinks are usually made from stainless steel because it is hardwearing, stain-resistant and easy to clean. A sink may have a single or double draining board; if it is single, try to have the draining board on the right. (Why?) It may be inset into the worktop, and is usually fitted over the cupboard units of a fitted kitchen. These provide storage for detergents, basins and other cleaning resources related to washing.

As with all plumbed fittings such as showers and baths, there is an S-trap (or U-bend) under a sink. This holds water and prevents unpleasant smells and germs entering the kitchen from the outside drain.

### How to unblock a sink

If a sink gets blocked frequently, it is a sign that you are emptying unsuitable things into it, e.g. grease, tea-leaves. When unblocking, try the simplest method first.

❶ Remove any debris from waste outlet. Half-fill the sink and cover the overflow with a cloth. Work a plunger up and down over the outlet to create suction. Repeat a few times.

❷ Place a lump of washing soda over the waste outlet and pour boiling water through it; or use a drain cleaner.

❸ Use rubber gloves. Place a basin under the S-bend and unscrew the fitting. Use a wire to loosen debris from the top, then pour boiling water through. Replace nut, then run cold water to fill S-bend.

## Burst pipes

❶ Frozen pipes can be unblocked by directing a hair-drier (medium heat) at the areas you think may be blocked, working backwards from the tap.

❷ Turn off the water at the mains and turn on all cold taps to empty the system.

**3** Turn off central heating and put out fire of back boiler.

**4** Call the plumber. If there is a delay and the water keeps flowing, wrap the leak as tightly as possible.

# Heating

Heat travels from a heat source in one of three ways:

| Conduction | Convection | Radiation |
|---|---|---|
| Heat travels along metal pipes. | Heaters heat the air, which rises and then falls as it cools. | Coal fires, gas and electric fires send out hot rays which heat the room. |

A home can be heated by:

**1** full central heating

**2** background heating, e.g. storage heaters, which partly heat the house

**3** individual heaters which are switched on when they are needed. Some are portable, e.g. electric and gas heaters, gas 'Super Ser' heaters. Others are fixed in place, e.g. coal fires, wood-burning stoves and electric and gas wall heaters.

LINK-UP

Heat travels to food in three ways, page 84

## Central heating

The term 'central heating' means that the whole house is comfortably heated from a central source, e.g. a boiler. The heat is pumped around the house in pipes and heats radiators in each room. The average room temperature should be 18–20°C. Many systems also heat water.

## Insulation

Whichever system of heating you choose, it will be expensive. For this reason it is important to trap the heat in the house and prevent heat loss. This is called **insulation**. A house can lose 75% of its heat if there is no insulation.

**Insulating materials** are made from poor conductors of heat. That means that heat doesn't travel through them easily. Poor heat conductors include trapped air, paper, fibreglass and loosely woven textiles such as wool. A duvet is a bad conductor – it's the air trapped inside the loose filling that keeps you warm.

❖ *Electric storage heater*

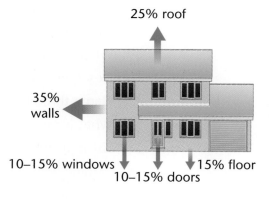

❖ *Average heat loss in an uninsulated house*

❖ *Lagging jacket*

❖ *Attic insulation*

## Forms of insulation

1. **Hot water cylinder** – a thick lagging jacket on your hot water cylinder saves energy and money.

2. **Draught excluders** – foam, plastic and metal draught excluders are good for keeping out draughts around doors. Seals around windows, carpets and underlays on the floor also keep out draughts.

3. **Attic insulation** – hot air rises, so most heat loss (up to 30%) is through the roof. A 10cm layer of fibreglass or loose-fill insulation will save lots of heat and money over the years.

4. **Cavity wall insulation** – cavity walls have a space between the blocks which retains heat. Sheets of polystyrene or insulating beads in this space will act like an overcoat, keeping more heat in the house.

5. **Window insulation** – double glazing (e.g. gas-filled glazing) is up to 20% more efficient than traditional double glazing.

## Energy efficiency

See page 331.

❖ *Cavity wall insulation*

**REVISION QUESTIONS**

1. List four guidelines for using gas in the home.
2. Explain the following electrical terms: consumer unit; meter; Nightsaver electricity; earth wire
3. What is a fuse? Describe how to replace a fuse in a plug.
4. What are the three colours of wire used in a plug and where should each go?
5. What is the function of lighting?
6. Name three types of light bulb. Describe one.
7. Describe how local authorities treat water in order to make it pure.
8. Name four methods of water heating.
9. Where is an S-trap or U-bend situated? What is its purpose?
10. Describe briefly how to deal with a gas leak.
11. Name three forms of heat transfer.
12. What is meant by a poor conductor of heat?
13. List four methods of insulating the home.
14. Outline two safety precautions that should be taken in the event of a gas leak at home.
15. Give two advantages of using CFLs in the home.

*Test Yourself* eTest.ie

# Chapter 41 The Environment and You

**Natural resources** include sunlight, air, water, wind, fossil fuels (oil, natural gas, coal and peat) and trees/wood. Many of these are not unlimited, and if we waste them there will be none left for future generations.

**Pollution** is a major environmental problem due to increased populations and greater use of consumer goods, packaging and chemicals.

| Air pollution | Water pollution |
| --- | --- |
| **Sources** | **Sources** |
| Carbon dioxide (from breathing) | Human sewage |
| Carbon monoxide | Animal slurry |
| (from burning fuels such as coal and petrol) | Industrial and chemical waste released into rivers |
| Sulphur dioxide (from industry) | Oil spills at sea |
| CFC gases, which destroy the ozone layer | Over-use of detergents, etc. causes foaming |
| (see page 330) | Marine dumping |
| | Fertilisers leaching into groundwater/rivers |
| **Effects** | **Effects** |
| Acid rain, which damages buildings and wildlife | Food-poisoning outbreaks |
| Respiratory problems, e.g. asthma and bronchitis | Reduction in oxygen, which can kill plants and fish |
| | Unpleasant smells |
| | Killing of fish and vegetation |
| | Eutrophication (too many nutrients in the water, leading to too much plant growth, which destroys other living organisms in the water) |

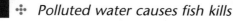

❖ *Polluted water causes fish kills*

## Other forms of pollution

❧ The **countryside** is defaced by discarded cars, illegal dumping, badly sited buildings.

❧ **Cities** are polluted by cars, dirt, litter and graffiti.

### Ozone

Older refrigerators and packaging used for fast foods contain chlorofluorocarbons (CFCs). In the past, many other products contained CFCs, especially aerosol cans. CFCs damage and reduce the ozone layer of the atmosphere, which protects us from the more harmful rays of the sun. This increases the risk of skin cancer and also causes the planet to overheat, leading to the 'greenhouse effect'. This means that the heat coming to earth from the sun becomes trapped and cannot escape, which causes the earth to warm up. This is a big problem because it leads to changes in weather, e.g. flooding, causes the polar ice caps to melt, and creates problems for wildlife.

We must use biodegradable products and avoid CFCs.

*Note:* **Biodegradable products break down naturally in the environment.**

❖ *The polar ice caps are melting as a result of the greenhouse effect*

**ACTIVITIES**

Name three biodegradable and three non-biodegradable products.

## What can we do? Lots!

❧ Avoid using products that contain CFCs.
❧ Reduce fossil fuel use.
❧ Recycle as many things as we can.
❧ Lower heating thermostats.
❧ Switch to energy-efficient lightbulbs.

Being a consumer society means we use a lot of products and a lot of packaging. Let's try to use less of everything – less energy, less water, fewer disposable products, fewer cleaning agents, less packaging, less petrol (walk or cycle instead).

## Energy efficiency

**Be economical with energy. not only will this save money, but more energy resources will be left for future generations.**

1. Insulate houses well (see page 327).
2. Switch off lights when leaving a room.
3. Switch off heaters when not needed.
4. Avoid blocking radiators with curtains and furniture.
5. Keep doors closed, and windows opened just enough for ventilation.
6. Turn down thermostats as the weather gets warmer.
7. Use energy-saving light bulbs (CFLs) (page 325).
8. Don't leave appliances on standby – this uses a significant amount of energy (as much as half as when the appliance is switched on).
9. Dry clothes outside where possible and don't always use the tumble drier. Turn off computers when not in use.
11. Buy energy-efficient equipment: look out for labelling.

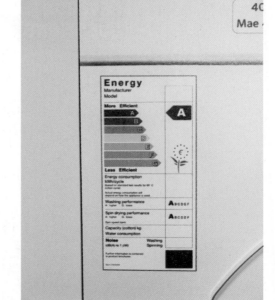

❖ *Heating thermostat*

## Water

1. Lag hot water cylinder.
2. Take showers instead of baths.
3. Fill up appliances before using, e.g. dishwashers.
4. Never wash things under running water, especially hot water.
5. Use the half-load economy wash on washing machines.
6. Have dripping taps, etc. repaired.
7. Service boilers regularly.

**CTIVITIES**

List some other ways in which you could save energy in your household.

# The consumer and the environment

One of the main problems with the increase in consumer goods is the effect they are having on our environment.

## How can we help?

- **Reduce** the amount of unnecessary things you buy. Have things repaired instead of replacing them.
- **Bring your own bag** to the supermarket or use boxes to pack your groceries.
- **Reuse** household items, e.g. plastic containers.
- **Recycle** all possible resources. Bring bottles, cans, newspapers and cardboard to recycling centres.
- Use a **compost heap** for plant and kitchen waste.
- **Clothing** can be given to charity, given to swap shops or recycled.
- **Don't litter** or deface the environment – it's the only world we have.

Plan a recycling awareness campaign for your school. Use the management formula (page 295).

1. Name five natural resources.
2. Describe three effects of air pollution.
3. Name three forms of water pollution and describe two of its effects.
4. What are the consequences of the 'greenhouse effect'?
5. What do we mean by biodegradable?
6. List six ways in which you could save energy in your home.
7. Suggest some practical ways in which we could help our environment.
8. Suggest four ways in which a consumer can reduce household waste.
9. What is the function of the ozone layer?

Basic hygiene in the home is essential if the family is to remain in good health. In the past century, standards of hygiene have improved enormously, yet there are still high rates of food poisoning and other diseases caused by lack of hygiene.

| Bacteria need | They are destroyed by |
| --- | --- |
| Food | Very high temperatures |
| Warmth | Soap and detergents |
| Moisture | Disinfectants |
| Time | Antiseptics |
| Air (usually) | Fresh air and sunlight |

 **Reminder:** Bacteria cause a wide range of diseases

Food hygiene,
pages 69–72

## Basic home hygiene requirements

1. Homes should be warm and dry – dampness leads to respiratory disease.
2. There should be enough space without overcrowding people.
3. There should be clean water and an efficient, hygienic drainage system.
4. Good ventilation is essential, particularly in kitchens and bathrooms.
5. Good lighting shows up dirt. Germs thrive in dirty dark places.
6. Kitchens and bathrooms should be well designed and easy to clean. Sinks, lavatories, floors and drains must be disinfected regularly.

## Hygiene in the bathroom

Many bacteria live in the bowel. For this reason they are frequently found in bathrooms, particularly on the lavatory bowl, flushing handle, surrounding floor and hand towel. These should be kept spotlessly clean and disinfected frequently. Clean the lavatory bowl weekly using a specialised lavatory cleaner. Keep other bathroom surfaces clean, and launder towels regularly. Avoid using carpets, toilet mats and seat covers in the bathroom, as these harbour germs.

## Waste disposal

There are two types of household waste:

**1** **Organic waste** consists of human waste or sewage, food waste, and natural materials such as paper, cotton, wood, etc. All are biodegradable. Much waste that can be recycled is collected by the local authorities in a separate colour-coded bin.

**2** **Inorganic waste** consists of metal, glass, delph, plastic and many household objects. Many inorganic materials can now be recycled (see page 332). Those that can't usually get collected in our bins by the local authority and go to landfill. This type of waste should be kept to a minimum.

### Bins

All bins that are used to store waste should be kept really clean in order to avoid attracting flies by their unpleasant smell.

**1** Empty kitchen bin regularly.

**2** Put out wheelie bin weekly.

**3** Keep bins covered/closed at all times to prevent vermin getting in.

**4** Wrap sharp objects and wet rubbish in newspaper before putting in bin.

**5** Wash bins regularly inside and out, rinse, disinfect and dry.

Work plans, page 295

## Cleaning and cleaning resources

### Sequence for cleaning appliances, e.g. cooker, fridge

**1** Protect self and surroundings, e.g. put on an apron, cover floor.

**2** Collect cleaning resources.

**3** Tidy away things that would get in the way, e.g. saucepans; empty the fridge

**4** Remove loose parts and steep, if necessary

**5** Work from the top down.

**6** Wash with hot or warm soapy water.

**7** Rinse and dry.

**8** Replace parts.

### Cleaning equipment

Store it all together in one cupboard. A basket or box keeps resources together for cleaning tasks.

- Sweeping brush
- Dustpan
- Handbrush
- Vacuum cleaner

- Wet (e.g. squeegee) mop
- Bucket
- Dusters and cloths

# Cleaning agents

**Store together out of reach of children. Many cleaning agents are poisonous.**

## Using cleaning agents

1. Many cleaning agents are dangerous. Store in original containers out of reach of children, e.g. in a locked cupboard.
2. Protect hands with rubber gloves; protect clothes, e.g. with an apron.
3. Use gentlest treatment first, e.g. soak in water or wash in warm water.
4. Follow directions for use.
5. Use mildest cleanser first; use strongest only as a last resort.
6. Rinse away all traces of cleaning agent.

**REVISION QUESTIONS**

1. Bacteria are destroyed by _____, _____, _____, _____.
2. List the basic requirements of a hygienic home.
3. List three guidelines for keeping a bathroom hygienic.
4. Name three types of organic waste and three types of inorganic waste.
5. Name six pieces of cleaning equipment.
6. Name four types of cleaning agent, and give examples of where they would be used.
7. List three guidelines to follow when using cleaning agents.
8. Make out a daily routine to be followed by an asthmatic to keep his/her room hygienic.
9. What rules should be followed when storing cleaning agents?

| Type | Example | Use | Cost* |
|---|---|---|---|
| Water | A solvent | For soaking, washing (hot water is better for grease) | |
| Detergents | Flash, Bold | To dissolve grease; for clothes, paintwork, floors | |
| Abrasives | Brillo | Stubborn stains on strong surfaces, e.g. metal | |
| Cream cleansers | Cif | Kitchen and bathroom surfaces, cookers | |
| Polishes | Spray (e.g. Pledge), wood polish | Shining furniture and floors | |
| | Metal (e.g. Brasso, Silvo) | Removing tarnish and polishing metals | |
| Window cleaners | Windolene | Cleaning and polishing windows | |
| Bleaches | | For removing stains, whitening sinks, etc. | |
| Disinfectants | Dettol | For killing germs – they do not remove dirt and stains | |

*Fill in cost and size of product, e.g. €1.70 for 300ml.

## Safety and accidents in the home

Many deaths and injuries are caused each year by accidents in the home. The dictionary defines 'accident' as 'something that happens by chance'. Very often there are more obvious causes, e.g. those listed below. We need to be aware of the possibilities of injury by making a conscious effort to make the home a safe place to be. Special attention must be given to safety if children or an elderly person lives in the home.

## Causes of accidents

1. Bad design features, e.g. internal glass doors, unnecessary steps.
2. Badly maintained houses, e.g. broken furniture
3. Incorrect use of electricity or equipment.
4. Careless storage of dangerous equipment or chemicals.
5. Untidiness – leaving things on floors and stairs; leaving flexes hanging down.
6. People's behaviour – curious children, forgetful older people.
7. Bad lighting.

❖ *Electricity and water don't mix*

## Electrical safety

1. Water and electricity should be kept apart. Never touch electric appliances with wet hands or bring anything electrical into the bathroom.
2. Appliances should be properly wired and earthed.
3. Buy reliable appliances and equipment which carry a safety symbol.
4. Keep equipment in good condition. Service when necessary and have faulty appliances repaired.
5. Avoid trailing flexes, overloaded sockets and faulty equipment and connections.

## Falls

1. Stairs and awkward corners should be well lit. Have a light switch at top and bottom of stairs.

2. Objects such as toys should never be left on the stairs or floors.

3. Install a safety gate at top and bottom of the stairs if small children are about.

4. Avoid slippery floors and frayed rugs. Non-stick backing is available for rugs.

5. Wipe up spills immediately.

6. Have hand grips on bath and shower, particularly for elderly people.

7. Use sturdy household steps instead of a chair, etc. to reach high places.

❖ *Two-way light switch*

❖ *Safety gate*

## Children

1. Keep dangerous objects out of reach of children. These include poisons, medicines, cleaning agents, gardening products, knives, plastic bags and small objects that might cause them to choke.

2. Keep small babies strapped into baby chairs out of harm's way while working in the kitchen.

3. Children in prams and buggies should be strapped into them. Use restrainers when they are older.

❖ *Hand grips*

4. Use safety gates on stairs, kitchen and garden if necessary to keep them out of harm's way.

5. Be conscious that children can drown in a few centimetres of water. Leave no filled basins, etc. about. They must always be watched near garden ponds and pools. Never leave them unattended in a bath.

❖ *Small children and babies should not be left alone in the bath*

❖ *Position medicine cabinets out of the reach of children*

Resource Management and Home Studies

## Fire safety

1. Install smoke alarms, and test batteries regularly to check that they are working.
2. Keep a fire extinguisher in the centre of the house.
3. Keep a fire blanket near the cooker in the kitchen.
4. Place a fireguard around fires.
5. Wear flameproof nightwear (particularly children).
6. Never leave a deep fat fryer unattended.
7. Be careful where you leave cigarettes, and NEVER smoke in bed.
8. Before going to bed, unplug TV and other appliances and close all doors to prevent a fire spreading.

### Fire drill

**A fire drill is an outline of how to behave in case of a fire.**

#### Small fire

1. Use fire extinguisher or blanket to put out fire.
2. Water may be used, but NEVER on electricity or burning fat.
3. If fire cannot be extinguished, call fire brigade.

#### Large fire

1. Raise the alarm. Get a neighbour to ring the fire brigade.
2. Remember there is more oxygen near the floor; cover face with damp cloth and crawl towards nearest exit.
3. Make sure everyone leaves the house, closing all doors to prevent fire spreading.
4. Never re-enter a burning house.
5. Have a family fire drill so that each person knows what to do.

**ACTIVITIES**

1. Make a list of people or organisations (apart from fire officers) responsible for our safety and protection.
2. List some common causes of fire.

## First aid

The aim in first aid is first to preserve life. This means dealing with small accidents quickly and calmly and, in the case of serious accidents, making the patient comfortable without worsening the condition until the arrival of a doctor or ambulance.

1. Avoid moving patient at all unless he or she is in immediate danger, e.g. of a car catching fire. Ring for an ambulance.
2. Check the pulse and see whether the patient is conscious.
3. Start mouth-to-mouth resuscitation if necessary.
4. Any bleeding must be stopped by applying pressure.
5. Avoid giving food or drink – patients must be fasting if they need an anaesthetic.
6. Guard against shock by covering with something light, and make the patient comfortable without moving them.

✛ *Taking a pulse*

## First-aid box

Keep a well-stocked first-aid box in a clearly visible place at home, e.g. in the kitchen. Keep it out of reach of small children. Keep it very clean and tidy with items in wrappings or small plastic bags to keep them clean. Medicines and drugs should be kept in a separate, locked medicine cupboard.

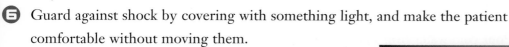

## Simple first aid
### Cuts and scratches

1. Stop bleeding by applying pressure.
2. Wash a dirty wound such as a graze from the inside out using sterile gauze dipped in warm water containing antiseptic.
3. Dry gently with cotton wool. Apply a clean dressing, e.g. plaster or sterile gauze and bandage.
4. If the cut is deep and blood is spurting, apply pressure and get medical help. A tetanus shot may be needed.

### Falls, strains and sprains

If the joint is in an unusual position or pain seems excessive, it may be a fracture or dislocation. Do not move the person. Send for a doctor or dial 999.

A strain is a pulled muscle; a sprain may involve torn or damaged ligaments. Treat with a cold compress using a cloth soaked in iced water.

✛ *Applying pressure to a cut*

Then dry and wrap firmly but not tightly in a crepe bandage. The patient should rest for a day or so.

### Burns and scalds

Burns are caused by dry heat; scalds by moist heat. The heat sterilises the wound, so avoid touching. Immerse in clean cold water for 5 minutes.

Cover with burn gauze or spray to exclude air.

### Major burns and scalds

1. If clothes catch fire, push patient to the ground, wrap in nearest blanket or coat to quench flames or, if this is not possible, simply roll them over on the ground.
2. Remove rings, watches, etc. before area swells.
3. Pour cold water over burnt area or, if the area is too large to do this, wrap in a clean dry cloth, e.g. a sheet, to exclude air.
4. Do not apply dressings, lotions or creams. Do not attempt to remove clothing.
5. Treat for shock and get medical help.

❖ *Heimlich manoeuvre*

### Choking

Choking is caused by a blockage in the airway. It must be dealt with very quickly.

1. If a child, place face down on the lap, with head lower than body. Slap sharply between the shoulder blades.
2. Adults: slap sharply on the back three or four times. If this doesn't work try the Heimlich manoeuvre:
   - stand behind the person and put your arms around him or her, clasping your hands so that the side of your fist is just above the waist
   - give a sharp upward thrust under the ribcage. Repeat four times.

### Shock

This is a physical reaction caused by a sudden drop in blood pressure. The patient looks pale and feels cold and clammy, even on a warm day. Pulse is rapid but weak, and he or she may feel dizzy, weak and sick.

1. Lie patient down with feet up. Loosen tight clothing around neck and waist.
2. Cover with a light coat or sheet but do not make him/her too warm.
3. Give nothing to eat or drink until shock has passed.

# Fainting

This is caused by a shortage of blood to the brain. If a patient feels weak, bring them into the fresh air, loosen tight clothing and get them to place their head down between their knees. If lying, place something under feet to raise them. Only give a drink of water if the patient is fully conscious.

1. Carry the faint person into the fresh air or near a window. Place lying flat with feet raised.

2. Loosen clothing round neck, chest and waist and cover with a light sheet or coat.

3. Apply a cold cloth to face. Allow patient to rest; do not move them too quickly. Give a drink when patient is fully conscious.

# Poisoning

Poisoning may occur in small children who have swallowed cleaning agents, or due to drug-taking or overdose.

1. Call an ambulance or bring patient quickly to hospital.

2. Try to find out what has been taken and, if possible, bring samples of poison, the bottle and patient's vomit.

3. Never try to make patient sick: if it is corrosive, the poison may damage the throat.

4. Keep patient lying in the recovery position in case of further vomiting.

# Recovery position

Never place a patient on their back, as they may choke if vomiting occurs. Place on their side as shown, with head to one side and arm and leg raised. Make sure nothing is blocking the airways.

❖ *Recovery position*

**REVISION QUESTIONS**

1. List five main causes of accidents in the home.
2. List four precautions to follow in order to prevent accidents with electricity.
3. List three precautions to prevent accidents to children.
4. List five fire safety precautions in the home.
5. What is the procedure to follow when a major fire occurs in the home?
6. Define first aid. Where would you store a first-aid box at home? Why?
7. List the first-aid procedure for dealing with a traffic accident victim.
8. Differentiate between a burn and a scald. Describe the first aid for a minor scald.
9. How would you deal with an adult who is choking?
10. You suspect that a friend has overdosed on drugs. Describe the first aid you would perform.
11. Describe the first-aid treatment for a sprained ankle.

*Test Yourself*
eTest.ie

Part

# 5

# Textile Studies

# Chapter 44 Textiles in Clothing

**A textile usually means a fabric or cloth.** However, textiles are also found in a wide range of articles such as soft furnishings, carpets, umbrellas, shoes, rucksacks and sails. One of the main uses of textiles is clothing.

❖ *Clothing giving protection from the cold*

❖ *Clothing for identification*

## Functions of clothing

**1** **Protection from the weather.** Clothes protect us from cold, wind, rain and sun. It is important to wear the right clothes for the weather. Certain clothes are treated to make them wind- or water-resistant; they may be padded to add extra warmth.

**2** **Safety.** Clothing is used to protect people from injury, e.g. protective overalls in garages and factories; reflective clothing for night-time. Surgeons and food workers wear clothes that help prevent infection.

**3** **Modesty.** Most people wish to preserve the privacy of their bodies. The idea of modesty varies in different cultures and religions, and has changed with time. In Victorian times people covered their bodies completely. Today less clothing is acceptable, e.g. people wear little clothing on the beach.

**4** **Identification.** Police, nurses, soldiers and airline staff are easily identified by their uniforms. National costumes give people a sense of identity and pride in their country. School uniforms identify the school you go to and help to make everyone feel equal. (Do you agree with this statement?)

**5** **Self-expression.** People use clothes to express their personality. Wearing clothes we like and colours that suit us

makes us feel more attractive. People like to dress up for special occasions such as weddings and parties. They wear dark clothes for mourning.

**6** **To influence others.** Judges wear wigs, etc. to show their status. Expensive designer clothes and logos are an important status symbol for some. The right clothes for an occasion such as work or an interview make us feel more confident and help us get (or keep) a job.

**❖** *Clothing showing status*

## Design using textiles

The main object in designing clothes and other textile products is to produce an article that looks well and fulfils its function.

**1** **Function.** Clothing should be well finished and use fabrics that fulfil the purpose of the garment, e.g. warm fabrics for winter clothes, cool absorbent fabrics for summer clothes. Household textiles should be washable and hardwearing.

**2** **Colour** is an important design feature in clothes. The colours we wear should suit our skin tone, eyes and hair. Other than that, the colours we choose are a matter of personal taste and often express our personality. Primary colours such as red, yellow and blue attract the eye and make one stand out in a crowd. Neutral colours – black, grey, cream, beige and camel – are classic and safe, and do not date.

**3** **Pattern** is often a matter of fashion and taste. As with interiors, pattern in clothes needs to be used with care or it can appear fussy. Few people look well in large patterns, except very tall people.

**4** **Texture** can add interest to a garment. Smooth textures flatter small people; rough textures such as fake fur are better avoided by short or overweight people except on small areas such as collars.

**5** **Form** refers to the shape or outline of the garment – a garment such as a short jacket or three-quarter-length coat can have a square shape; wide shoulders and a narrow skirt can give an attractive triangular shape. The form or shape of a garment should suit the figure of the wearer.

Design in the home, page 300

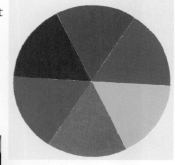

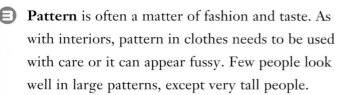

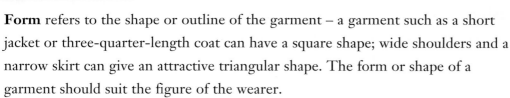

345

**6** **Line** can be used to emphasise your good features or draw attention from your bad ones.

- **Vertical lines** make people look taller and thinner. Stripes are an obvious example, but even things like buttoning can alter our perception, e.g. a single-breasted jacket gives a vertical line and makes people look thinner. Double-breasted coats and suits can make those wearing them look wider.

- **Horizontal lines** widen the figure and make people look smaller.

- **Curves** give a soft, feminine look.

- **Diagonal lines** are unusual and striking.

- **Asymmetrical** buttoning or fastenings can be dramatic.

**7** **Balance** means that there is harmony and proportion between the parts of the design, that nothing is too big or too small, e.g. a huge collar on a skimpy jacket, a huge frill on a mini skirt.

**8** **Emphasis.** Contrasting colour can be used to give emphasis to an outfit, e.g. black collar and cuffs on a red coat; contrasting braid around a jacket. Accessories and jewellery are also useful for adding emphasis.

## Fashion

The word 'fashion' is used to describe the style of clothing that is popular at a particular time.

In the past, only the wealthy could afford to dress fashionably, so royalty set the standards. Today, mass production of clothes and a wide variety of shops mean that most people can wear the latest fashion, if they choose to do so.

### Fashion trends

Fashion is constantly changing. Fashion **trends** are **changes in fashion** such as colour, skirt length and style, e.g. the short mini skirts of the 1960s. They might last from six months to a year or two or longer. Fashion **fads** are often more extreme, e.g.

strong colours; they are usually worn by younger people and have a **short life**. Recent examples include maxi dresses, wet look leggings and fedora hats.

Fashion trends are influenced by:

- **Famous people**, often called trend-setters, e.g. music stars, models, actors, fashion designers.
- **The media**, e.g. magazines, TV, film. American programmes in the 1980s, together with women gaining more powerful positions in work, resulted in 'power dressing' – masculine suits and wide, padded shoulders.
- **Historical events**, e.g. wars. During the First World War, when women took over factory work from men at war, clothes and fabrics became more practical and full skirts disappeared. Fabric was scarce during the Second World War, so skirts became straight and shorter. After the war, Dior celebrated by creating the 'New Look' – a fitted bodice and full skirt which used lots of fabric.
- Protests against the Vietnam war encouraged a peaceful 'hippy' lifestyle and flowing 'flower power' fashions.
- **Street fashion** is when everyday clothes rather than designers influence fashion. Examples: jeans, cycling shorts, baseball caps.
- The **fashion industry** is the main influence on high street fashion trends. In order to create turnover in fashion, the industry promotes new colours, styles, etc. as part of the 'new season'. This makes last year's fashion out of date, so that more clothes are sold.

## The fashion industry

The 'rag trade' employs a large number of people. Twice a year, top fashion designers show a collection of new designs at international fashion shows in London, Paris, Milan and New York. These set the fashion for the next season – October collections show fashions for the following spring/summer; March collections for the following autumn/winter. These **haute couture** (high fashion) clothes are original, hand-made and very expensive. **Prêt-à-porter** (ready-to-wear) clothes are less expensive machine-made ranges from top designers. Manufacturers buy or copy these designs using cheaper fabrics and mass production methods to produce cheap off-the-peg clothes which are sold in chain stores.

# What influences your choice of clothes?

1. **Age.**
2. **Cost** – what you can afford.
3. **Personal taste** – what you think suits you.
4. **Peers** – what other people your age are wearing.
5. **Lifestyle** and **occupation**, e.g. whether a student or solicitor.
6. **Fashion trends** (see above) and advertising.
7. **Culture** – what is acceptable in your culture, e.g. shorts are unlikely to be worn by Muslim women.

# Practical considerations when shopping for clothes

- Cost – is it within my price range?
- Need – I need a warm sweater for winter more than the dress I'd like.
- Size and figure type – what suits me.
- Fit – does it fit well?
- Comfort.
- Good quality and value for money.
- Properties, e.g. warm or cool depending on the season.
- Suitability for the occasion, e.g. work, sport.
- Care – is it easy to launder or must it be dry-cleaned? Look at the care label.

## Fashion style

This is a total look – clothes, accessories, jewellery, hairstyle and often make-up. Examples of fashion styles include retro (retrospective) – looking back to a fashion style of the past, e.g. 1950s or 1960s – sporty, casual, business, classic or trendy.

## Accessories

These help to complete a look. They include shoes, gloves, ties, hats, belts, scarves, bags, jewellery, socks and tights. Good-quality classic accessories are best, in dark or neutral colours. Do you agree? Why/why not?

**ACTIVITY**

1. Name some jobs in which certain types of clothing are worn to protect people from danger.

2. Discuss things other than clothes that go in and out of fashion.

3. Begin a textile folder. Design an attractive title page using a collage of fabrics. Collect fashion photographs and use the next two pages to illustrate current fashions for teenagers. Continue to use this folder for fabric samples, photos, design briefs, etc. as a record of your textile studies.

4. How do you think age influences our choice of clothes? Describe what the priorities of (a) a teenager and (b) a pensioner might be.

5. Suggest accessories for (a) Paula's dark grey business suit; (b) Paul's summer jeans and polo shirt.

6. Pat is going on holiday in the sun for one week. Make a list of the minimum amount of clothes he or she should bring. Name the fabrics that would best suit hot climates, and say why.

7. Make a simple sketch of an outfit you would wear to a job interview for (a) a sales person in a boutique or (b) a bank official. Explain the reasons for your choice.

**REVISION QUESTIONS**

1. What is a textile?

2. Name four functions of clothing, giving one example of each.

3. Describe two ways in which line can be used in clothes.

4. What is a fashion trend? Name four influences on fashion trends.

5. Name two ways to add emphasis to an outfit.

6. What influences people's choice of clothes?

7. Name four guidelines for buying clothes.

8. Explain the terms 'haute couture' and 'prêt-à-porter'.

9. Why are accessories worn with clothing?

Test Yourself
eTest.ie

# Chapter 45 Textiles in the Home

Textiles are not simply for clothing fabrics – they are used in a wide range of products.

## Uses of textiles

- Clothing
- Curtains
- Shoes
- Luggage
- Seat belts
- Carpets

From this list we can see that textiles have to be suitable for different kinds of jobs. Choosing a textile for a job means looking at its **properties**.

A **property** or **characteristic** is a **special quality which is typical of the object**, e.g. silk is smooth.

| Some properties of textiles | | |
| --- | --- | --- |
| Soft | Heavy | Crease-resistant |
| Rough | Elastic | Warm |
| Resilient (bounces back) | Absorbent | Waterproof |
| Strong | Drapes well | Open-textured |
| Washable | Cool | Smooth |
| Light | Stretchy | Insulating |
| Close-textured | | |

A textile item should have properties to suit its purpose. For example, underwear should be soft and absorbent; a rucksack should be strong, lightweight and waterproof.

**ACTIVITY**

| | | |
|---|---|---|
| Duvet | Armchair | Curtains |
| Carpet | Oven gloves | Anorak |
| Track suit bottoms | Work overalls | |

What properties would be required for the objects above?

## Household textiles

Textiles have many uses in the home. Examples:

| | | |
|---|---|---|
| Curtains | Cushions | Chair covers |
| Duvets | Blankets | Carpets |
| Bed linen | Towels | Kitchen cloths |

### Considerations when buying household textiles

1. Cost
2. Durability
3. Ease of cleaning
4. Properties: suited to purpose?
5. Colour, pattern, texture (soft furnishings)

## Soft furnishings

Soft furnishings are room furnishings made from textiles, e.g. curtains, cushions and duvet covers. Soft furnishings add warmth, comfort and style to a room.

### Properties to look for in soft furnishings

- **Curtains** – hang and drape well, resistant to fading, fire-resistant, washable, pre-shrunk, closely woven (to keep out light).
- **Cushion and bed covers** – attractive, washable, durable, fire-resistant, resistant to dirt and fading.
- **Upholstery\* fabrics** – tough and durable, resistant to fading, stain-resistant, washable or spongeable, closely woven, comply with fire safety regulations.

❖ *Fire-resistant label*

**\*Upholstery refers to both the covering fabric on chairs, sofas, mattresses, etc. and the filling inside them.** New upholstered furniture must use fabrics and filling materials that resist burning by matches and cigarettes (1988 safety regulations). In the past, polyurethane foam was used in upholstery, which released toxic fumes during fires. Only combustion-modified foam (CMF) may now be used. Look out for these labels – the square one is used on the more fireproof furniture.

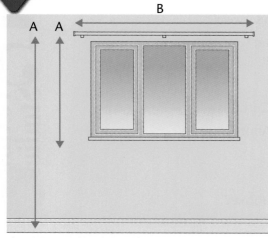

❖ *Measuring curtains*

# Curtains

Functions:

- ◆ shut out light
- ◆ insulate
- ◆ give privacy

- ◆ are decorative
- ◆ shut out noise
- ◆ reduce draughts.

Measurements required:

(A) Length – from rail to 5cm below sill (short) or 2cm from floor (long).

(B) Width – 2.5 times width of rail or window.

## Suitable fabrics

Cotton, linen, Dralon, velvet, polyester or cotton net. Lining helps curtains to hang better. It improves insulation and reduces light, noise and draughts.

## Carpets

Carpets have been made for thousands of years. They originated in the East, and many of the most beautiful carpets still come from countries such as Iran (originally Persia), India, China and Turkey. Most are hand-made, sadly many by child labour. Manufactured carpets are made on huge looms by weaving or fixing tufts of yarn into a strong backing.

The pile or surface hairs can be long, short, twisted or embossed (a raised design).

## Carpet textiles

**Wool** (the oldest material) – warm, resilient, hardwearing, but expensive.

**Man-made** (e.g. nylon, acrylic) – hard-wearing but flattens easily and produces static which attracts dirt.

**Blends** – for example, a mixture of 80% wool and 20% nylon combines the properties of both and is cheaper than wool.

## Carpet grading

Carpets are graded according to quality and durability, e.g.

- ◆ light domestic – for bedrooms
- ◆ general domestic – for living rooms
- ◆ heavy domestic – for the busiest areas of the home, e.g. living rooms, halls and stairs.

## Bedclothes

Bedclothes include sheets, pillowcases, duvet covers, valances, etc.

Properties to look for: absorbent, smooth, comfortable, easy to wash and dry, minimum iron.

Blankets and duvets should be warm, light, comfortable, easy to wash and dry. Warmth of duvets is measured by a tog rating: summer weight, 4.5 tog; warmest, 15 tog.

## Textiles used in bed clothes

1. **Bed linen** – rarely made from linen (too expensive); cotton, polyester or a blend of both.

2. **Duvets** – cover made from cotton, polyester or a blend of both; filling from down or polyester.

3. **Blankets** – wool, a wool and nylon mixture, or a man-made fibre e.g. Acrilan. Man-made fibres are easier to wash and cheaper, but not as warm as wool.

**Towels** are usually made from cotton. The looped weave makes them more absorbent. **Dishcloths** are usually made from cotton or man-made fibres. Disposable cloths such as J-cloths are made from a non-woven man-made fibre. They are hygienic and they wash and dry quickly.

Test Yourself eTest.ie

**ACTIVITY**

Resilience is an important property in a carpet. What does it mean? What other properties are important in carpets?

**REVISION QUESTIONS**

1. Name four uses for textiles other than clothes.
2. What properties would you look for in: (a) babies' nappies; (b) a winter coat; (c) a track suit; (d) bed linen?
3. Name two properties you should find in (a) soft furnishings, (b) upholstery.
4. Name four functions of curtains. What are the advantages of lining curtains?
5. Name three properties suitable for carpets.
6. Name two textiles used in (a) sheets and (b) blankets.
7. Name a property that is important in towels.
8. Explain what is meant by 'tog rating'.
9. Why are soft furnishings used in the home?

# Chapter 46 Fibres and Fabrics

Most textiles begin as very fine fibres. These are twisted together to make yarn or thread. Yarn is woven or knitted to make a fabric or textile. (More about this later.)

Fibres come from several sources.

| Natural fibres | | Man-made fibres | |
|---|---|---|---|
| **Plants** | **Animals** | **Synthetic** | **Regenerated** |
| Cotton | Wool | Nylon | Acetate |
| Linen | Silk | Polyester | Viscose |

## Natural fibres (animal)

| Silk Types | Source and production | Properties Desirable | Uses Clothes |
|---|---|---|---|
| Raw silk<br>Chiffon<br>China silk<br>Crêpe de Chine<br>Charmeuse<br>Jacquard | Silkworm. Feeds on mulberry leaves. Spins a cocoon of silk around itself. If left alone it will transform into a moth and lay eggs which will hatch into silkworms. Instead the cocoons are immersed in hot water to soften the silk. This is wound off as fine threads, then spun into yarn which is used to make silk fabric. | 1. Lightweight but warm<br>2. Crease-resistant<br>3. Strong and smooth<br>4. Absorbs moisture<br>5. Drapes well<br>6. Dyes well<br>7. Good heat resistance to ironing<br><br>**Undesirable**<br>1. Expensive<br>2. Flammable<br>3. Damaged by moths, chemicals and sunlight<br>4. Weak when wet; wash carefully | Shirts, blouses<br>Dresses<br>Suits<br>Trousers<br>Scarves, ties<br>Night wear<br><br>**Household**<br>Cushion and sofa covers<br>Curtains<br>Lampshades |

Pure silk symbol

❖ *Pure silk*

## Natural fibres (animal)

| Wool Types | Source and production | Properties Desirable | | Uses Clothes |
|---|---|---|---|---|
| Tweed | Sheep (or goats, camels, rabbits). Sheep are sheared annually, fleece is graded, washed and dried. Wool fibres are carded with wire-covered rollers. Longer fibres are combed into tops, then spun into worsted yarn for fine suitings or gaberdine. Shorter fibres are used to make woollen yarns for lambswool sweaters and soft woollen cloths such as blankets. | 1. | Warm – insulates well | Coats |
| Flannel | | 2. | Soft and comfortable | Shawls and scarves |
| Crêpe | | 3. | Absorbent | Skirts |
| Jersey | | 4. | Wears well, e.g. carpets | Trousers |
| Gaberdine | | 5. | Elastic, resilient | Dresses |
| | | 6. | Does not burn easily | Jumpers |
| | | | | Hats |
| **WOOLMARK** ® | | **Undesirable** | | **Household** |
| ❖ *100% pure wool* | | 1. | Weak when wet; shrinks and felts if washed carelessly | Carpets |
| | | 2. | Irritates sensitive skins | Rugs |
| **WOOL BLEND** ® | | | | Upholstery |
| | | 3. | Scorches easily | Cushions |
| ❖ *Wool blend* | | 4. | Damaged by moths | Blankets |
| | | 5. | Pills easily | |

## Natural fibres (vegetable)

| Cotton Types | Source and production | Properties Desirable | | Uses Clothes |
|---|---|---|---|---|
| Muslin | Grown in hot countries, e.g. Southern USA, India, Egypt. After flowering, cotton plants develop bolls (pods). These burst when ripe, releasing white fluffy fibres. After harvesting, the seeds are removed and the cotton is graded and cleaned. It is carded (brushed), combed into long strands and spun into thread. | 1. | Strong, wet or dry | Shirts, blouses |
| Flannelette | | 2. | Absorbs moisture | Dresses |
| Denim | | 3. | Cool – good for summer | Sweatshirts |
| Towelling | | 4. | Easy to wash and dry | Trousers, e.g. jeans |
| Corduroy | | 5. | Can be bleached and dyed | T-shirts |
| Canvas | | 6. | Easy to dry clean | Overalls |
| Chenille | | 7. | Doesn't pill easily | |
| Velvet | | **Undesirable** | | **Household** |
| | | 1. | Creases easily so often blended with e.g. polyester | Towels |
| **PURE COTTON** | | | | Bedclothes |
| | | 2. | Little elasticity | Kitchen cloths |
| | | 3. | Shrinks, unless pre-shrunk | Curtains, cushions |
| | | 4. | Burns easily | Duvet covers |
| | | 5. | Damaged by mildew (mould) | |

## Natural fibres (animal)

| Linen | Source and production | Properties Desirable | Uses Clothes |
|---|---|---|---|
| This is the strongest of the vegetable fibres: 2–3 times stronger than cotton  **Types** Lawn Cambric Damask Slub | Linen is a fibre taken from the stalk of the flax plant, a plant grown in damp climates, e.g. Ireland, France, Belgium, Netherlands. The flax is pulled and left to soak until the tough outer stem rots away (retting) and the fibres are exposed. Fibres are dried and then combed, spun into threads and bleached. Irish linen is famous world-wide, both for damask table linen and designer clothes (e.g. Paul Costelloe). | 1. Strong, wet or dry 2. Cool to wear as it conduct  heat away from the body 3. Absorbs moisture 4. Dirt-resistant 5. Washes well 6. Smooth and lint-free 7. Can withstand a lot of heat  **Undesirable** 1. Creases easily 2. Shrinks a lot 3. Difficult to dye 4. Burns easily 5. Damaged by mildew | Shirts Blouses Dresses Trousers Suits and coats   **Household** Curtains Cushions Table linen Tea towels Handkerchiefs |

## Man-made fibres

These were invented at the end of the nineteenth century when scientists looked at how the silkworm produces its long fibres. It digests the cellulose in mulberry leaves, then spins it out as silk through tiny holes in its head. Scientists used cellulose from plants which they pulped and treated with chemicals, then forced it through tiny nozzles to create a sheer fibre called artificial silk. This process of regenerating (re-forming) cellulose was developed to make rayon, viscose and acetate.

Later, **synthetic fibres** were invented which were made entirely from chemicals such as petroleum. The first, called nylon, was made in the late 1930s. This new fabric replaced silk for making stockings (called nylons) and parachutes.

## Artificial fibres

| Regenerated fibres | | Synthetic fibres | |
|---|---|---|---|
| *Examples* | *Production* | *Examples* | *Production* |
| Rayon Viscose Acetate Tri-acetate | Spruce wood or cotton waste is pulped into a thick liquid, mixed with chemicals and heated. The liquid is forced through a spinneret, and dries as it cools to form a long continuous filament.* This is twisted to form a yarn or chopped to make short fibres. | Nylon Polyester Acrylic PVC | Made from coal, petroleum and other chemicals. These are heated, forced through a spinneret, then dried and cooled to produce long filaments or chopped to make short fibres. |

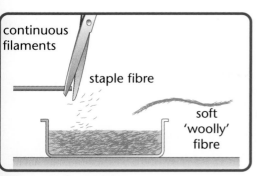

continuous filaments

staple fibre

soft 'woolly' fibre

*A continuous filament is a long, thin, unbroken thread. It is twisted to make a very smooth yarn and therefore very smooth silky fabrics. The filament can be chopped to make short staple fibres. When these are twisted together, they give a soft, fluffy fibre and fabric.

❖ *Continuous filaments*

## Properties of man-made fibres

| Strong | Warm | Absorbent | Crease-resistant | Flame-resistant | Elastic | Water-repellent |
|--------|------|-----------|------------------|-----------------|---------|-----------------|
| Nylon | Viscose Polyester Acrylic | Viscose Acetate | Polyester Elastane | Modacrylic | Lycra | Nylon |

## Disadvantages

All man-made fibres are flammable; some, like nylon, cling, cause static and can be clammy to wear in hot weather. Regenerated fibres are not very hardwearing.

## Uses

All man-made fibres and fabrics have many uses, as they can be altered during manufacture to give various properties. For example:

- **Polyester** can be made into suits, trousers, shirts, dresses, sheets and sheer net curtains. It is used to make wadding, e.g. for anoraks, and filling for pillows and duvets. It is often mixed with cotton because of its wrinkle-resistant property and its ability to retain its shape. Since the items mentioned are frequently worn and washed, its stain-resistance and durability are also desirable.

- **Nylon** is used for anoraks, linings, underwear and tights. It is also used for tents and rainwear. (Why?)

- **Acrylic** is used for sweaters, fleecy linings and blankets because it is warm and fluffy.

- **Lycra** is used in sportswear, swimwear, underwear, socks and tights. (Why?)

- **Dralon** is an acrylic fibre used for curtains and upholstery.

- **Regenerated fibres** such as viscose and rayon are often used for sheer, silky products such as evening wear, blouses and dresses and items such as tablecloths and napkins.

| Chemical name | Brand name |
|---|---|
| Viscose | Rayon, Modal, Tencel |
| Tri-acetate | Tricel |
| Polyamide | Nylon, Bri nylon, Enkalon |
| Polyester | Dacron, Trevira |
| Acrylic | Acrilan, Dralon, Courtelle, Orlon |
| Polyurethane | Lycra |

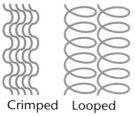 

Crimped   Looped   Soft, fluffy fibre

## Fibres to fabrics

### Making yarn

Take any textile and pull out a thread. Tease this out and you will see that it is made from very fine fibres. Most fibres are too thin to be used in weaving, as they would break. For this reason, **several fibres are twisted together to make a thicker, stronger thread or yarn.** This is known as **spinning**. It is done today at high speed by machines in factories.

Yarn can be treated to give different effects.

- It can be crimped, much as you would crimp hair – this makes it more stretchy.
- It can be looped to give a rough look, e.g. some tweeds.
- It can have short hairs spun into it to make it fluffier.

Two or more types of fibre can be blended to improve the properties of a yarn or fabric. This is done by spinning two different fibres or yarns together. Examples:

- **polyester/cotton** blends the coolness of cotton with the easy-care qualities of polyester
- **80% wool/20% nylon**, often used in carpets, blends the resilience of wool with the strength of nylon.

**Denier: a measurement of the fineness of silk and man-made fibres,** particularly hosiery, e.g. tights. Fine threads have a lower number, e.g. sheer tights are 10 denier; opaque tights 40 denier.

**Ply: the number of yarns twisted together** to make a wool, e.g. 3 ply, 4 ply.

### Yarn to fabric

Yarn can be made into fabric in three ways:

1. weaving
2. knitting
3. bonding.

# Weaving

**Woven fabric is made on a loom by passing one set of yarns over and under the other.** The stronger yarns (**warp**) are stretched lengthwise on the loom. The weaker crosswise yarns (**weft**) fill in the weave by passing over and under the warp threads.

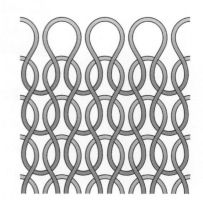

The **selvage** (or selvedge) at the edges of the fabric is where the weft thread turns to go back and the warp threads are closer together: this gives extra strength and prevents fraying.

There are several types of weave:

- **plain** weave is used in fabrics such as lawn
- **diagonal** weave, in denim and gaberdine
- **looped** weave, e.g. towelling
- weaves with a **pile**, e.g. cut loops such as velvet, corduroy.

Look at the fabrics you are wearing. Can you recognise the weave? Perhaps they are not woven at all – read on.

# Knitting

**Knitted fabrics or garments are made by interlocking (looping) threads into one another by hand or machine.** All knitted fabrics are stretchy. There is a huge variety of knitting stitches, all of which give different effects – more or less stretchy, chunky or decorative (e.g. Aran, Fair Isle). Most are based on two simple stitches – plain and purl.

## Properties

Knitted fabrics are stretchy, comfortable and crease-resistant, and need little ironing.

## Uses

Stretchy fabric, such as crêpe and jersey. Sportswear, such as track suits, fitness wear, swimwear. Jumpers, socks, tights, hats, underwear, upholstery (e.g. stretch covers), dish cloths and stretch bandaging.

## Bonded or non-woven fabrics

**These are made by bonding (sticking) together short fibres, usually by moisture, heat and pressure. Interfacings** (e.g. Vilene) contain latex. These are used for stiffening certain areas of clothes, e.g. collars and cuffs.

Bonding also describes a method of applying iron-on interfacing to fabrics. Iron-on interfacings have adhesive on one side which is bonded to fabrics using heat and pressure (i.e. an iron).

**Examples** of bonded fabrics: felt, interfacings, disposable fabrics, wadding.

### Uses

Hats, toys, hospital gowns, disposable cloths (J-cloths), cheap blankets, carpet underlays.

| Advantages of bonded fabrics | Disadvantages of bonded fabrics |
| --- | --- |
| Do not fray | Do not wear well |
| Hold their shape well | Felt is damaged by water |
| Can be washed (except felt) and dry-cleaned | Blankets not as warm, as they don't trap air. |

**ACTIVITY** Make a collage or fabric picture using different fabrics. List the names of the fabrics on the back.

## Fabric finishes

A fabric can be made to look and feel very different. Take cotton – it can be soft and stretchy in a tracksuit; waterproof in a jacket; tough and strong in jeans; and soft, thick and absorbent in a bath towel. These differences are due to the methods of construction and the finishes given to the fabric.

**A finish is a way of treating fabrics to give them extra properties, e.g. crease-resistance, or to improve their appearance.**

| Finish (trade name) | Function | Use |
| --- | --- | --- |
| Flame-retarding (Proban) | Makes fabric less flammable | Children's nightwear, furnishings |
| Stiffening (Trubenising) | Saves starching; gives crisp finish | Shirt collars, cuffs |
| Polishing (Mercerising) | Makes fabric stronger, smooth | Sewing thread, glazed cotton |
| Brushing | Fabric feels warmer and softer | Brushed nylon, cotton, e.g. flannelette |

| Finish (trade name) | Function | Use |
|---|---|---|
| Waterproofing (Scotchguard) | Prevents water penetrating | Raincoats, anoraks |
| Water-repelling (Scotchguard) | Resists water soaking in | Coats, casual jackets |
| Anti-static (Antistat) | Prevents static, which causes clinging and slight shocks | Underwear, clothes, carpets |
| Stain-repellent (Scotchguard) | Prevents stains from penetrating | Clothing, upholstery, carpets |
| Non-shrink (Sanforized) | Prevents shrinking | Clothing and furnishing fabrics |
| Mothproof | Protects fabrics from moths | Clothes, furnishing and carpets |
| Crease resistance and drip-dry (Easycare, Tebilising) | Reduces creasing and saves ironing | Clothing, e.g. shirts and trousers, and soft furnishings, e.g. curtains |
| Permanent pleating (Koratron) | Saves ironing; pleats don't fall out | Clothing, e.g. skirts, trousers |
| Stretch finish (Lycra is woven or knitted in) | Makes fabric more stretchy | Swimwear, tights, trousers |

## Adding colour to fabric

Colour may be added to fabric by weaving, printing and dyeing.

### Weaving

Blocks of different coloured threads are inserted in the warp to make stripes, or in the warp and weft to make checks such as gingham and tartan.

### Dyeing

The natural colour of most fibres is neutral, e.g. cream or beige. Clothes can be dyed to add colour at several stages during manufacture: as a yarn, as fabric, or as a finished garment.

Originally all dyes were from natural sources – animal, mineral and vegetable, e.g. onion skins, beetroot. Modern dyes are made from chemicals and are more **colour-fast** – they don't run or fade.

Home dyeing is simple, using commercial dyes such as Dylon. Hot-water dyeing is used for cotton and linen; cold-water dyes for wool and synthetics. Washing machine dyes are useful when large quantities are to be dyed. Tie-dyeing and batik (using wax to create designs before dyeing) are interesting ways to add pattern to fabrics and clothing. Fabric crayons are a simple way of applying your own design.

### Printing

This involves applying dye in a pattern to one side of the fabric, using a block, screen or roller.

# Technology and textiles

The Industrial Revolution saw the beginning of major changes in the production of textiles and clothing. Machines took over from methods that had been used for thousands of years. Advances in technology have brought down the cost of manufacture, making a wide range of fabrics and clothing available to everyone through mass production.

❶ The invention of high-speed **spinning machines** replaced hand spinning on the spinning wheel.

❷ **Automatic weaving and knitting machines** replaced hand weaving and knitting. As a result, elaborate fabrics could be made quickly and cheaply.

❸ Production of fibres, fabric and clothes moved from home to **factory**.

❹ The invention of **man-made fibres** gave us a vast new range of fabrics with properties for every purpose.

❺ **Fabric finishes** were developed which gave fabrics new properties, e.g. flame-proofing and waterproofing.

❻ The invention of the **sewing machine** over 100 years ago made production of clothes in the home and factory quicker and cheaper. In recent years computerised machines have given a greater choice of stitches, patterns, etc.

❼ **Computer-aided design (CAD).** This is a system in which clothes and textiles can be designed on a computer screen. The designer can view colour, drape, etc. These designs are then transferred easily and quickly to the machines that make the products, e.g. the lasers that cut out the pattern pieces.

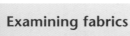

**Examining fabrics**

1.  **Types of fabric.** Compare samples of a woven, a knitted and a non-woven fabric. Pull out threads with a pin and examine under a magnifying glass. If a microscope is available, compare a sample fibre of wool, silk, cotton and man-made fibre. Place a single fibre on a slide, add a drop of water, cover with a cover slip and place under the lens.

2.  **Pattern.** Make a collection of patterned fabrics. Divide them into those patterned by weaving and by printing. (Looking at the back will help you.)

3.  **Dyeing.** Is the dye fast? Wet coloured fabric and place between two pieces of white cotton. Press with a hot iron. If no dye seeps into the cotton, it is fast.

4. **Crease resistance.** Crush a piece of fabric tightly in your hand. If it wrinkles, that fabric will need ironing.

5. **Burning tests.** You will need a metal tongs, a metal tray, a long taper, matches and a report sheet. Using the tongs, hold a sample of the fibres or fabric over the metal tray. Light the taper and move it slowly towards the fibres. Once fibres are burning, remove taper. Observe the way fibres burn, the odour and the residue. Fill in the report sheet after each test.

| Fibre | Odour | How it burns | Residue |
|---|---|---|---|
| Protein fibre (wool, silk) | Burning hair or feathers | Very slowly | Dark ash |
| Nylon | Celery | Melts; burns unevenly | Hard grey bead |
| Cellulose fibres (cotton, linen, viscose) | Burning paper | Quickly, yellowish | Grey paper-like ash |

**REVISION QUESTIONS**

1. Name two natural and two man-made fibres, and suggest a use for each.
2. Name two desirable and two undesirable properties of wool.
3. Name four household articles commonly made from (a) cotton and (b) linen.
4. Explain the term 'regenerated'. Name two regenerated fibres.
5. Name two advantages and two disadvantages of man-made fibres.
6. Explain three of the following: warp; weft; selvage; denier; bias; nap.
7. Name three fabric 'finishes' and the purpose of each.
8. Name two non-woven fabrics. List their advantages.
9. Describe how to identify two fibres by burning.
10. Describe two ways of identifying the properties of a fibre/fabric.
11. Draw and explain what is meant by the Woolmark.
12. Outline the stages involved in the production of cotton.
13. List three examples of cotton fabric.
14. Suggest three fabric finishes which can be applied to cotton.
15. Sketch the symbol which indicates that a fabric is pure cotton.
16. What is a colour-fast fabric?
17. Suggest three ways yarn can be made into a fabric.

Test Yourself
eTest.ie

# Chapter 47 Textile Care

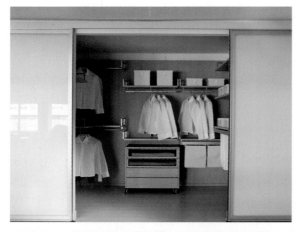

## Caring for your clothes

Clothes that are well looked after last longer and look better.

- Mend clothes before storing.
- Never put away soiled or stained clothes; stains will be harder to remove.
- Always hang clothes straight after use. Close zips, top buttons, etc. Use shaped or padded hangers.
- Fold knitwear and store it flat, e.g. in a drawer.
- Polish shoes and leather accessories to preserve them and keep them looking smart.

## Care labelling

Most clothes and textile items have care labels sewn into them. These state the manufacturer's name, the size, fibre content and clear instructions for washing, drying and ironing the fabric.

Many of the instructions are in symbols. Do you think this is a good idea? Discuss.

The international care labelling code has five basic symbols:

- a **washtub**, showing the washing temperature to be used
- a **triangle**, indicating whether chlorine bleach may be used.
- a **square** – drying instructions
- **ironing** instructions
- **dry cleaning** instructions, for the information of the dry cleaner.

A cross through the symbol means the treatment should not be done.

# Washing instructions

Washing processes are divided into groups. A chart giving washing instructions is usually printed on detergent packets.

| DRYING | IRONING | BLEACH | DRY CLEANING |
|---|---|---|---|
| Dry flat | Hot iron | Bleach may be used (Cl) | (A) |
| Line dry | Warm iron | Do not bleach | (P) |
| Drip dry | Cool iron | | (P) |
| Tumble dry | Do not iron | | (X) |
| Do not tumble dry | | | Do not dry clean |

❖ *Care labels*

| TEXTILE/MACHINE CODE | MACHINE WASH | HAND WASH | FABRIC |
|---|---|---|---|
| 95 | Maximum wash in Cotton cycle. | Hand hot (50°C) or boil. Spin or wring. | White cotton and linen articles without special finishes. |
| 60 | Maximum wash in Cotton cycle. | Hand hot (50°C). Spin or wring. | Cotton, linen or viscose articles without special finishes where colours are fast at 60°C. |
| 50 | Medium wash in Synthetic cycle. | Hand hot. Cold rinse. Short spin or damp dry. | Polyester/cotton mixtures. Nylon polyester. Cotton and viscose articles with special finishes. Cotton/acrylic mixtures. |
| 40 | Maximum wash in Cotton cycle. | Warm. Spin or wring | Cotton, linen or viscose where colours are fast at 40°C but not at 60°C. |
| 40 | Medium wash in Synthetic cycle. | Warm. Cold rinse. Short spin. Do not hand wring. | Acrylics, acetate and triacetate, including mixtures with wool; polyester/wool blends. |
| 40 | Minimum wash in Wool cycle. | Warm. Do not rub. Spin. Do not hand wring. | Wool, wool mixed with other fibres; silk. |
| ✋ | Hand wash only. | See article care label for washing instructions. | Articles which must not be machine washed; glass fibre fabrics and some pleated fabrics. |
| ✕ | Do not wash. | Do not wash. | Articles which cannot be washed. See article care label for cleaning instructions. |

❖ *Washing instructions*

## The bar symbol

This tells you which washing action should be used in the machine.

- No bar – maximum washing action and spin.
- Single bar – medium washing action, short spin.
- Broken bar – minimum washing action. This is the wool cycle.

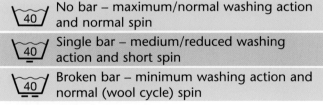

| | |
|---|---|
| 40 | No bar – maximum/normal washing action and normal spin |
| 40 | Single bar – medium/reduced washing action and short spin |
| 40 | Broken bar – minimum washing action and normal (wool cycle) spin |

❖ *Bar symbols*

You can wash a mixture of fabrics as long as their bar symbols correspond and they are washed at the lowest temperature, e.g. if one label shows 60°C and one 40°C, wash at 40°C.

## Preparing to wash

**1** Repair tears and holes in clothes. (Why?)

**2** Empty all pockets.

**3** Close zips, buttons and tie strings to avoid tangling.

**4** Examine for stains and remove any that are unlikely to come out in the wash.

**5** Sort clothes according to wash care labels.

**6** Follow any written instructions on the care label, such as 'Use non-biological detergent' or 'Wash dark colours separately'. If in doubt, test for colour fastness (see page 362).

## Delicate fabrics

Certain fabrics such as silk and wool require special handling. Follow the care label exactly.

- They should be washed separately, by hand.
- They usually require a low temperature and gentle detergent.
- Handle gently. Squeeze; do not rub.
- Rinse several times until the water is clear.
- Gently squeeze out water; do not wring or twist. Roll in a towel, if necessary.
- Dry flat or drip dry, as instructed.
- Check instructions for ironing temperature – usually a cool iron.

*Note:* Machine-washable wool may be washed on the wool cycle in a washing machine.

**ACTIVITY**

1. This is an example of a care label on a viscose fabric.
   What does it mean?

2. Look at the labels on four different items of clothing. Draw the symbols shown on each and say what they mean.

3. Draw the label you would expect to see on (a) a woollen jumper, (b) a white towel, (c) a swimsuit.

4. List 4 different textile items that you consider should be treated as 'delicate'.

# Stain removal

Most dirt and stains, such as dust, food and grease, can be removed by normal washing. If the fabric cannot be washed you may have to use another method. Treatment depends on: (a) type of stain, (b) type of fibre, (c) whether or not the fabric is washable.

## Guidelines for removing stains

1. Act quickly or the stain will set.
2. Remove excess by blotting gently, but do not rub.
3. Check fabric care label to see whether fabric is washable.
4. Some stains (e.g. oil paints) are removed before washing, but modern washing powders remove many stains, such as food and body stains (e.g. blood).
5. Use the least harmful method first, e.g. steep in cold water if washable. (Hot water often sets stains.)
6. Test stain remover first on an inconspicuous part of the item such as the hem. Many commercial stain treatments are sprayed on first and then left to work. Powders to assist stain removal are also available.
7. If using a special solvent, place a pad of white cotton under the stain and dab stain with solvent, using white cloth.
8. If stain cannot be removed or fabric is non-washable, take to a specialist dry cleaner.

## Stain removal chart

| Stain | Treatment | Precautions |
|---|---|---|
| **Protein** (gravy, egg, blood, perspiration) (Urine) | Soak in cold water, then a warm solution of enzyme detergent. (Soak nappies in Napisan.) | Hot water sets protein. (Do not use biological detergent.) |
| **Grease** (oil, make-up, fats, chocolate) | Wash in hot, soapy water. If not washable, use a solvent, e.g. benzene. | Many solvents give off toxic fumes (see below). Work near a window and air well. |
| **Tea, coffee, felt pen** | Soak in warm biological detergent. | Do not use on flame-proof fabrics. |
| **Grass, ink, biro** | Dab with methylated spirits. | Flammable liquid. |
| **Paint** (oil-based) | Rub on white spirit, turpentine. | Flammable liquid. |
| **Chewing gum** | Freeze, then pick off. A grease solvent may then be needed, or use a special solvent e.g. Stain Devil. | See precautions below. |
| **Nail polish, adhesives** | Nail polish remover. | Do not use on acetate fabrics. |
| **Mildew and difficult stains** | Soak in warm biological detergent. White cotton, linen may be bleached. | Do not use on flame-proof fabrics. |

*After treating all washable fabrics for stains, wash, rinse and dry.*

### Precautions when using commercial stain removers

Most commercial stain removers are solvents, which can be very dangerous if inhaled.

**1** Follow manufacturer's instructions.

**2** Use in a well-ventilated room, e.g. near a window. Air well after use.

**3** Do not use near flames.

**4** Use rubber gloves and wash hands after use.

**5** Label clearly and lock away from children.

## Detergents

**A detergent is something that removes dirt.** It does this by softening water and removing grease and stains. In the past the main detergent was soap. Today, washing detergents are made from a mixture of chemicals. They may contain:

- water softeners
- bleach
- phosphates
- optical brighteners (which make colours seem brighter)
- enzymes
- cleaning chemicals
- perfume.

The cleaning chemical contains an **emulsifier**. This has a **water-loving end** which attaches itself to the water, and a **water-hating end** which attaches itself to the dirt and helps to float it away.

### Types of detergent

- Powder or liquid detergents
- Gel detergents
- Liquitabs
- Solid powder tablets
- Hand washing detergents for delicate fabrics
- Sensitive skin detergent
- Biological detergents* contain enzymes which break down protein stains at under 40°C. They then wash as usual as the temperature in the machine rises.

*Note: Flame-resistant and waterproof finishes are damaged by biological detergents.

## 'Green' detergents

Some detergents cause damage to the environment. Look for environmentally friendly products and containers.

## Fabric conditioners

These are added to the final rinsing water (a) to soften clothes, (b) to reduce static electricity, (c) to reduce wrinkling so that little ironing is needed. Fabric conditioners make fabrics such as nappies and towels less absorbent.

# Washing equipment

Today, most clothes are washed by machine, either in the launderette or at home.

## Washing machines

Most washing machines today are automatic front-loading machines designed to fit under a worktop. Washing machines have a stainless steel drum, which tumbles the clothes in water and detergent. A pump pumps water into the machine, which is heated by an element. Water is removed from clothes by the high-speed spinning of the drum, and is then pumped from the machine.

## Using a washing machine

Always follow the instructions on the machine.

❶ Check clothes for mending and stains, and treat if necessary.

❷ Sort clothes according to wash care labels and place in machine.

❸ Choose the correct washing programme for the fabric load.

❹ Put the detergent in the dispenser.

❺ Turn on the machine – the clothes are washed, rinsed and spun automatically.

✦ Some machines have a half-load economy programme. This saves water and electricity.

✦ Some have a built-in tumble dryer.

(See also page 312.)

# Drying

There are several ways to dry clothes.

❶ Line drying costs nothing. Clothes remain soft and smell fresh.

❷ A pulley or clothes-horse can be used indoors, but drying causes condensation. Ventilate the room well when drying indoors.

≡ Tumble dryers. Clothes are tumbled in a rotating drum. A heating element heats the air in the machine, evaporating the water from the clothes. Some dryers have an air vent, which removes the damp air to outside the house; others condense the steam back into water and this water is emptied out when the collection tray fills up. These are called condenser dryers and require no hole in the wall to carry steam outside. Tumble dryers are costly to run, but they remove wrinkles and therefore reduce ironing.

## Irons

There are two basic settings on modern irons: (a) **dry iron** and; (b) **steam iron**. An iron contains a heating element which heats the shiny ironing surface. A thermostat controls the temperature, and a light turns off when the correct temperature is reached. Irons contain a small water tank which creates steam when the iron is heated, releasing it through holes in the base.

Some have additional features, such as self cleaning, which means that the steam chamber is cleaned when you put the iron to that setting. Cordless and travel irons are available, which can be convenient.

### Using irons

- Keep the iron upright when not ironing.
- Unplug when filling with water.
- Empty water tank after use.
- In hard water areas, use distilled water to prevent clogging.

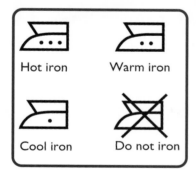

### Ironing guidelines

Hot – cotton, linen.

Medium – wool, polyester, silk.

Cool – nylon, acrylic and viscose.

- Check the care label, then set the temperature dial to the correct heat for fabric.
- Most fabrics are best ironed on the 'wrong' side.
- Iron clothes when they are very slightly damp.
- Iron carefully to avoid creasing.

Modern fabrics and finishes, fabric conditioners and tumble drying have reduced the amount of textiles that need ironing.

**ACTIVITY**

Visit your local electrical shop and look at automatic washing machines. Compare them under these headings: cost, design, number of programmes, convenience.

(a)  Find out the monthly cost of buying a machine on hire purchase.

(b)  Compare this with the cost of using the launderette three or four times a week.

(c)  What other costs must you take into account when comparing the two?

(d)  What other types of washing machine are available?

**REVISION QUESTIONS**

1.  Explain these symbols.

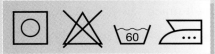

2.  Explain the bar symbol in washing instructions.
3.  List four steps to follow when preparing clothes for washing.
4.  How would you remove the following stains: (a) chewing gum; (b) lipstick; (c) oil-based paint; (d) ink (biro)?
5.  List four precautions to follow when using stain removers.
6.  List five guidelines for washing delicate fabrics.
7.  What is a detergent? Explain how they work.
8.  What is the most environmentally friendly way of drying clothes, in your opinion?
9.  What is a condenser dryer?
10.  List three guidelines for ironing clothes.
11.  What heat setting would you use for (a) linen, (b) viscose and (c) wool?
12.  State two advantages of using a fabric conditioner.

# Chapter 48 Textile Skills

Sewing is a useful and creative skill. It is used to make clothes and soft furnishings, for crafts, and for repairing and altering clothes. Creative sewing, e.g. embroidery and quilting, is an interesting hobby.

❖ *Sewing resources*

## Hand sewing guidelines

Although much sewing is done by machine, the first step in sewing is learning to sew by hand.

1. Use a single thread which is not too long. (Why?)
2. Most stitching is worked from right to left, unless you are left-handed.
3. Pin seams and hems, then tack if necessary, to hold them together.
4. Start and finish off with a secure stitch.
5. Stitches should be even and not too large.
6. Use a thimble for tough fabrics like denim. (Why?)

❖ *Tacking*

### Tacking

**Tacking is temporary stitching used to hold the fabric together** while the permanent stitching, e.g. machining, is being done. It can also act as a guide for machining. When making clothes, use secure tacking to hold a garment together for fitting. Use a contrasting thread so that it shows up easily.

1. Pin the two pieces of fabric in position, usually with raw edges together. Match any notches, etc.
2. Make a knot in the thread and start with a small back stitch (make a stitch and go back into the same stitch).
3. Work from right to left, making stitches about 1cm in length. Stitches and spaces should be equal. Do not pull or tacking will pucker.
4. Finish by making two or three back stitches to secure.

# Running stitch

This is worked **like tacking except that it is much smaller (1–2mm)**. It is used for **sewing seams** or for **gathering fabric** if you have no machine.

❖ *Running stitch*

# Gathering stitch

This is used when you want **to make a wide piece of fabric fit into a narrower piece**, for example a gathered skirt into a waistband. Running stitches or machining may be used.

❶ Loosen the tension on the machine.

❷ Machine two parallel rows about 1cm in from the edge to be gathered.

❸ Carefully pull the looser threads (at the back) until the gathering fits.

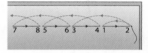

❖ *Gathering stitch*

# Back stitch

This is a **secure stitch used instead of machining to sew seams**.

❶ Pin and tack fabric in position.

❷ Begin with a double stitch but bring the second stitch out 2–3mm beyond the previous stitch.

❸ Insert the needle into the end of the previous stitch and bring the needle out 2–3mm beyond again.

❹ Continue in this way to the end. Finish with a double back stitch, pass needle through fabric and cut thread.

❖ *Back stitch*

# Hemming

Hemming is a **small, slanted stitch used to hold down the back of facings, collars and waistbands**. It is not used for the hems of clothes, as it would show on the outside.

❶ Slip the needle through the fold from left to right as shown, leaving a 'tail' of thread which is tucked under the fold.

❷ Sew from right to left in small slanted stitches, picking up just two or three threads of the single fabric and the fold in one stitch. (Follow the angle of the needle in the diagram.) Stitches should be small, even and fairly tight.

❸ Continue to the end, then sew back into the last stitch twice, making a small V. Pass the needle through the fold and cut thread.

❖ *Hemming*

# Slip hemming

This is used to **sew the hems of clothes such as skirts, dresses and trousers**. If correctly done, it is almost invisible on the front. It can be made more secure by sewing a back stitch now and then on the fold. Work from right to left.

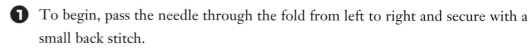

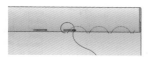

**1** To begin, pass the needle through the fold from left to right and secure with a small back stitch.

**2** Take a tiny stitch on the single fabric, picking up only one or two threads.

**3** Slip the needle through the fold for about 5–10 mm, depending on the type of fabric and the depth of hem.

**4** Continue in the same way, leaving the stitches quite loose.

**5** Finish securely by making a double back stitch in the fold.

❖ *Slip hemming*

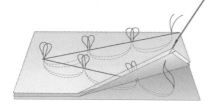

### Tailor tacking

This is used **to transfer pattern markings from paper pattern pieces on to doubled fabric.**

**1** Use a fairly long double thread without a knot.

**2** Take a small stitch through the pattern mark and both layers of fabric.

**3** Repeat stitch, leaving a loop.

**4** Cut thread, leaving a long 'tail'. The loop may be cut.

**5** Remove pattern carefully. Separate both layers of fabric and cut the threads between them.

❖ *Tailor tacking*

## Embroidery stitches

Embroidery is used to decorate fabrics. It can be done by hand or machine. Embroidery thread is sold in skeins. Each thread is made up of six strands. These are usually divided in two (three strands in each) unless you are embroidering very thick fabrics.

- Use a crewel needle for embroidery – this has a large eye.
- Start embroidery by making a few running stitches along the line to be stitched. These will be covered with embroidery stitches as you work.
- Finish by weaving the needle through the 'wrong' side of the finished stitches, pull thread through and then cut.

❖ *Embroidery thread*

### Stem stitch

This is used for outlines, flower stems, etc.

**1** Begin with a back stitch.

**2** Work from left to right along the line of the design as shown, taking even, slightly slanted stitches. The thread should come out above the previous stitch.

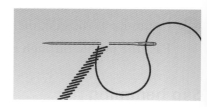

❖ *Stem stitch*

# Satin stitch

This is used to fill shapes such as leaves and petals.

**1** Pass the needle in through one side of the design and out the other.

**2** Stitches may be straight or slanted but they must be close together.

**3** Padding: a running stitch may be used within the outline before satin stitching to give extra thickness.

**4** Do not make stitches too long or they will drag the fabric. A long and short stitch is more suitable if the space to be filled is too wide.

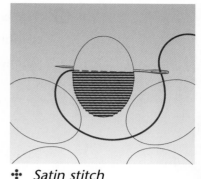

❖ *Satin stitch*

# Long and short stitch

This is used to fill designs which are too large to be filled by satin stitch. It also gives a realistic, shaded appearance to designs such as petals and feathers.

**1** First row: the stitches are worked alternately long and short.

**2** Second row: make all long stitches, putting needle into holes of previous stitches. Continue with long stitches to maintain the long and short effect.

**3** For a shaded effect, use shaded embroidery thread or gradually change shades of thread after every two or three lines.

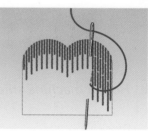

❖ *Long and short stitch*

# Chain stitch

Used both as an outline stitch and to fill a design.

**1** Start with a back stitch at the top of the outline.

**2** Work downwards, holding the thread with the left thumb, to form a loop.

**3** Insert the needle inside the loop, beside where the thread came out, as shown.

**4** Finish with a secure stitch catching in the loop. Bring the needle through to the back of the work and weave it through the last few stitches. Cut thread.

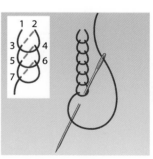

❖ *Chain stitch*

# The sewing machine

## Threading

This varies according to the machine.

**1** Bring thread from the spool pin to the guide (1).

**2** Bring it around the tension (2), and up through the take-up lever (3).

**3** Pass thread down through guides (4) then through the needle (5) from the direction of the last guide.

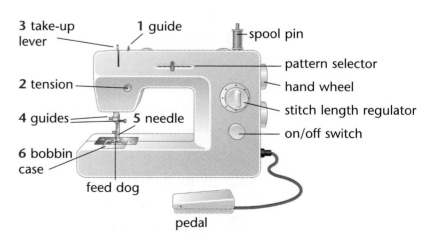

❖ *Sewing machine*

**❹** The bobbin (6) must be inserted correctly. Pass the thread through the bobbin tension, then leave it loose, to be caught up by bringing the needle down and pulling it up by the needle thread.

❖ *How a machine stitches*

## How a machine stitches

Each machine stitch is formed by two threads which twist around one another – one from the spool and needle, the other from the bobbin. Tension is the tightness of the stitch. For even stitching, upper and lower threads must be equally tight. Tension is adjusted by the tension regulator. Tension that is too tight causes puckering; tension that is too loose causes looping at the back of the stitch.

❖ *Correct tension*

❖ *Top tension too loose*

❖ *Top tension too tight*

## Using a sewing machine

**❶** Follow the instruction book for threading and general use.

**❷** Use a suitable needle and thread. The thread of the spool and bobbin should match each other and the fabric.

**❸** Adjust stitch length and tension to suit fabric. Test stitch on a scrap of fabric before starting.

**❹** Remove pins before sewing.

**❺** Start with the needle at its highest point, insert fabric from front, then lower presser foot.

**❻** Turn hand wheel towards you to lower needle onto fabric, then press pedal – lightly if you want to go slowly, heavily if you want to go fast.

**❼** Guide fabric into the machine – do not push or pull fabric.

**❽** Keep the bulk of the fabric to the left when sewing. (Why?)

**❾** If you need to stop in the middle of a line, or turn a corner, leave the needle in the fabric.

**❿** When finished, reverse for a few stitches if wished. Raise needle by turning hand wheel towards you.

**⓫** Lift presser foot. Pull fabric to the back and cut thread, leaving 4cm.

**⓬** Check stitching after every line.

**ACTIVITY** Test your stitching. When you have had some practice doing straight machining, try sewing the following designs. Draw them on to the fabric three or four times the size shown here. Go very slowly.

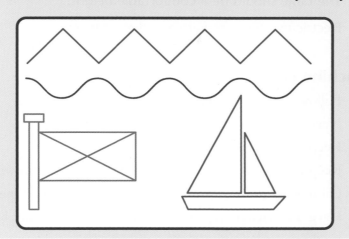

## Machine stitches

**Straight stitch** – used for most sewing tasks, e.g. seams. Length can be adjusted – usually, the higher the number, the longer the stitch. Long stitches are used for thick or loosely woven fabrics.

**Zigzag** – useful for neatening seams, sewing on elastic. A slight zigzag is used for 'give' on stretchy fabrics.

**Buttonhole stitch** – usually worked in four stages using the buttonhole symbol on the machine.

**Blind stitch** – used for hems and simple decoration.

**Embroidery stitches** – some machines can be used for a wide variety of embroidery stitches. Even a simple zigzag stitch is useful for working attractive designs and appliqué.

## Choosing a sewing machine

- Consider how much you can afford to pay.
- Do you want a simple straight stitch machine, or is it worth paying more for elaborate stitching?
- What attachments and other 'extras' are included?
- Is it a reliable brand and a reliable retailer?
- Is there a guarantee and after-sales service?
- Is a demonstration available? Try out the machine yourself before you buy.

------------------

❖ *Straight stitch*

❖ *Zigzag stitch*

❖ *Buttonhole stitch*

❖ *Blind stitch*

❖ *Machine embroidery stitches*

### Position

+ Place the machine in a good light.

+ Place on a large flat surface, e.g. a table.

+ The table should be a comfortable height.

+ Electric machines require a socket near by.

### Machine care

1. Follow instructions regarding use, care and cleaning.
2. Never run a threaded machine without fabric.
3. Keep covered when not in use.
4. Keep working parts clean and free from dust. Clean with a brush occasionally.
5. Oil moving parts occasionally, depending on use. (One drop in each point.)
6. Have the machine repaired and serviced occasionally by a sewing machine mechanic.

| Machine fault | Possible cause |
|---|---|
| Uneven or skipped stitches | 1. Pushing or pulling fabric into machine<br>2. Needle incorrect size or inserted the wrong way round<br>3. Blunt or bent needle<br>4. Needle set too high or too low<br>5. Needle incorrectly threaded |
| Thread breaking | 1. Tension too tight<br>2. Incorrect threading of needle or bobbin<br>3. Thread too fine or of poor quality<br>4. Needle too fine, bent, blunt, wrong way round |
| Looped stitches | 1. Incorrect threading, especially through tension<br>2. Upper tension too loose<br>3. Bobbin incorrectly threaded |
| Puckered seams | 1. Top or bobbin tension too tight<br>2. Top and lower threads of different quality<br>3. Stitch too long, especially in fine fabrics<br>4. Blunt needle |
| Needle breaking | 1. Upper tension too tight<br>2. Needle too fine, bent or incorrectly inserted<br>3. Fabric pulled roughly during or after sewing<br>4. Loose presser foot |

# Seams

Seams are used to join pieces of fabric together. Seams are part of the basic structure of clothes – you will find them on the sides of trousers and shirts, and where collars and sleeves join on to a garment. They can also be used as a feature by being outlined with piping or contrasting stitching, e.g. on jeans.

## Flat seam

A flat seam is the simplest seam to sew. It can be taken in or let out easily. Flat seams are sewn 1.5cm from the raw edge – this seam allowance is standard on most commercial patterns.

1. Place the two pieces of fabric together, right sides facing, and match any notches or balance marks (tailor tacks).
2. Pin and tack on fitting line. Remove pins.
3. Machine from the very top of the seam to the bottom 1.5cm in from the edge.
4. Remove tacking and press seam open.
5. Neaten raw edges according to fabric type.

❖ *Flat seam pinned*

❖ *Machined flat seam*

## Seam finishes

Seams are neatened to give a better finish and to prevent fraying.

1. Zigzag machining
   - Set machine to a suitable zigzag stitch and test. Adjust stitch length, if necessary.
   - Trim seam turnings evenly, then machine along the edge.
   - Turnings may be stitched separately or together.
2. Edge machining
   - Use on fine and medium-weight fabrics only.
   - Turn under a narrow fold to the back of each seam allowance.
   - Tack and machine about 2mm from the outer edge.
   - Remove tacking and press lightly.
3. A pinking shears is a quick way to neaten edges of closely woven fabrics.

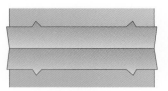

❖ *Finished flat seam*

❖ *Zigzag finish*

# Textiles for sewing

## Guidelines for choosing

1. Fabrics are sold in the following widths: 90cm; 115cm; 120cm; 140cm; 150cm.
2. Calculate the amount you need before you shop, e.g. from the pattern grid.
3. Beginners should choose fabric which is easy to handle and sew – avoid fabrics

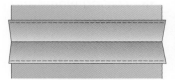

❖ *Edge machining finish*

that are stretchy or slippery, or have a nap or one-way design*. Medium-weight cotton would be a good choice.

**4** Choose a textile suitable for the task. Fabric should be without flaws and washable – care instructions are usually on the roll.

**5** Make a list of the sewing requirements for your task and buy them at the same time. You may need needles, pins, matching thread, zips, buttons, binding or braid.

## Straight grain

Woven fabrics, as mentioned in Chapter 46, are made from warp (selvage) and weft threads. The **warp threads are stronger and run down the length of the fabric**; the **weft are the cross-wise threads**. When cutting textiles, **make sure the warp (called the straight grain in patterns) runs down the length of the article**, whether it is a curtain, trousers or wall hanging. This makes it hang well.

On areas where there is strain, such as waist bands, the warp should run around the article. You can identify the warp/selvage by pulling the fabric sharply. It makes a sharp noise and will not give as you pull it.

**The bias is the diagonal of the fabric (an angle of 45° to the selvage).** Clothes cut on the bias drape very well and cling flatteringly to the body. Fabric cut on the bias is very stretchy. Strips of bias binding can be used to neaten curves or hems and pipe cushions.

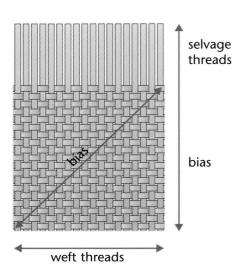

* Warp and weft

## Cutting out

**1** Arrange pattern on fabric, following the straight grain lines and instructions for placing on fold. Pin in position.

**2** Use sharp cutting out scissors.

**3** Leave a seam allowance of 1.5cm, unless included in pattern.

**4** Cut along cutting line of pattern, cutting notches outwards.

**5** Hold fabric flat on the table with one hand while cutting with long, even strokes. Never lift fabric.

**6** Before removing pattern, transfer important markings on to the fabric. This is done using

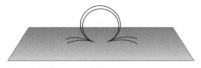

* Tailor tacking

* Tracing wheel and carbon paper

* Tailor's chalk

- ✦ tailor tacking
- ✦ tracing wheel and special carbon
- ✦ tailor's chalk.

**\*Nap and one-way designs.** Fabrics with a **nap** or **pile** have hairs or 'fur' which is smooth if brushed one way, rough if brushed the other way. Velvet and corduroy are nap fabrics. **One-way designs** have pictures or writing which must face in the same direction. Both must be laid out and cut so that the design runs one way. This requires extra fabric.

# Designing a textile item

**Design brief:** Design a textile item for use in the kitchen. It must not cost more than €15. Make up and complete the item in four weeks.

1. **Analyse the factors to be considered**
   - A textile must be used – not wood or leather.
   - For kitchen – should be washable and heat-resistant, match colour scheme.
   - Cost – less than €15.
   - Amount of time to complete – four weeks.
   - Your ability, e.g. sewing skills.

2. **Research/investigation**

   Look through magazines, craft books and other HE resources. Find out cost of suitable fabrics and other possible resources. What equipment is available (e.g. sewing machine)?

3. **Consider possible solutions**

   Tea cosy; table mat; draught excluder; oven glove; tray cloth.

4. **Decide on a solution**

   Oven glove. Reasons – attractive, practical, fairly cheap, not too difficult.

5. **Plan assignment**
   - Check resources: make a list of resources you have, e.g. pins, needles, scissors, binding.
   - Draw two patterns from old oven gloves; measure amount of fabric, etc. needed.
   - Make shopping list of materials required, e.g. fabric, wadding, matching thread.
   - Buy fabric, wadding, thread. (Be conscious of cost.)
   - Collect all resources and keep together in a bag for length of assignment.
   - Make work plan or time schedule.

6. **Action** – carry out practical work (see below)

7. **Evaluate result:** Did you achieve your goal?
   - Is the item suitable for kitchen use? Is it washable and heat-resistant?
   - Is it well made? Attractive? Useful? Does it co-ordinate with kitchen colour scheme?
   - Did I keep within my budget?
   - Was it finished within the time limit?
   - Could I improve it in any way, e.g. by embroidery, patchwork or quilting?

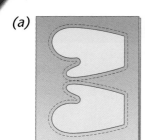
*(a)*

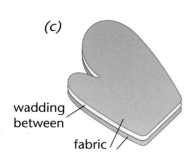
*(b)*

## Making an oven glove

❶ Lay fabric on table, right sides together.

❷ Lay pattern on double fabric. Pin and cut out twice, leaving 1cm seam allowance (a).

❸ Mark sewing line around pattern with tailor's chalk before removing.

❹ Lay pattern on wadding. Cut out two (b).

❺ Arrange two fabric glove shapes wrong sides together, wadding in between, pin (c).

❻ Repeat with remaining two fabric shapes and wadding. Pin.

❼ Lay 6 pieces together. Pin, tack and machine, leaving opening for hand (d).

❽ Trim wadding and clip turnings, zigzag raw edges and turn right side out (e).

❾ Use bias strips of fabric or contrasting binding to neaten opening and form loop (f).

❿ Machine in place. Press, if necessary.

*(c)*

wadding between
fabric

*(d)*
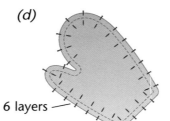
6 layers
Pin, tack, machine

*(e)*
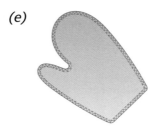
Trim and zigzag

*(f)*

Finish off opening

## REVISION QUESTIONS

1. Name five basic requirements for making a textile article.
2. Give two uses for (a) tacking, (b) back stitching, (c) hemming.
3. List six guidelines for using a sewing machine.
4. Explain the following terms: (a) tension, (b) feed dog.
5. Suggest two reasons for each of the following faults: (a) needle breaking, (b) puckering, (c) looped stitches.
6. Name two methods of neatening a flat seam.
7. List four points to consider when buying textiles for sewing.
8. Explain the following terms: (a) nap, (b) straight grain, (c) bias.
9. Describe one method of transferring pattern markings to fabric.
10. What factors might someone consider before buying a sewing machine?
11. Name two machine stitches and give a use for each.
12. Name two embroidery stitches and suggest a use for each.

Test Yourself eTest.ie

# Part

# 6

## Options

# Option 1 Childcare

## Becoming a parent

Bringing a baby into the world is a happy and joyful occasion. It is also a serious business. Both parents are **legally responsible** for looking after their children. A child is totally dependent on its parents for everything. It needs responsible and loving parents to provide its needs.

**A child needs:**

1. nourishing food
2. proper clothing
3. a healthy environment
4. security and protection
5. love and affection
6. a stimulating environment in which to grow and develop
7. loving and consistent guidance and discipline.

## Pregnancy

A new life begins at the moment of conception.

From now on the mother should:

1. avoid smoking, alcohol and drugs, including medicines
2. eat a nourishing, well-balanced diet – particularly foods rich in protein, iron and calcium
3. avoid rich, spicy or fatty foods, strong tea and coffee
4. avoid unpasteurised cheeses, raw or lightly cooked eggs and cook–chill foods, due to the dangers of serious food poisoning by Listeria bacteria
5. avoid gaining too much weight e.g. over 12 kilos
6. get plenty of exercise and rest
7. have regular antenatal visits* and a dental check-up.

*Antenatal (before birth) check-ups are necessary to monitor development of the foetus and prevent complications.

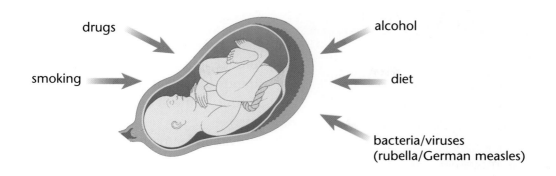

drugs

smoking

alcohol

diet

bacteria/viruses
(rubella/German measles)

## Human development

### Development in the uterus

The length of pregnancy is 40 weeks. Very important development takes place during the first 14 weeks, when the embryo develops very rapidly.

| | | |
|---|---|---|
| 6–8 weeks |  | The heart develops; arm and leg growth begins; then brain, lungs and internal organs develop. The embryo is about 60mm long. |
| 10–14 weeks |  | The developing baby, now called a foetus, is fully formed. It has all its organs – bones, limbs, fingers and toes. It begins to move. The first antenatal visit is due now. |
| 15–22 weeks |  | Face recognisable; finger and toenails growing; body covered with fine hair. Considerable increase in size. |
| 28 weeks |  | Could survive if born prematurely. Skin covered with waxy waterproof layer; eyelids open. |
| 28–40 weeks |  | Continues to grow, gradually turns so the head is downwards, ready for birth. |
| Full term | | Baby weighs an average of 3kg, although this varies considerably. |

Birth, page 281

# Child development

All children develop in a certain sequence or pattern, although the rate at which they develop varies. The health services provide screening checks on the development of children from birth to five years.

Health and childcare facilities, page 396

## Child development

### Physical development

This includes:

- increase in height and weight
- learning to use senses, e.g. focusing of eyes, developing sensitivity to noise and touch
- motor skills, i.e. movement such as crawling, sitting, standing, walking
- manipulative skills, e.g. learning to use fingers to pick up and grasp, feeding itself, using toys
- co-ordination – using different senses to do things, e.g. the eyes see a mobile and hands reach for it.

### Emotional development

Emotional development is the way children learn to cope with feelings. Babies and children need to feel secure. If their parents make them feel wanted and loved, they're more likely to grow up to have good self-esteem. To develop emotionally, children need:

- unconditional love – being loved for themselves rather than for how they behave (conditional love)
- protection and security
- physical contact, e.g. cuddling, hugging
- attention, e.g. being picked up when they cry, talked to and played with.

### Intellectual (mental) development

This is how a child uses its mind to do things such as talk, learn, play, explore and read. Children learn more by example than by people telling them what to do. They imitate and repeat the behaviour until it is learned. Much information is picked up through the senses – looking, touching. A child should not be too confined except for its own safety. Normal children are curious and want to learn and explore.

Parents can encourage this by:

- providing a stimulating environment – things to look at (mobiles, pictures), hear (music, rattlers, bells, etc.) and touch (toys, etc.)
- providing learning materials such as water, sand, paper and crayons
- giving time and attention to the child
- giving encouragement and praise.

### Physical development is influenced by

- heredity (what you inherited from your parents) – height, eye and hair colour
- a balanced diet
- a healthy environment, e.g. fresh air, exercise, rest and sleep
- play and stimulation, which help develop motor and manipulative skills.

### Emotional development is influenced by

- home environment, especially love and security
- encouragement and praise
- discipline – children feel more secure when they are given boundaries and know what is allowed and not allowed. Discipline should be firm, fair and consistent.
- consistency – this means that parents don't keep altering the way they treat their child, e.g. 'blowing hot and cold'. Children feel happier with a routine – meals and bed at regular times. Otherwise they get confused and insecure.

### Intellectual development is influenced by

- heredity
- environment
- unconditional love
- communication – talking with a child is important for speech development, social development and emotional development
- encouragement and praise.

# Play

Play is an important part of child development. It is through play that children learn. Play helps:

- physical development, e.g. motor and manipulative skills
- co-ordination, balance
- development of the senses and intelligence, through creative and imaginative play
- social development – learning to play with others, share and take turns.

## Stages of development

| Age | Physical | Emotional | Intellectual |
|---|---|---|---|
| First weeks | Feels hunger, cold<br>Can suck, grasp<br>Sleeps most of day<br>Uncontrolled limb movement | Needs comfort, security<br>Likes to be cuddled, fed and changed regularly | Five senses developing<br>Eyes not focused<br>Blinks at strong light<br>Startled by loud sounds |
| 6 weeks | Head movement more controlled<br>Limb movement smoother | Smiles<br>Recognises parent's voice<br>Recognises faces | Watches face of parent/minder<br>Makes small noises |
| 3 months | Can sit up<br>Watches own hands moving<br>Good head control | Makes cooing noises<br>Gets excited when food is seen | Shows interest in surroundings<br>Plays with its fingers<br>Enjoys noise of rattle |
| 6 months | Sits with support<br>Can roll over, grasp objects and hold up arms to be lifted | Friendly with parents and strangers<br>Laughs | Puts things in its mouth<br>More interested in surroundings<br>Listens to sounds |
| 9 months | Sits unaided<br>Attempts to crawl<br>Pulls up to standing position with help<br>Chews food | Afraid of strangers<br>Often cries when mother leaves<br>Responds to other family members | Understands 'no'<br>Can clap hands and wave 'bye-bye'<br>Can play peek-a-boo<br>May say first word, e.g. 'Dada' |

## Stages of development

| Age | Physical | Emotional | Intellectual |
|---|---|---|---|
| 12 months | Crawls well<br>Stands and attempts to walk with support<br>Learns to climb<br>Picks up small objects | Recognises own name<br>Plays with objects, e.g. toys | Understands several words<br>Uses some single-syllable words<br>Understands commands and often responds |
| 18 months | Walking well<br>Learns to climb stairs<br>Uses a spoon to feed | More confident<br>Has temper tantrums if angry or frustrated | Language developing – vocabulary increases, makes short sentences<br>Imitates parents |
| 2–3 years | Can run and throw<br>Can get dressed and undressed<br>Usually toilet-trained by age of three | Learning to play with others<br>Independent<br>Shows jealousy, e.g. of new baby | Obeys commands<br>Very talkative<br>Curious – investigates everything<br>Enjoys being read to<br>Looks through picture books, turning pages |

**ACTIVITY**

1. Keep a childcare folder while you are studying this option. Use it to keep any information you gather on children and childcare.

2. Social development is how a child learns to get on with others. A small baby first gets to know those closest to it – its mother and father. However, it must learn to get used to other people. List some ways in which a child might learn social skills.

## Food and nutrition

Babies live on milk alone for the first three months of life. Milk provides a baby with all the nutrients it needs in the right amounts for healthy growth. Babies may be fed by breast or bottle. In both cases hands must be thoroughly washed before feeding.

### Breast-feeding

It is not always possible for a mother to breast-feed, but if she can it has many advantages.

6 Options

1. Nutrients are in the correct proportion for the baby's needs.
2. It is free and convenient – no need to prepare a bottle.
3. It is safer – no dangers from careless sterilising.
4. It helps the uterus to return to normal size.
5. Breast-fed babies are less likely to be overweight, suffer digestive problems or suffer from allergies.
6. Mother's immunity to many diseases is passed to the baby.
7. The close contact is enjoyable for mother and child, and encourages bonding.

**Problems that can occur during breast-feeding**

1. May cause soreness of breasts.
2. Mother is restricted by feeding times as child is fed on demand.
3. Other family members such as fathers are excluded from feeding unless milk is expressed.
4. It may be awkward to breast-feed in public. Few suitable areas are available in restaurants, etc.

**Bottle-feeding**

- The mother may feel this gives her greater freedom.
- It allows the father and others to be more involved in feeding or to do night feeds.
- It is clear from the measurements on the bottle how much the baby has drunk.
- It is more expensive and more time-consuming.

Milk for bottle-feeding is made up so that it is in the same proportion as mother's milk. It is available as a dried milk formula. Soya milk formula is available for babies who are allergic to cow's milk.

1. Make up bottles exactly according to formula. Incorrect proportion of powder to water can cause serious dehydration.
2. Store made-up feeds in refrigerator.
3. Milk may be warmed or not according to baby's taste. Stand the bottle in a jug of hot water. Microwave warming can be dangerous, as milk is heated unevenly. Shake bottle well and test on inside of wrist.
4. Baby should be closely cuddled during bottle-feeding to encourage bonding. Never allow a baby to feed itself, e.g. from a propped-up bottle. (Why?)
5. Sterilisation of bottles, teats, etc. must be carried out carefully to prevent sickness.

Sterilising bottles,
page 392

## Making up a feed

1. Boil water. Allow to cool for up to half an hour.
2. Wash hands.
3. Pour required amount of water into bottle.
4. Use scoop provided to measure dried formula exactly.
5. Add required number of level scoops to bottle.
6. Cover bottle and shake well.
7. Fix teat on bottle. Store in refrigerator until needed. If using straight away cool down so it is slightly warm. Check on inside of wrist.
8. Empty left-over feed within 2 hours; rinse and wash bottle and teat before sterilising.

## Winding

Babies swallow air during feeding, which may cause discomfort and pain. To bring up wind, place the baby against your shoulder, or on your knee sitting up while supported and gently rub or pat its back until wind is released. Do this once or twice during feeds and at the end of a feed.

## Weaning

**Weaning is the change from milk to solid food.** In our culture weaning takes place at about 4-6 months. At this stage babies are becoming more active and hungry, therefore their milk needs to be supplemented with energy-rich foods. Weaning should be a very gradual process to allow a baby's digestive system to get used to the extra food. Weaning too early, e.g. before three months, can lead to obesity. A baby is ready for weaning when it wakes early for its next feed and sucks its fists vigorously.

### Weaning guidelines

- Continue normal milk feeds.
- Introduce one new food at a time.
- Foods should be smooth and easy to digest.
- Give small amounts of food from a spoon.
- At eight to nine months introduce more variety, e.g. yoghurt, other baby cereals, scrambled egg, puréed white fish and chicken, stewed fruit, banana.

| Suitable foods | Unsuitable foods |
| --- | --- |
| Baby rice | Salt – puts strain on kidneys |
| Puréed soup or gravy | Sugar – gives baby sweet tooth, rots new teeth |
| Puréed cooked fruit | Wheat foods – baby may be allergic to gluten |
| Puréed cooked vegetables | Egg white, rich foods – indigestible |

## Teething

Teething babies need to chew on harder foods such as rusks, fingers of toast, crusts, carrots, peeled apple and pear quarters. Never leave a baby alone with these foods. (Why?)

## Feeding young children

Babies and toddlers need

* protein for growth
* carbohydrate (starch rather than sugar) and digestible fat for energy
* calcium for growing bones and teeth
* iron for healthy blood
* vitamins and other minerals for general health.

By the age of one year, babies should be able to eat many of the foods eaten by the rest of the family, chopped or mashed if necessary. By the age of two, toddlers should be feeding themselves and should be encouraged but not forced to eat most foods. Milk remains an important food for toddlers and young children, as it supplies many important nutrients. Skimmed milk is unsuitable as it lacks fat and fat-soluble vitamins.

## Commercial baby foods

A wide variety of commercially prepared baby foods is available. They usually just need reheating. They include canned, bottled and dried foods. These are useful:

* when both parents are working
* for emergencies
* for travelling.

Follow instructions on label for storage and reheating.

1. Investigation: Conduct a survey on ready-prepared baby foods.
   (a) Compare them under the following headings – type, cost, food value, hygiene.
   (b) Make a collection of baby foods or their containers. Examine the labels and list the ingredients and nutrients in each.
   (c) What other information is given on the label?
2. Compare a home-made dish for a baby with a commercial version of a similar food. Use these headings: nutritive value, convenience, taste, texture, cost.
3. Suggest a packed lunch for a four-year-old's first day at school. What drink would you include? Give reasons for your choices.

# Hygiene and safety

## Preventing infection

Cleanliness is very important in the life of a young baby, particularly when preparing its food. Because they have little resistance to bacteria, babies are very vulnerable to illness and must be protected by good hygiene. No one should smoke near children – it causes serious respiratory diseases.

## Food hygiene

Lack of hygiene when preparing food can cause serious food poisoning.

1. Wash hands before handling a baby's food and before feeding a baby.
2. Use cooled boiled water for mixing feeds and for drinks.
3. Prepared feeds must be stored in a refrigerator and not kept longer than 24 hours.
4. Throw out unfinished feeds. Rinse bottle and teat in cold water.
5. Wash bottle and teat thoroughly using warm water and a bottle brush. Rinse and sterilise carefully.

trapped air

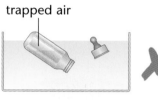

*Chemical sterilisation*

## Sterilising bottles

Bottles, teats, soothers, etc. can be sterilised by:

- boiling
- steaming
- chemical sterilisation – make up the sterilising solution, e.g. Milton, according to instructions. Place washed bottles, etc. in solution, making sure there are no air pockets. Leave for at least 30 minutes. Rinse in cooled boiled water to remove taste of solution.

## Bathing

A regular bath is the best way to keep a baby clean. When a bath is not possible a baby can be 'topped and tailed' – first the head and then the nappy area is washed and dried. Bathing a baby can be an enjoyable time for parent and child, but precautions must be taken to avoid chills and accidents.

- Make sure bathing area is warm.
- Collect all requirements: towels, soap, etc.
- Fill bath and test bath water with your elbow.
- Remove all baby's clothes except nappy, and wrap baby in towel.
- Clean face area and shampoo hair before bathing.
- Remove nappy, clean baby's bottom, then lift gently into bath water.
- Support at all times in the crook of the elbow, holding baby's off-side arm with your hand.

- Wash gently, using the minimum of baby soap and being particular about groin and underarms.
- Rinse, then lift from bath and dry gently with a soft towel.

## Nappy changing

Be particular about nappy hygiene – change nappies regularly and keep nappy area clean and dry. Use waterproof cream, e.g. petroleum jelly, to protect against nappy rash. Wash your hands after changing a nappy.

## Toilet training

A child cannot be toilet-trained until it is ready. It needs to be able to understand instructions, have sufficient co-ordination to be able to remove its pants, and have some control over bladder and bowel movements. Gentle encouragement is more effective than forcing the issue.

Make it easier for the child by:

1 using towelling training pants instead of nappies
2 using a steady attractive potty, and later a training seat (a smaller seat that fits over a normal toilet seat)
3 using praise and reward for achievements to give the child confidence.

Train the child from the start to wash their hands after using the toilet.

# Care of teeth

Although teeth are present from birth, they only break through the gums at about the sixth or seventh month. Signs of teething: (a) flushed cheeks, (b) dribbling, (c) chewing fists.

All 20 baby teeth are present by about the age of three years.

It is important to keep first teeth healthy in order that decay does not pass into permanent teeth which are growing in the gums. Make sure that children:

- eat plenty of high-calcium foods – milk, cheese, yoghurt
- avoid sugary foods such as biscuits, sweets and bars
- avoid sweetened drinks and fruit juices; use cooled boiled water instead

Adults should never dip soothers in sweet substances to keep children quiet, or bribe children with sweet treats.

Clean children's teeth when they appear, and encourage them to clean their own as soon as they are able.

## Preventing accidents

1. Put babies to sleep on their backs without a pillow.
2. Never allow a baby to feed alone.
3. Never leave babies or young children unattended in a bath or near water.
4. Toys and equipment, e.g. buggies, should be safe.
5. Keep dangerous objects out of reach of children: small objects, e.g. beads or toy parts, can cause choking. Matches, cleaning agents, pills, medicines, knives and plastic bags should be locked away.
6. Use stair gates at top and bottom of stairs, and a fireguard on fires and heaters.
7. Use a cooker guard to protect against burns and scalds. Turn saucepan handles in.
8. Electricity – avoid trailing flexes; use shuttered sockets.

1. Suggest some safety precautions to follow when children are (a) in a car; (b) in the garden.
2. Make a collection of leaflets on safety, hygiene and baby care from health boards etc.
3. Make up a rhyme that teaches a child safety rules in the home and outside the home.

## Clothing

It is not necessary to buy a lot of clothes for a new baby (0–3 months), as they are soon outgrown. On the other hand, babies regularly soil and wet clothes, e.g. by bringing up feeds, so a good supply of washable clothes and bed clothes is essential from then on.

### Buying baby clothes

1. They should be comfortable – soft, with no rough seams or trimmings.
2. They should be absorbent.
3. They should be machine washable, tumble dryable and need no ironing.
4. They should allow freedom of movement. Stretch suits, e.g. Babygros, are ideal; they are soft and stretchy, keep feet warm and have no gaps.
5. They should be easy to put on and take off, e.g. with envelope necks and Velcro fastenings, or poppers at neck and inside of legs.
6. Avoid strings, buttons and lacy finishes which catch in babies' fingers.
7. They should conform to safety standards, i.e. flame-resistant nightwear, no cords around neck.

| Suitable fibres | Suitable fabrics |
|---|---|
| Cotton | Brushed cotton (winceyette) |
| Polyester | Cotton/synthetic jersey |
| Cotton/polyester mix | Stretch towelling |
| Acrylic | Quilted or fleece finishes for outdoor garments |
| Nylon (outer clothes) | Machine-washable wools |

## Layette

A set of clothes for a new baby is sometimes called a layette. The number of items depends on budget and washing/drying facilities. Babies need (approximately):

- 6–7 envelope neck vests
- 6–7 Babygros
- 3–4 jumpers or jackets
- 2–3 washable shawls/blankets for wrapping
- 2–3 all-in-one winter suits, hats, mittens, etc.
- several bibs.

Other items, e.g. dresses, are optional.

Footwear is unnecessary until a child is walking well. Make sure shoes fit properly – allow room for growth and movement. Shoes that are too tight restrict growth and cause deformity.

## Nappies

Nappies are a necessary and costly consideration when budgeting for a baby. There is a choice between disposable and towelling nappies. Disposable nappies are available in several sizes, e.g. newborn, baby and toddler size.

**ACTIVITY**

1. Discuss (a) towelling nappies and (b) disposable nappies under the following headings: cost; convenience; shopping; laundering; environment; ease of use. A baby needs an average of 6 to 8 nappy changes a day. Calculate the cost of a year's supply of (a) towelling nappies and (b) disposable nappies. Name two brands of disposable nappy.
2. List the important properties of fabrics used for baby clothes.
3. List the five pieces of equipment you consider most necessary to buy for a new baby. Find out the average cost of each.

# Health and childcare facilities

## Public health services for children

All babies are entitled to free health care until the age of five.

1. The public health nurse visits newborn babies at home, checks each baby's health and development, advises mothers on care and feeding, and provides information on clinics, etc.

2. Health centres run baby clinics which provide a series of developmental checks, e.g. on hearing, sight, physical progress, to make sure that there are no health problems. If there are problems, babies are referred to specialists for treatment, free of charge.

3. Immunisation (vaccination) is available at clinics and from GPs. Immunisation helps the body produce antibodies which fight off dangerous diseases. Vaccinations include those against tuberculosis (up to six weeks), diphtheria, whooping cough, tetanus, polio, meningitis (2–6 months); and the MMR vaccination against measles, mumps and rubella (15 months). Some boosters are given later.

## Community services

In some areas the following services may be provided subsidised or free of charge. Childcare facilities are also available through voluntary organisations such as Barnardo's. Check what is available in your area.

- Parenting classes
- Crèches
- Playgroups
- Nursery schools, e.g. Montessori schools.

Child-minding is usually arranged privately.

Childcare facilities should be:

- staffed by responsible, caring individuals who understand children's needs
- well equipped – with stimulating and educational play equipment and toys, child-sized furniture and a rest area for naps
- clean and hygienic – with adequate toilet facilities for the number of children
- roomy – enough space for children to play indoors and outdoors
- safe – sockets covered, kitchen closed off, dangerous objects locked away
- fire-aware – fire extinguishers visible; fire drill routine established.

## Voluntary organisations for parents and children

1. Irish Society for the Prevention of Cruelty to Children (ISPCC)
2. Irish Pre-school Playgroups Association
3. Parentline (organisation for parents under stress)
4. Single Parents Support Group
5. La Leche League (breast-feeding information)

**ACTIVITY**

1. Find out what community services are available for mothers and children in your area. Make an appointment to visit one, and write a report on the services provided in your childcare folder.

2. Visit the child clinic in your local health centre. Prepare a questionnaire before you go, and complete a businesslike report on the visit including the answers to these and similar questions:
   - Name and address of clinic.
   - Name of district nurse and other staff present.
   - Services provided, e.g. vaccinations, developmental checks.
   - Age at which a baby must visit.

   Collect information on other services for babies/children in your area.

# Children with special needs

All children need lots of love, care and guidance. One in ten children, however, need extra help and assistance. These are children with disabilities.

**A disability is something that affects or weakens one's normal ability.**

A disability may be congenital (a child is born with it) or the result of an illness or accident. Children may be affected in one of the following ways:

- chronic illness, e.g. asthma, epilepsy
- disability of the senses, e.g. blindness, deafness
- physical disability, e.g. unable to walk or move properly
- mental disability, e.g. difficulty in understanding or learning
- emotional disability, e.g. difficulty relating to others, e.g. autism.

Children may also suffer from emotional disability if they were abused or neglected as babies.

**Four common disabilities in children are:**

**Down syndrome** – a defect in part of the cells (the chromosomes). The child is born with characteristic appearance and learning needs. They frequently suffer other health problems.

**Cerebral palsy** – brain damage before or during birth. Symptoms: jerky, uncontrolled movements.

**Cystic fibrosis** – overproduction of mucus in the lungs, causing severe breathing difficulties.

**Spina bifida** – malformation of the spine and spinal cord. Symptoms: may be unable to walk; difficulty with bladder and bowel control.

## Attitude

People who have not had much contact with children with special needs often have difficulty in communicating with them. Remember that each disability is separate – don't treat children with one disability as if they had others, i.e. don't talk down to them. Special children should be treated as far as possible as normal children.

Because of a disability, a child may have difficulty communicating and be slower to learn. With love, patience and the correct stimulation a special child, like any other child, will be able to reach his or her full potential.

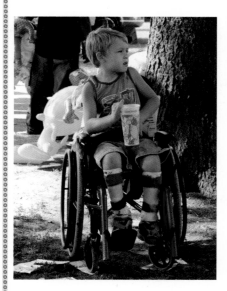

## Children with disabilities have special needs

These may include:

- extra loving care and attention
- specialised medical care, nursing, physiotherapy, e.g. massage
- special needs teaching – for children who are deaf, blind or have learning difficulties
- aids for hearing, walking, etc.
- special transport, e.g. wheelchairs
- speech therapy, occupational therapy, psychotherapy
- special accommodation, e.g. access for wheelchairs, hand rails at toilet, wide doorways.

## Help available

The responsibility of caring for a child with special needs can be demanding on family members. Help is available from organisations that have a special interest and knowledge of each condition, for example:

- Irish Society for Autism

♣ National Association for the Deaf

♣ Down Syndrome Ireland.

See also the Golden Pages under 'Charities and caring groups'.

1. Explain what is meant by speech therapy, occupational therapy and psychotherapy. Give an example of each, and name a disability that would benefit from each therapy.

2. Look up four more organisations for children with disabilities. Find out more about one of them. Use these headings: address; aims; services provided for disabled child and parents.

3. Describe four problems that a physically handicapped child might face in a normal home. Suggest one way of resolving each problem.

## The family and the law

Parents are obliged by law to provide children with food, clothing, shelter and protection. They are also responsible for the education of their children. Parents who fail in their legal duties to their children may have them removed and placed in care.

The **Family Home Protection Act** makes sure that children are provided with shelter by preventing one parent from selling the family home against the wishes of the other.

The **Family Law (Maintenance of Spouse and Children) Act** makes sure that the dependent spouse and children are provided for.

The law can also bar a violent spouse from the family home.

## Family breakdown

Modern society has placed many pressures on the family. One of the results is that more couples are divorcing or separating and more families are breaking down. Organisations that help families in difficulties include:

♣ Accord (formerly CMAC) – for couples who have problems in their marriage

♣ Family Mediation Service – run by the Department of Justice to help separating couples work out the conditions of their separation, e.g. custody and maintenance of children

- Alcoholics Anonymous, Gamblers Anonymous – help people overcome addictions which damage family life. Al Anon, Al Ateen help the spouses and children of alcoholics
- Women's Aid – helps abused women and their children.

**PROJECT**

### Childcare project

If you follow the childcare option for your Junior Certificate, you must complete a project relating to children. This represents 15% of your total marks. Choose a topic which interests you and which it will be possible to research. It must be original (do not copy material closely from books, etc.) and all your own work. Examiners look for a well-thought-out, interesting project, original research, and some practical work, e.g. interviews, surveys and visits to organisations, clinics, etc. It should be thoroughly researched in a scientific way, with evidence of how you gathered your information, e.g. correspondence. The project must be no longer than 1,500 words and must be well presented (see below).

### Resources/research

- Books – from home, school, public libraries.
- Internet.
- Interviews – with mothers; professionals, e.g. public health nurses, doctors.
- Questionnaires and surveys.
- Visits – to clinics, hospitals, playgroups, specialist organisations, etc.
- Community resources – community information centre, voluntary groups, etc.
- Specialist sources such as manufacturers, government departments, e.g. Health Promotion Unit.

### Presenting your project

The project should be presented in this order.
- Title.
- Table of contents.
- Statement of the aim of the project.
- Background research.
- Main project.
- Conclusion – whether you have achieved your aim.
- Bibliography – acknowledgements of books, people and other resources you used.

Use a neat layout, clear headings, good writing and correct spellings, with photographs, labelled diagrams, etc. to illustrate it. Samples, etc. should be stapled or glued to pages.

## Suggestions for research project

- Preparing for birth – clothes and equipment.
- A booklet for babysitters.
- Commercial baby foods.
- Health services for children in my area.
- Parenting courses.
- Preschool care in my area.
- Mental handicap in children.
- Child development – a case study.
- A child-based craft, e.g. wall hanging, play mat, soft toy. This may form only part of your total project: in other words, a project on learning might include a play mat to demonstrate some research. (Making a craft item – see page 405.)

# Option 2 Design and Craftwork

## Craft in Ireland

 Craft is the creation of objects that are both beautiful and useful.

Ireland has a long tradition of craft. The art of craftworkers can be seen in our museums – Bronze Age ornaments, religious objects such as chalices, and illustrated manuscripts such as the Book of Kells. Many examples of medieval craftwork – pewter vessels, jewellery and even woven textiles – were found buried in Wood Quay in Dublin. We have a history of producing magnificent crafts which are exported all over the world.

Crafts began to die out when the Industrial Revolution made it possible to mass-produce goods by machine. Crafts such as textiles, furniture and pottery were too slow and expensive to make by hand – factory goods could be produced more cheaply.

Today, however, people have a renewed interest in crafts. This revival has been helped by the huge increase in tourism – visitors are buying indigenous crafts to bring home with them. The term 'craft' is now associated with goods that are beautiful, special and 'one of a kind'.

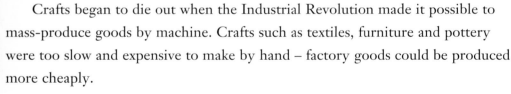

The major sectors in the Irish craft industry are pottery, glass, jewellery, textiles (particularly knitwear) and furniture. Irish craft businesses are generally small and are spread all over the country, but taken nationally the industry is a significant employer. It is important in providing viable, sustainable enterprises in all areas, including those isolated rural communities ignored as unsuitable by other manufacturers.

## The Crafts Council of Ireland

This is the national design and economic development agency for the craft industry in Ireland. It helps to create employment for craft workers. It is funded by the Department of Enterprise, Trade and Employment. The council holds almost 1,700 members in its register of craft enterprise.

Its functions are:

- to enhance and promote Irish design
- to help craftspeople develop their business
- to provide information and training courses to those involved in craft and design
- to raise the profile of Irish crafts at home and abroad.

**ACTIVITY**

1. Visit a craft centre or a craft shop in your locality. Examine the different groups of crafts and make a list of them, describing each under these headings: medium used, aesthetic value, function, evaluation (does it fulfil its function?).
2. If a particular craft is made in your locality, you might be allowed to visit the premises. Write a report on the visit, how the product is made, the types of product available and a history of the craft or business.

# Craft skills

Craftwork is the use of personal skills to design and create objects that are both beautiful and useful.

A well-designed crafted item:

- looks pleasing
- fulfils its function
- has a high standard of workmanship.

## Skills required by craftworkers

1. Ability to design.
2. Manual dexterity (being skilled with your hands).
3. Artistic ability and aesthetic sense – often called 'good taste'.

**LINK-UP**

Design in the home, page 300

**LINK-UP**

Design in textiles, page 345

## ACTIVITY

1. Start a craftwork folder. Collect ideas for crafts from magazines, etc. and small samples of crafts, if suitable. Collect samples of textiles, e.g. left-over fabric, which you may be able to use in a craft such as patchwork.

2. Choose a craft that appeals to you, research and make a report on it, including some samples in your presentation which show the versatility of the craft.

## Textile crafts

These are crafts that use threads and/or fabrics. Textile crafts have been in use for hundreds of years. Jacobean embroidery was popular in Stuart times. Petit point and cross-stitched 'samplers' were worked by Victorian ladies and their daughters. Patchwork began as a thrifty way of using up old clothes and fabric scraps and became particularly popular in America. Lacemaking developed in Europe in the 15th century, particularly in France, Italy and Belgium – Brussels lace is still world famous. Lacemaking was brought to Ireland by nuns to give employment to poor girls, e.g. in Limerick and Carrickmacross.

❖ *Carrickmacross lace*

| Textile crafts | | |
|---|---|---|
| Appliqué | Tapestry | Quilting – plain and raised (Trapunto, Italian) |
| Collage | Smocking | Embroidery – hand, machine, creative |
| Crochet | Patchwork | Weaving – card, frame |
| Knitting | Lacemaking | Printing, hand painting, fabric markers |
| Macramé | Toy-making | Dyeing – batik, tie-dyeing |

## Modern crafts

Traditional crafts and designs will always be popular, but there is a strong emphasis today on using your imagination to make up your own designs when creating textile crafts.

Creative design can take its inspiration from:

- ❧ scenery – mountains, rocks, grasses, sea, sky and clouds
- ❧ nature – birds, insects, flowers, leaves, bark, shells, feathers, roots
- ❧ self-expression – use your imagination to create 'stream of consciousness' blobs and squiggles.

**Creative embroidery** – uses the imagination rather than using embroidery transfers. Different textiles and yarns are used to produce interesting textures and shapes. Other objects, such as buttons, braid, lace, shells, feathers, sequins and even safety pins, can be used in the design to give different effects.

## Machine embroidery

Machines are useful for quilting, patchwork and other decorative effects. Elaborate machines can sew a huge range of decorative stitches. Even a simple zigzag stitch is useful for creative needlework such as appliqué. When embroidering by machine, hold fabric taut to avoid puckering. An embroidery frame is useful when doing freestyle machine embroidery (using a lowered feed dog).

**ACTIVITY**

1. Personalise an item of clothing by using embroidery or appliqué to put your initials on it.
2. Using a textile craft, create and work a design for a T-shirt.
3. Choose a craft object which you have the skills to make. Price a similar one in a shop. Design and make the object, using the design process. Compare it with the shop item under the headings cost, time, appearance, function.
4. Using a textile, design a storage system suitable for small items, e.g. a cloth bag; a hanging storage system containing pockets.

## Making a craft item

If you choose the craft option for your Junior Certificate you are required to make a craft item from textiles. There is a wide range of useful textile items to choose from. You can also make use of some of the textile crafts listed on page 404. Decide whether to use the skills you have or to learn new skills in order to make the item.

### Suggested craft items

| | |
|---|---|
| Tissue box covers | Draught excluders, e.g. stuffed snake |
| Clothes peg holders | Christmas stockings or wreaths |
| Lampshades | Matching oven gloves, tea cosy and table mats |
| Cushion covers | Patchwork quilt |
| Bean bags | Hats and other accessories |
| Knitted clothes or toys | Wall hangings, appliqué pictures and collages |
| Soft toys | Baby's play mat or pocketed nappy changing mat |
| Cloth bag | Padded towelling sun mat with pockets |

## Maximise your marks

Remember that your finished craft must:

1. meet your brief, i.e. be made from textiles (thread or fabric)
2. be aesthetically pleasing, i.e. attractive, creative, well made and finished
3. be functional – the materials used must suit its function
4. be suitable for your level of skill
5. be within your budget.

You must also present a design folder for inspection. This should show the design process. Make sure to include details of research, costs, sketches, designs or patterns, samples of fabric, etc.

6 Options

## Sample design process

**1** **Design brief**

'Make and decorate a craft item suitable for your bedroom from a textile.'

**2** **Analyse the factors to be considered**

What do I need in my bedroom? Available time; cost; washability; skills.

**3** **Research/investigation**

Look up craft books, visit craft shops, etc. Discuss with teacher.

**4** **Consider possible solutions**

Hanging storage, laundry bag, cushion, etc.

**5** **Decide on a solution**

A cushion, for example.

**6** **Plan assignment**

Draw various designs. Collect fabric and other samples. Make a work plan.

**7** **Action**

Make the cushion, keeping a step-by-step record.

**8** **Evaluation**

Did you achieve your goal? Modifications, if any.

## Making a cushion cover

A cushion can be round, square, sausage-shaped (bolster) or even star-shaped. It can be piped, pleated, smocked, frilled, embroidered, appliquéd, quilted, crocheted, tie-dyed or patchworked.

**1** Buy cushion pad first. Measure, allowing some room to spare.

**2** Make pattern and pin onto fabric or draw cushion shape on fabric using tailor's chalk. Leave a 1.5cm seam allowance and cut out.

**3** *Note:* Decoration such as embroidery or quilting is done before assembling.

**4** Tack and machine one seam, right sides together, leaving space for zip, if using. Press flat. (Alternatively, have an overlap opening at the back of cushion.)

**5** Neaten seam. Insert zip.

**6** Machine remaining sides of cushion cover, trim corners and zigzag.

**7** Press well and turn right side out.

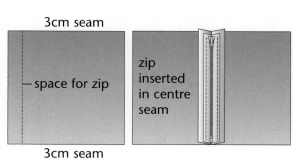

3cm seam

space for zip

3cm seam

4

zip inserted in centre seam

5

zigzag

machining

cut off corners

6

## Preparation

Making your own clothes can be a useful and money-saving hobby. Before you buy a pattern, it is necessary to take your measurements. It is easier to have another person do this.

### Taking measurements

1  Wear the minimum of clothing, and underclothes that fit well.
2  Stand straight and measure snugly but not too tightly.
3  The usual measurements are shown below; write down each as it is taken.

- ♦ Bust/chest (measure round widest part)
- ♦ Waist (tie a string around to find natural waist)
- ♦ Hips (around fullest part – 15–25cm below waist)
- ♦ Length of back (from bone at neck to waist)
- ♦ Neck (around base of neck, adding 12mm for ease)
- ♦ Sleeve length (shoulder edge to wrist bone with elbow slightly bent)
- ♦ Length of skirt (from waist to required length)
- ♦ Outside leg (trousers – from waist to required length)
- ♦ Inside leg (from crotch to required length)

### Buying a pattern

1  Know your measurements and buy the correct size.
2  Choose a design that suits your figure.
3  Consider the purpose of the garment.
4  Consider your ability (skills) – don't buy a pattern that is too difficult.

Patterns for beginners have few pieces, few seams and little detail. They are often labelled 'Easy to make'.

Commercial patterns, e.g. Style, Burda, Vogue, are chosen from catalogues in fabric shops. When you have decided on a pattern ask for it, giving name, number and size. Pattern illustrations often show different garments or variations, e.g. long and short sleeves; a dress, jacket and skirt. This means that patterns for each item or variation are included in the envelope. If in doubt, check pattern or ask the assistant.

## The pattern

Patterns contain lots of information on the envelope, the instruction sheet and the pattern pieces. Read these before you start and when making up the garment.

### The envelope front

This shows:

- pictures of the patterns enclosed – different views are numbered or lettered A, B and so on
- sizes (patterns usually include more than one size)
- name and number.

### The envelope back

This gives the following information:

- the back view (if not shown on the pattern front)
- a description of the garment
- standard body measurements – check them against your own
- fabrics suitable for the design
- measurements of finished garment – useful for alterations
- it may show numbered pattern pieces
- a chart for calculating the amount of fabric required for each size
- notions (sewing needs for making garment, e.g. 18cm zip, 20cm interfacing).

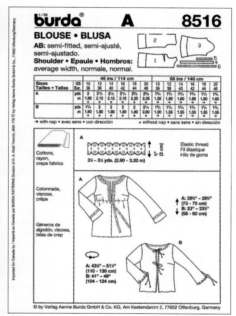

## The instruction sheet

This usually shows:

- illustration of garments, front and back
- a list and illustration of pattern pieces needed for each view
- instructions for preparing pattern
- instructions for altering pattern
- instructions for laying out pattern on different fabric widths
- cutting instructions
- step-by-step instructions on how to make the garment.

---

### burda
<sup>1/03</sup>

**ENGLISH**

**PATTERN PIECES:**

A B 1 Front 2x
A B 2 Back 1x
A B 3 Sleeve 2x
A B 4 Bias Strip / Neck Edge 1x
    B 5 Tie Band 4x
    B 6 Tie Band / Sleeve 2x

CUTTING LAYOUTS ARE ON THE PATTERN SHEET

**PREPARING PATTERN PIECES**

Choose your size according to the Burda measurement chart: dresses, blouses, jackets, and coats according to your bust measurement and pants and skirts according to your hip measurement. Adjust the pattern pieces, if necessary, by adding or subtracting the number of inches that your measurements differ from the measurements given in the Burda chart.

**AB**
Cut out the following pattern pieces in the required size:
for the BLOUSE, view **A**, pieces 1 to 4 and
for the BLOUSE, view **B**, pieces 1 to 6.

**LENGTHENING OR SHORTENING PATTERN**

Our pattern is calculated for a height of 5 feet, 6 inches (168 cm). If you are taller or shorter, you may adjust the pattern to fit your size at the lines marked "lengthen or shorten here". This ensures proper fit.

Make sure that you adjust all pieces of one model by the same amount at the same lines.

**How to lengthen or shorten pattern pieces:**
Cut pattern pieces along marked lines.
**To lengthen,** slide the two halves of the pattern piece as far apart as necessary.
**To shorten** overlap the two halves of the pattern piece as far as necessary.
Even out side edges.

**CUTTING**

**FOLD (— — —)** means: Here is the center of a pattern piece, but in no case a cut edge or a seam. The piece should be cut double, with the fold line forming the center line.

Pattern pieces that are outlined with a broken line in the cutting layout are to be placed face down on the fabric.
**AB**
**The cutting layouts on the pattern sheet show how the pattern pieces should be placed on the fabric.**

**SEAM AND HEM ALLOWANCES are included on pattern pieces: 5/8" (1.5 cm)** for hem and at all other seams and edges.

## Pattern symbols

| Straight grain | | Pattern piece must be placed with the arrow lying along the warp or lengthwise grain of fabric. |
|---|---|---|
| Fold line | | Arrows point to a line which must be placed on the lengthwise fold of fabric. |
| Notches | | These show where parts of garment must be joined. Cut notches outwards. |
| Cutting line | | The thick outline of the pattern is where you cut. If your pattern does not have a cutting line you must allow 1.5cm extra for the seam allowance when cutting. |
| Stitching line | | Sew (machine) on the broken line in the direction of the arrows. |
| Balance marks | | These show important points, for example the centre of the garment or (dots) where to stop sewing. |
| Construction marks | | These are lines and dots showing position of darts, pockets, pleats, etc. |
| Alteration lines | | Cut between these lines to lengthen or shorten. |
| Button position | | |
| Buttonholes | | |

## The tissue pattern

This comes in large sheets which must be separated by cutting on the line indicated for your size. Each pattern piece is usually half of what is required. It is then cut on the double. Example: a shirt front is shown here – it should be cut on the double to give the left and right front. Any exceptions are labelled 'cut one' or 'cut four' etc.

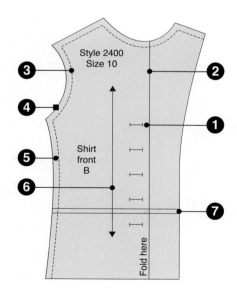

Pattern pieces show:

- name, number and size of pattern
- number and name of pattern piece
- symbols such as balance marks
- some instructions.

Identify the following on this pattern piece

1. _____    5. _____

2. _____    6. _____

3. _____    7. _____

4. _____

Textiles for sewing,
page 379

# Choosing fabric for sewing

**1** Fabrics are sold in 90cm, 115cm, 120cm, 140cm and 150cm widths.

**2** Check pattern chart to find out how much fabric you need. The wider the fabric, the less you will need.

**3** Choose a fabric suitable for the design you are making. The fabric envelope suggests suitable fabrics. Choose stiff, closely woven fabrics such as linen or worsted for a tailored look. Soft, silky fabrics suit draped, unstructured lines.

**4** Buy thread, zip, interfacing, etc. at the same time as the fabric, so that you can match colours and start the garment straight away.

**ACTIVITY** List the properties of a fabric that would be suitable for a beginner.

# Altering patterns

When you check your measurements against the pattern measurements you may need to adjust the length or width. Small alterations may be done by letting in or out the seam allowance when sewing. For larger adjustments, alter the pattern as shown below before laying it on the fabric.

- If the pattern has to be altered a great deal, it is better to adjust in two places rather than adding/taking too much in one place, which would alter the proportions of the garment.

- If you alter one pattern piece, e.g. a shoulder seam, the pattern piece that joins it must also be altered or it will not fit.

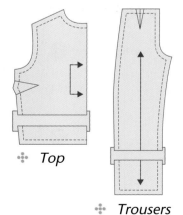

* Top

* Trousers

## Lengthening

**1** Cut the pattern between the alteration lines.

**2** Use a sheet of tissue or paper large enough for alteration.

**3** Draw two parallel lines on paper the required distance apart.

**4** Lay pattern pieces on the new lines and secure with pins or Sellotape. Mark new cutting line.

## Shortening

**1** Fold pattern on alteration line half the depth of alteration required. Pin or Sellotape in place.

**2** Mark new cutting line.

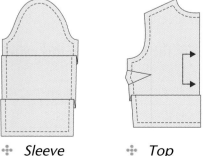

* Sleeve   * Top

## Increasing width

1. Draw a vertical line from top to bottom of pattern and cut.
2. Draw two lines the width required on a sheet of paper/tissue, as for lengthening.
3. Place divided pattern pieces on alteration marks and secure with pins or Sellotape.
4. Redraw cutting and fitting line and construction marks such as darts, if necessary.

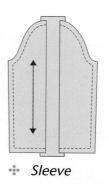 *Sleeve*  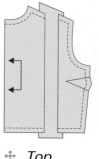 *Top*

## Decreasing width

1. Draw a vertical line from top to bottom of the pattern.
2. Fold along line, half width of alteration required. Secure with pins or Sellotape.
3. Redraw cutting and fitting lines and construction marks such as darts.

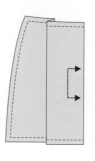 *Skirt*   *Top*

# Making clothes

## Preparing the fabric

1. Examine fabric for flaws, mark them with chalk and work around them when cutting out.
2. Press if creased and straighten cut ends to a thread.
3. Fold fabric according to layout instructions and lay flat on a table.

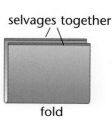

*Selvage to selvage*

## Preparing the pattern

1. Check instruction sheet for pattern pieces needed for your view. Remove.
2. Mark layout for your view, size and fabric width.
3. Alter pattern if necessary.

## Laying the pattern on the fabric

1. Place pattern pieces on folded fabric, following layout suggested in instructions.
2. Place large pieces first, and those placed to the fold. Then fit in smaller pieces.
3. Check that the straight grain line on the pattern corresponds with the straight grain of the fabric. Check this with a ruler or tape measure.
4. Check that all pieces have been placed on the fabric. Note those that must be cut twice or on the single.
5. Pin in position, placing pins at right angles to edge and within seam allowance.

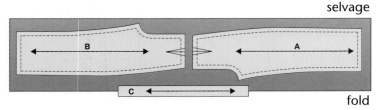

selvage

fold

❖ *Cutting out (pattern laid on fabric)*

**ACTIVITY** Pile fabrics must be laid out a special way. Explain how and why. (Hint: See 'Textiles for sewing', page 379.)

❖ *Cutting round a pattern piece*

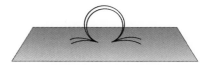

❖ *Tailor tacking*

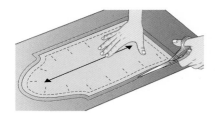

right side of fabric

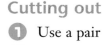

tracing wheel   tracing paper

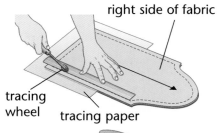

❖ *Tailor's chalk*

## Cutting out

1. Use a pair of sharp cutting-out scissors.
2. Leave a seam allowance of 1.5cm, unless included in pattern.
3. Cut along cutting line of pattern, cutting notches outwards.
4. Hold fabric flat on the table with one hand while cutting with even strokes. Never lift fabric.
5. Before removing pattern, transfer important markings on to the fabric.

## Transferring pattern markings

It is essential to transfer construction marks from pattern to fabric pieces in order to make up the garment. They act as a guide for joining sections together and indicate important details of the construction.

- **Tailor tacking:** See page 374.
- **Tracing wheel:** Fold fabric right side out. Insert two sheets of coloured carbon between fabric layers, waxed side facing wrong sides of fabric and trace, using a ruler to guide tracing wheel.
- **Tailor's chalk:** Useful for marking stitching line when pattern has no seam allowance, or for marking cutting lines when there is no pattern, e.g. for crafts.

## Making up a garment – step by step

While garments may differ in some details, most clothes are made up in much the same order. Tack the basic garment together on the fitting lines, for a first fitting. Alter if necessary, then tack, machine and press at each stage of garment construction. Neaten seams before proceeding to the next stage.

**Always follow the instruction sheet of your pattern.**

- Sew darts and tucks.
- Make and attach pockets.
- Sew shoulder seams.
- Make and attach facings/collar to top of garment.
- Sew side seams.
- Make and insert sleeves.
- Join top to lower half of garment.
- Insert zip or make buttons and buttonholes.
- Turn up hem.
- Final pressing.

## Fitting

Major alterations should have been made on the pattern before cutting out. However, to make sure a garment fits well it is necessary to try it on several times during its construction, altering it if necessary. A 'good fit' means that the garment:

- looks well
- hangs properly
- is comfortable
- is neither too tight nor too loose.

Fit of garments often alters with fashion.

## Fitting guidelines

1. Pin basic garment together and tack securely.
2. Try on right side out (there are often differences between one side of the body and the other).
3. Close opening with pins. Make sure centre of garment is at centre of body.
4. Stand in front of a mirror.
   - Does it hang correctly without pulling or dragging?
   - Is it too loose or too tight?
   - Are darts and other shaped features positioned correctly?
   - Are the shoulder seams on the shoulder line?
   - Is the waistline exactly on the waist?
   - Are vertical seams straight?
   - Are armholes and neckline in correct position? Are they too loose or too tight?

5. Mark alterations with pins or chalk. Remove garment and transfer alterations to inside.

6. Tack along new fitting lines. Try on again before machining.

## Alterations

1. **Too loose or too tight:** take in or let out vertical darts and/or side seams. The alteration should be equal on both sides.

2. **Shoulders too narrow for sleeve:** unpick top half of sleeve and lift sleeve inwards to edge of shoulder; pin, tack and machine, tapering to original seam at notches.

3. **Sloping shoulders:** take in outside of shoulder seam, tapering to nothing at the neck.

4. **Waist too tight:** separate bodice from skirt. Let out darts by sewing inside existing dart. Let out side seams on bodice and skirt, tapering to original seam at bust and hips.

5. **Waist too loose:** as (4) above, but taking in darts and seams.

6. **Hips too tight:** let out side seams gradually from waist to hip.

7. **Fitting trousers:** crotch can be lengthened or shortened by lifting or lowering the waistline. Wrinkles at the back below the waist can be removed by lowering the back of the waistband.

**LINK-UP**

Irons, page 370

## Pressing

### Equipment

Steam iron, ironing board, sleeve board (like a small ironing board), pressing cloths.

### Guidelines

Pressing gives garments a good finish. It involves steam and pressure. It is not a gliding movement like ironing – the iron is lifted and pressed firmly on to the fabric, then lifted and pressed on to the next section.

1. Press on the wrong side using a steam iron. Use a pressing cloth to protect fabric if you must press on the right side.

2. Test iron for correct temperature on a scrap of sewing fabric.

3. Remove pins and tacking before pressing.

4. Press at each construction stage, e.g. darts, seams, before proceeding to the next stage.

**⑤** Press smaller items, e.g. pockets, collars, sleeves, before attaching to main garment.

**⑥** When garment is complete, give a final press.

## Decorative finishes

Plain clothes can look attractive and smart, but if we wore them all the time they would be boring. Consider how different jeans would be without pockets, welt seams and contrasting stitching. You can add interest to home-produced and ready-made clothes by decorating them to your own style and taste. Decoration on clothes can add colour, pattern, texture and emphasis.

- **Bias binding** or **braid** can add emphasis to an otherwise plain garment. One of the trademarks of Chanel suits is the use of braid to edge jackets.

- **Embroidery and lace** can be used creatively to decorate underwear and evening clothes, adding pattern and texture.

- **Buttons and beads** can lift a chain-store suit or dress into the designer league.

- **Zips and pockets** can be both functional and decorative.

It's all a matter of using your imagination to make your clothes look attractive, different and personal.

**ACTIVITY** Suggest two ways of adding colour or texture to the following: (a) a pair of old jeans; (b) a white T-shirt; (c) a grey track suit; (d) a sweater that is too short.

## The textile industry

The Irish textile industry employs a large number of people in several sectors.

- Raw material production – sheep rearing, growing flax.
- Manufacture of fibres – spinning.
- Man-made fibre production.
- Fabric production – weaving and knitting.
- Dyeing and finishing.
- Fashion design and clothes manufacture.
- Wholesaling and retailing.

Most of the raw materials for textiles are imported; most of the finished textiles are exported. Many of the larger textile companies are in foreign ownership.

| Irish clothing manufacturers | Irish fashion designers |
| --- | --- |
| Avoca Handweavers | Richard O'Brien |
| Blarney Woollen Mills | John Rocha |
| Jack Murphy Clothing | Louise Kennedy |

The principal textile industries in Ireland are:
- Irish tweed – the main producers are located in the West, e.g. Donegal, and the South-west
- Irish linen – centred on Belfast
- carpets
- knitwear
- clothing – mainly centred on Dublin.

Can you name some more?

**ACTIVITY**

1. Visit a textile factory in your locality and report on the processes used in making the textile.
2. Arrange to visit the showroom or workplace of a fashion or textile designer and describe the products in which the designer specialises. Interview the designer and find out the training required for his or her work.
3. Read some current fashion magazines and note five of the current fashion trends, e.g. colour, style, skirt length. Visit some clothes shops and chain stores in a local shopping area and report on how many of the current trends are available in the stores.

# INDEX

abrasives, 335
absorption of food, 26
accessories, 348
accident prevention, 336–8, 394
accidents, first aid, 338–41
acetate, 356–8
acne, 254–5
acrylic, 356–8
addiction, 289
additives, food, 159–60
adolescence, 272–7
  dietary needs, 34
adulthood, 278–82
advertising, 240–3
advice agencies, 214–15
aerobic exercise, 247
air pollution, 329
alcohol, 284–7
alimentary canal, 25–7
allergies, 160
altering clothes, 416
aluminium foil, 73
amenities, 298
amino acids, 8–9, 25
anaemia, 16
anger, 250
anorexia nervosa, 48
antenatal check-ups, 384
antioxidants, 160
anti-perspirants, 254
apple cake, 194
apple tart, 193
arteries, 261
ascorbic acid, 14
ATM cards, 237
attitude, 249–50
au gratin, 81

babies, 384–99
  bathing, 392–3
  clothing, 394–5
  feeding, 33, 388–92

hygiene and safety, 337, 392–3, 394
  teething, 391, 393
  toileting, 393
bacon, Dublin coddle, 188
bacteria, 68–72, 333
Bakewell tart, 194
baking, 87, 106–10
  blind, 81
  recipes, 164–7, 189–201
baking parchment, 74
baking powder, 107
banana and raisin cookies, 199
banana nut bread, 165
banana smoothie, 168
barbecue sauce, 176
bar codes, 237
barley, 103
basal metabolic rate (BMR), 19
basting, 81
bathroom hygiene, 333
batter, 203
bean salad, 182
béchamel sauce, 99
bedclothes, 353
bedroom design, 306–7
behaviour, 275–6
berry smoothie, 168
bias of fabric, 380
bile, 25
biodegradable products, 330
birth, 281
biscuits, 198–201
blanching, 154
blankets, 353
bleaches, 335
blood and blood vessels, 261–2
blood pressure, 45
body odour (BO), 254
boiling, 84
  vegetables, 117
bonded fabrics, 360

bottled food, 155–6
bottle-feeding, 389–90
  sterilising bottles, 392
botulism, 69
bouquet garni, 81
boutiques, 234
bowel, 26
bran, 43, 102
bread, 105–7
  freezing, 154
  recipes, 164–6
bread and butter pudding, 175
bread soda, 107
breakfast fruit salad, 168
breakfasts, 90–1
breast-feeding, 388–9
  dietary needs, 35
breathing, 263–4
brief, 60
brine, 81
brittle bone disease, 15
broth, 96
budgeting, 229–33
buffets, 58
bulimia, 49
bulk buying, 238
buns, rock buns, 167
burns, first aid, 340
burst pipes, 326–7
butter, 125–6
buttercream filling, 200–1
buttermilk, 123
buying checklist, 209–10

cabbage salad, 182
CAD (computer-aided design), 362
cakes, 106–10
  freezing, 154
  icings and fillings, 197, 200–1
  recipes, 194–7
calcium, 14–15
  food composition table, 28–30

RDA, 18
cancer, 249, 255, 283
canned food, 155–6
carbohydrates, 10–11, 18
    food composition table, 28–30
care labels, 364–6
carotene, 13
carpets, 352
carrot and coriander soup, 169
carrot and raisin salad, 182
casseroling, 85
cellulose, 41
central heating, 327
central vacuum systems, 312
cereals, 101–10
cerebral palsy, 398
CFCs, 330
CFLs, 312–13, 325
chain stores, 234–5
cheese, 126–9
    cheese pastry, 190
    cheese scones, 167
cheques, 237
chicken, 137–8
    recipes, 178, 187–8, 192
childbirth, 281
children and childcare, 384–401
    child development, 272–5, 385–8
    dietary needs, 33–4, 388–91
    facilities, 396–7
    hygiene and safety, 337, 392–3,
      394
    rights, 266
    roles, 269
chilli con carne, 185
chocolate and peanut butter
    blondies, 200
chocolate cake, 196
chocolate chip cookies, 198
chocolate fudge icing, 197
choice, 208–10
choking, first aid, 340
cholesterol, 43–4
chowder, 170
chyme, 25
circulatory system, 260–2
Citizens' Information Centres,
    214–15

cleaning, 312
    agents and equipment, 334–5
    schedule, 295–6
clingfilm, 73
clostridium botulinum, 69
clothes making, 408–17
clothing, 344–9
    babies, 394–5
    washing and care of, 364–71
coddle, 188
coeliac disease, 50, 105
colcannon, 189
coleslaw, 182
colon, 26
colour, 301–2
    clothes, 345
    fabrics, 361
    home interiors, 302
colourings in food, 159
communication, 268
community, 299
community services, 299
    childcare, 396–7
complaints, 213, 220–2
compost heap, 332
computers, 313
condensed milk, 124
conduction, 84, 327
conflict, 276
consommé, 96
constipation, 42
Consumer Information Act, 242
Consumer Protection Act, 218–19
consumers, 206–44
    choice and decisions, 207–10
    complaints, 213, 220–2
    information, 211–15, 242
    quality of goods, 223–8
    rights and protection, 211–22
Consumers' Association of Ireland,
    219, 222
convalescents, dietary needs, 36–7
convection, 84, 327
convenience foods, 156–7
cook-chill foods, 157
cookers, 316–18
    oven management, 79–80
cooking, 83–9

methods, 84–9, 117–18
    planning and preparation, 60–7,
      75–80
    terms, 81–2
co-ordination, 386
coronary heart disease, 43–4
costing a recipe, 62–3
cottage pie, 186
cotton, 355
courts, 216, 222
Crafts Council of Ireland, 403
craftwork, 402–7
cream, 125
cream cleansers, 335
crease resistant test, 363
crèches, 396
credit, 232
credit cards, 238
credit notes, 217
crème fraîche, 125
crêpes, 203
cross-contamination, 71, 133
croûtons, 81
crumble, fruit, 168
curry recipes, 187–8
curtains, 352
cushion cover, how to make, 407
custard, 174–5
cuts, first aid, 339
cystic fibrosis, 398

dairy products, 122–9
dairy spreads, 126
debit cards, 237
decision-making, 207–10
deficiency diseases, 13–16
dehydration, 155
deodorants, 254
department stores, 234
design, 300–3
    clothing, 345–7
    craftwork, 402–7
    home, 300–10
detergents, 335
    laundry, 368–9
development of children, 272–5,
    385–8
diabetes, 49

diet, 31–52
  balanced, 31–8
  dietary needs, 33–7
  high-fibre, 41–3
  low-fat/cholesterol, 43–4
  low-salt, 44–5
  low-sugar, 45–6
  weight-reducing, 46–8
dietary fibre, 11, 41–3
  RDA, 18
digestion, 24–7
disabilities, 397–9
discipline, 386
dishcloths, 353
divorce, 265–6, 399
dough, 81
Down syndrome, 398
dressmaking, 408–17
dried food, 155
  fruit and vegetables, 112, 117
  milk, 124
drinking, 284–7
drugs, 288–9
drying clothes, 369–70
Dublin coddle, 188
durability, 300
duvets, 353
dyeing, 361

E. Coli, 69
E numbers, 159–60
eating disorders, 48–9
eating, healthy, 2–6, 41–8
  modifying recipes, 162–3
eggs, 145–8
  omelettes, 202
elderly, dietary needs, 36
electrical appliances, 314–20
  heaters, 327
  safety, 336
  wiring a plug, 323–4
electricity, 322–5
embroidery, 374–5, 377
  craftwork, 405
emotional development, 273–4,
  386–8
emotional disability, 397
emotional needs, 266, 298

emotions, 250
Employment Equality Act, 270
emulsifiers, 160
endosperm, 102
energy, 19–22
  content of foods, 28–30
energy balance, 22
energy efficiency, 331
environment, 329–32
enzymes, 24, 68
equality, 270
ergonomics, 308
evaluation, 295
evaporated milk, 124
excretory organs, 252
exercise, 246–7
extended family, 265

fabric conditioners, 369
fabrics, 354–63
faeces, 26
fainting, first aid, 341
family, 265–71
  breakdown, 265–6, 399–400
  family law, 399–400
  home management, 293–5
fan ovens, 317
fashion, 346–7
fats/oils, 11–12
  food composition table, 28–30
  RDA, 18
  saturated/unsaturated, 11
fatty acids, 12, 24
fear, 250
feet, care of, 256
fertilisation, 280
fibre, dietary, 11, 41–3
  RDA, 18
fibres, 354–63
filleting fish, 143
Financial Regulator, 219
fire safety, 338
first aid, 338–41
fish, 140–4
  recipes, 170, 171–5
fish cakes, 172
flavourings, 159
floor plan, 305

flour, 105
fluorescent lights, 325
fluoride, 258
foetus, 281
foil, 73
food, 2–52
  balanced diet, 31–8
  choices, 2–6
  composition of, 28–30
  GM (genetically modified), 161
  healthy/unhealthy, 2–6, 31, 41–8
  nutrition, 7–23
  staple foods, 4, 101
food additives, 159–60
food allergies, 160
food hygiene, 68–74, 75, 158
  babies, 392
food management, 60
food mixers, 80
food poisoning, 69
food preparation, 75–80
  hygiene, 71, 75
food presentation, 58–9, 65
food preservation, 149–57
food processing, 41–2, 102, 149
  fruit and vegetables, 116–17
food processors, 80
food pyramid, 31
food spoilage, 68–74, 149–50
food storage, 72–4
  fish, 142
  fruit and vegetables, 116
  meat, 132–3, 138
fortified foods, 102
French dressing, 183
French savoury omelette, 202
frozen food, 151–4
  fish, 141, 142
  fruit and vegetables, 116
  home freezing, 152–4
  keeping times, 73, 153
fruit, 111–21
  freezing, 154
fruit crumble, 168
fruit salad, 168
fruit smoothie, 168
frying, 86
furnishings, 351–2

fuses and fuse boxes, 322–3

garnishing food, 65
gas, 321–2
gas ovens, 317
gender equity, 270, 294–5
gender roles, 269–70, 294–5
germs, 68–72, 333
gingerbread, 167
glaze, 81
global warming, 330
glucose, 10
gluten-free foods, 50, 105
glycerol, 12, 24
GM (genetically modified) foods, 161
goals, 293
greaseproof paper, 74
greenhouse effect, 330
grill, 316
grilling, 86
guarantees, 217, 224

haemoglobin, 16
hair, 255–6
hand care, 256
HBV foods, 9
health, 246–51
  hazards, 283–9
health checks, 249
healthy eating, 2–6, 41–8
heart, 260–1
heartbeat, 261
heart disease, 43–4, 283
heating, 313, 327–8
hemming, 373–4
heredity, 274, 386
hobs, 316
home, 297–8
home design, 300–10
home hygiene, 333–5
home management, 293–6
home services, 321–8
homogenised milk, 124
hormones, 278, 279
household textiles, 350–3
housing, 297–8
hygiene

babies, 337, 392–3
  food, 68–74, 75, 158
  home, 333–5
  personal, 252–6
hypertension, 45

icing, 197
illness, precautions against, 249, 283–9
immersion heaters, 326
immunisation, 249, 396
information for consumers, 211–15
infusion, 81
insomnia, 248
insulation, 327–8
insulin, 49
intellectual development, 273, 386–8
intestines, 25–6
invalids, dietary needs, 36–7
iodine, 16
iron, in diet, 15–16
  food composition table, 28–30
  RDA, 18
ironing, 370
irradiation, 150
Italian shepherd's pie, 185

jam making, 156

kettles, 315–16
kidneys, 252
kilocalories/kilojoules, 20–1
  food composition table, 28–30
kitchen, 307–10
  hygiene, 72
  safety, 75–6
  sinks, 326
kneading, 81
knitting, 359

labelling, 158–9, 226–7
  care of clothes, 364–6
  eggs, 145–6
  fruit and vegetables, 116
  nutritional information, 21, 159
lacemaking, 404
lactovegetarians, 39, 41
larynx, 263

lasagne, smoked fish, 174
lasagne, vegetarian, 181
Laser cards, 237
laundry, 364–70
layette, 395
LBV foods, 9
leek and potato soup, 169
leisure, 248, 313
leisure amenities, 298
lemon biscuits, 199
liaison, 81
lightbulbs, 312–13, 324–5
lighting, 324–5
linen, 356
lipids, 11–12
listening, 268
listeria, 69
logos, 228
long-life milk, 124
loss leaders, 239
love, 250, 386
LPG (liquid petroleum gas), 321
lungs, 263–4
lycra, 357, 358

macaroni cheese with mushrooms, 179
macronutrients, 7
Madeira cakes, 195
maize, 103
malnutrition, 4
management, 60, 292
  home management, 293–6
marinade, 81
marketing techniques, 237, 239, 243–4
maturity, 273
mayonnaise, 183
meal planning, 53–67
measurements, clothes, 408
measuring and weighing, 76–7
meat, 130–9
  freezing, 153
  recipes, 184–9
  substitutes, 139
melanin, 252–3
menopause, 279
menstrual cycle, 279

mental development, 273, 386–8
mental health, 249–51
menus, 55–7
meters, 322
micronutrients, 7, 13
micro-organisms, 68–72
microwave cooking, 87–8
    vegetables, 118
milk, 122–5
milling, 102
mince pies, 201
minced meat, 136
    recipes, 184–6
minerals, 14–17
mineral water, 18
mixers, 80
modesty, 344
money management, 229–33
monopoly, 212
monosodium glutamate, 159
moral development, 275
motor skills, 386
moulds, 68
mouth, 25
mushroom soup, 170

nappies, 393, 395
National Consumer Agency, 219
natural resources, 329
needs, 266, 298
    distinct from wants, 208
norms of behaviour, 275
nuclear family, 265
nursery schools, 396
nut and banana bread, 165
nutrients, 8
nutrition, 7–23
    babies, 388–91
    food labelling, 21, 159
    malnutrition, 4
nylon, 356–8

oats, 103
obesity, 46–8
oesophagus, 25
offal, 136
Office of the Director of Corporate
    Enforcement, 219

oils, 11–12
Ombudsman, 219
omelettes, 202
online shopping, 238
organs, 252
osteoporosis, 15
oven glove, how to make, 382
ovens, 79–80, 316–17
ovulation, 279
oxidation, 19
oxygen, food spoilage, 68
ozone, 330

packaging, 224–5
    when storing food, 73–4
packed meals, 91–4
pancakes, 203
pancreatic juice, 25
parboil, 82
parenthood, 266, 384
    roles, 268–9
pasta, 104
    recipes, 173–4, 179, 181–2, 184
pasteurised milk, 124
pastry, 109–10
    recipes, 189–92
patchwork, 404
pattern in design, 302, 345
patterns, 408–13
peanut butter and white chocolate
    blondies, 200
pectin, 156
peer group/peer pressure, 274
pepsin, 25
peristalsis, 25
personal hygiene, 252–6
personality, 274
phosphorus, 16
photosynthesis, 10
physical development, 273, 386–8
physical needs, 266, 298
pimples, 254–5
pipes, frozen, 326–7
pizza, 204
planning a meal, 53–67
plaque, 257–8
plasma, 262
platelets, 262

play, 387–8
playgroups, 396
plugs, fuses and wiring, 323–4
poaching, 85
poisoning
    first aid, 341
    food poisoning, 69
polishes, 335
pollution, 329–30
polyester, 356–8
pork curry with jasmine rice, 187
posture, 247
potassium, 16
potato recipes
    colcannon, 189
    potato and leek soup, 169
    potato salad, 182
poultry, 137–8
power stations, 322
pregnancy, 280–1, 384–5
    dietary needs, 35
    smoking, 283–4
presentation of food, 58–9, 65
preservatives, 159–60
preserving food, 149–57
pressing clothes, 416–17
pressure cooking, 85
preventative medicine, 249, 283–9
printing fabric, 361
priorities, 208–9
processed food, 41–2, 102, 149
    fruit and vegetables, 116–17
proportion, 303
protein, 8–10
    food composition table, 28–30
    RDA, 18
puberty, 278
public health nurses, 396
pulses, 114, 127
purée, 82
pyroclean, 317

quality control, 223
quality marks, 223–4
queen cakes, 195
quiche Lorraine, 191

radiation of heat, 84, 327

raisin and banana cookies, 199
raising agents, 106–7
rayon, 356
receipts, 238
recipes, 76
  costing, 62–3
  modifying, 162–3
recommended daily allowance
  (RDA), 8
  vitamins and minerals, 18
recovery position, 341
recycling, 226, 330, 332
red cabbage salad, 182
refined food, 41–2, 102
refrigerators, 318–20
refunds, 217–18
reheating food, 71, 135
relationships, 267–8
relaxation, 247–8
rennin, 25
reproduction, 279–81
resource management, 60, 292
respiratory system, 263–4
responsibilities, 211
rest, 247–8
rice, 103–4
  recipes, 177–8, 181–2
rice pudding, 178
rickets, 15
ricotta and basil tart, 179
rights of children, 266
rights of consumers, 211–22
risotto recipes, 178, 181
roasting, 86
roasting bags, 74
rock buns, 167
roles, 268–70, 294
room planning, 304–10
rotisserie, 317
roux sauces, 98–9
rubbish bins, 334
rye, 103

safety, 336–42
  children, 337, 392, 394
  kitchen, 75–6
safety of goods, 212–13
  labels, 227, 351

salads, 119–20
  dressings, 183
  recipes, 182–3
Sale of Goods and Supply of
  Services Act, 216–18
sales staff, 214, 224
saliva, 25
salmon recipes, 171, 173
salmonella, 69, 146
salt, 16, 18, 44–5
sandwiches, 92–4
saturated fats, 11
sauces, 97–100
  recipes, 174–7
sausage rolls, 190
sausages, 137
sauté, 82
saving, 233
scalds, first aid, 340
scales, 77
scones, 164, 166, 167
scratches, first aid, 339
scurvy, 14
seafood, 140
  recipe, 173
seams, 379
self-esteem, 249–50, 273, 386
selvage, 359, 380
services, 206, 218, 224
services to home, 321–8
sewing, 372–82
sewing machines, 375–8
sex role, 269–70, 294
sexual reproduction, 279–81
sexual responsibility, 281
sheets, 353
shellfish, 140
  recipe, 173
shelter, 297
shepherd's pie, 185
shock, first aid, 340
shopping, 234–9
  decision-making, 207–10
  for clothes, 348
  for electric appliances, 314–15,
  318
  for food, 65–6
  online, 238

quality of goods, 223–8
  rights of consumer, 211–22
shops, types of, 234–5
shortcrust pastry, 189
shortening, 82
silk, 354
  artificial, 356
simmering, 82
sinks, 326
skimmed milk, 123
skin, 252–5
sleep, 247–8
slimming, 46–8
smoked fish, 142
  recipes, 171, 174
smoking, 283–4
smoothies, 168
social development, 274, 388
social needs, 298
soda bread, 165
sodium, 16, 18
soft furnishings, 351–2
solar panels, 311
soup, 95–7
  recipes, 169–70
soured cream, 125
soya milk, 124
soya protein, 40, 139
spaghetti Bolognese, 184
special needs, 397–9
spina bifida, 398
spinning, 358, 362
spoilage of food, 68–74, 149–50
sponge cake, 195
sprains, first aid, 339–40
stabilisers in food, 160
stain removal, 367–8
stairs, and safety, 337
staphylococci, 69
staple foods, 4, 101
starches, 10
statutory services, 299
steam cleaners, 312
steaming, 85, 118
stereotype, 269–70
sterilising bottles, 392
stewing, 85, 118

stir-fried vegetables, 118
    recipe, 180
stitches, types of, 373–5, 377
stock, 95
stomach, 25
storage heaters, 327
storage of food, 72–4
    fish, 142
    fruit and vegetables, 116
    meat, 132–3, 138
store cards, 238
stress, 251
sugar, 10, 45–6
sunbathing, 253, 255
supermarkets, 234, 235–6
sweat glands, 254
sweet and sour sauce, 176
Swiss roll, 196
synthetic fibres, 356–8

table setting, 57–9
tacking, 372
    tailor tacking, 374, 414
tailor's chalk, 414
tarts, savoury, 179
tarts, sweet, 193–4
tax credits, 231
technology, 311–14, 362
teeth, 257–9
    babies and children, 391, 393
television, 313
textiles, 344–82
    care of, 364–71
    clothes-making, 408–17
    clothing, 344–9
    crafts, 404–7
    fibres and fabrics, 354–63
    household, 350–3
    Irish industry, 417–18
    properties of, 350–1
texture, 300, 345
Thai pork curry with jasmine rice, 187
thermostat, 79
time management, 292, 295–6

time plan (cookery), 63–4
timers, 317
tinfoil, 73
tinned food, 155–6
tins, baking, 108–9
tofu, 139
toilet training, 393
tomato bread, 166
tomato sauce, 176
tongue, taste areas, 3
towels, 353
tracing wheel, 414
tumble driers, 370
tuna and pasta salad, 182
TVP (textured vegetable protein), 40, 139

UHT milk, 124
unit pricing, 238
unsaturated fats, 11
upholstery, 351
utensils, cookery, 78

vaccination, 249, 396
vacuum cleaners, 312
values, 275–6
vegans, 39, 41
vegetables, 114–21
    freezing, 154
    recipes, 169, 179–81
vegetarians, 39–41
    meat substitutes, 139
    recipes, 169, 179–81
veins, 261
velouté, 99
ventilation, 309
villi, 26
vinaigrette, 183
viscose, 356–8
vitamins, 13–14
    food composition table, 28–30
    food preparation, 17
    RDA, 18
voluntary services, 299

Waldorf salad, 182
wants and needs, 208
warp, 359, 380
washing clothes, 364–70
washing detergents, 368–9
washing machines, 312, 369
waste disposal, 334
water in food, 17–18
    food composition table, 28–30
water pollution, 329
water supply, 325–7
weaning babies, 33, 390
weaving, 359, 361, 380
weft, 359, 380
weighing ingredients, 76–7
weight, losing, 46–8
wheat, 103
wheat grain, 102
whisking, 107
white sauces, 98–9, 177
winding babies, 390
window cleaners, 335
windows, 311
wool, 355
work triangle, 308

yarn, 358–60
yeast, 107
yoghurt, 126
Yule log, 200–1

# Photo Credits

For permission to reproduce photographs the author and publisher gratefully acknowledge the following:

The Advertising Archives: 209TR, 240, 241CR, 241BR; Courtesy of Advertising Standards Authority for Ireland: 243; Alamy: 32, 34, 35T, 46, 47, 48, 58, 92, 97, 104, 124, 125, 130, 132CBL, 135T, 136, 157, 159, 168, 172, 175, 188, 191, 193, 201, 203, 206BL, 211, 212BR, 227TR, 234CL, 236BL, 237TR, 237BR, 238CL, 238CR, 241TR, 246, 254, 260, 265CR, 266, 273T, 273B, 274C, 274B, 283, 284, 285B, 296, 297T, 301BC, 311T, 312BL, 313BR, 313CTR, 316, 317B, 319, 321C, 322BL, 325C, 326, 327, 328TL, 328CL, 329, 330T, 330C, 331T, 331C, 334c, 336, 337TR, 337C, 337BR, 339T, 339C, 351B, 352, 358, 359T, 361T, 368, 372, 391, 393, 398, 404, 417; Courtesy of An Bord Gáis: 321T, 322TL; Courtesy of An Garda Síochána: 344B; Courtesy of Australian Wool Innovation Limited: 228TL, 355R, 355C; Courtesy of Avonmore: 123; Courtesy of Batchelors: 225CR; Courtesy of Bank of Ireland: 232, 238TL; Courtesy of Beam Central Systems: 312TL; Courtesy of Bord Bia: 145, 146; Courtesy of Brown Thomas: 234BL; Courtesy of Burda: 409C, 409CR; Courtesy of Coeliac UK: 50, 105TR; Corbis: 33B, 35B, 36, 105BR, 112, 198, 206CL, 209BR, 223TR, 256, 267, 303BR, 304, 308, 309CR, 313TR, 324, 328CR, 330B, 337TC, 345BL, 350, 353, 359B, 362, 387, 395, 396, 406CL; Courtesy of Currys: 226; Courtesy of Donegal Catch: 151; Courtesy of Erin: 156BR; Courtesy of Excellence Ireland Quality Association: 223C; Courtesy of Fields: 234TL; Fresh Food Images: 93B, 137, 165; Getty: 2BR, 3B, 9CL, 9CR, 31, 33T, 73, 85, 87, 90, 128B, 132TL, 132CBR, 135C, 141, 186, 228BL, 251, 255CR, 275, 301TC, 301TR, 301C, 301BR, 302T, 302C, 302B, 309T, 311B, 317T, 323TC, 325TC, 325TR, 334b, 338, 339B, 340, 345TR, 345CR, 346T, 346C, 347T, 347C, 347B, 389T, 389B, 390, 394, 416; Courtesy of Guaranteed Irish: 223CR; Courtesy of the HSE: 286CL, 286BR; Imagefile: 2BL, 3C, 14, 83, 86, 93T, 107, 115, 120, 128T, 132CCL, 132CCR, 133, 139T, 139C, 153C, 155, 160B, 169, 180, 184, 196, 227BR, 237CR, 247, 297B, 301CR, 303BC, 313CBR, 333, 337BL, 344C, 345BC, 351C, 361B, 364B, 405; Courtesy of Jacob Fruitfield: 156CL, 225BR; Courtesy of National Consumer Agency: 214, 228CL; Courtesy of National Standards Authority of Ireland: 224TL; Courtesy of Nicholas Mosse: 402T; Photocall: 212TL, 402B; Photolibrary: 153T, 164, 166, 167, 225TR, 236CL, 244, 265BR, 269, 295, 298, 301BL, 303T, 303C, 309BC, 317C, 364T, 369, 406CR; Rex Features: 345BR; Science Photo Library: 11, 140, 158, 160T, 249, 255BR, 258, 285C, 323TR, 341; Courtesy of Shopdirect: 235; Courtesy of Siúcra: 156BL; Courtesy of Uncle Ben's: 100; Courtesy of Whirlpool: 210CL.

The author and publisher have made every effort to trace all copyright holders, but if any has been inadvertently overlooked we would be pleased to make the necessary arrangement at the first opportunity.